D1756553

Springer Series in Applied Biology

Biodegradation: Natural and Synthetic Materials

Springer Series in Applied Biology

Series Editor: Prof. Anthony W. Robards PhD, DSc, FIBiol

Published titles:

Foams: Physics, Chemistry and Structure

The 4-Quinolones: Antibacterial Agents in Vitro

Food Freezing: Today and Tomorrow

Proposed future titles:

Application Potential of Immobilised Macromolecules
Ed. U. B. Sleytr

Probiotics: Bacterial Prophylaxis
Ed. S. A. W. Gibson

Drug Resistant Enzymes
Ed. J. R. Warr

Biodegradation:
Natural and Synthetic Materials

Edited by W.B. Betts

Springer-Verlag
London Berlin Heidelberg New York
Paris Tokyo Hong Kong
Barcelona Budapest

W B Betts, BA, MSc, PhD
Mycotech, Institute for Applied Biology, Department of Biology,
University of York YO1 5DD

Series Editor
Professor Anthony William Robards, BSc, PhD, DSc, DipRMS,
FIBiol
Director, Institute for Applied Biology, Department of Biology,
University of York, York YO1 5DD, UK

Cover Illustration: Photomicrograph of soft-rot fungal growth on
lignin model compound - by permission of Betts WB, Dart RK,
Ball MC (1987) Holzforschung vol 41, Walter de Gruyter & Co,
Berlin

ISBN 3-540-19705-2 Springer-Verlag Berlin Heidelberg New York
ISBN 0-387-19705-2 Springer-Verlag New York Berlin Heidelberg

British Library Cataloguing in Publication Data
Biodegradation:natural and synthetic materials.
I. Betts, W. B. (Walter Bernard), 1953-
620.11223
ISBN 3-540-19705-2

Library of Congress Cataloging-in-Publication Data
Biodegradation:natural and synthetic materials / edited by W. B. Betts
p. cm. - (Springer series in applied biology)
Includes index.
ISBN 3-540-19705-2. - ISBN 0-387-19705-2
1. Materials - Biodeterioration. I. Betts, W. B., 1953-
II. Series.
TA418.74.B538   1991
620.1' 1223 - dc20   91-22058
                                                                    CIP

Set by Institute for Applied Biology, Department of Biology, University of York
12/3830 - 543210 Printed on acid free paper

Foreword from Series Editor

The Institute for Applied Biology was established by the Department of Biology at the University of York to consolidate and expand its existing activities in the field of applied biology. The Department of Biology at York contains a number of individual centres and groups specialising in particular areas of applied research which are associated with the Institute in providing a comprehensive facility for applied biology. Springer-Verlag has a long and successful history of publishing in the biological sciences. The combination of these two forces leads to the "Springer Series in Applied Biology". The choice of subjects for seminars is made by our own editorial board and external sources who have identified the need for a particular topic to be addressed.

The first volume, *"Foams: Physics, Chemistry and Structure"*, has been quickly followed by *"The 4-Quinolones: Antibacterial Agents in Vitro"* and *"Food Freezing: Today and Tomorrow"* and the range of seminars will extend from genetic engineering to ecotoxicology and biodegradation to plant micropropagation. The aim is to keep abreast of topics that have a special applied, and contemporary, interest. The current volume, dealing with *Biodegradation*, highlights the importance of biotransformation as one possible solution to the problem of diminishing availability of resources for chemicals and energy, and considers this problem in the context of environmental pollution.

Up to three volumes are published each year through the editorial office of *IFAB Communications* in York. Using modern methods of manuscript assembly, this streamlines the publication process without losing quality and, crucially, allows the books to take their place in the shops within four to five months of the actual seminar. In this way authors are able to publish their most up-to-date work without fear that it will, as so often happens, become outdated during an overlong period between submission and publication.

The applications of Biology are fundamental to the continuing welfare of all people, whether by protecting their environment or by ensuring the health of their bodies. The objective of this series is to become an important means of disseminating the most up-to-date information in this field.

York, June 1991   A. W. Robards

Editor's Preface

Two major problems encountered as we approach a new century are the availability of resources for chemicals and energy, and environmental pollution. This book highlights the importance of biotransformation as a solution to these problems and considers traditionally separate areas as one interdependent discipline, in terms of the underlying mechanistic biochemistry and the research techniques employed.

The provision of resources has largely centred around non-renewable materials, especially oil. Diminishing reserves of these, together with uncertainties of supply and cost have stimulated great interest in renewable resources. These are largely lignocellulosic materials (e.g. wood and straw) which are available through natural biomass turnover, farming and forestry and from wastes generated by industrial processes. An excellent example is that of kraft lignin, a by-product of pulp and paper production, amounting to 60 million tonnes per annum and which is largely wasted by burning or landfilling. This aromatic polymer has enormous potential as a feedstock to the chemical industry.

Environmental pollution is no longer accepted as inevitable for a technological society. Over the past decade there has been a tremendous increase in awareness of the effects of pollution and public pressure has influenced both industry and government. However, to be realistic, it is not possible to replace all processes generating polluting wastes with clean alternatives. Instead, treatments of pollution, both at source and after an incident, are alternatives in many instances and a great deal of emphasis is currently being placed on these.

When considering the technologies currently available to utilise renewable resources and remove pollutants from the environment it is apparent that physical and chemical methods are often unsatisfactory and uneconomical. There has therefore been a movement towards biological conversion and remediation procedures which can be more specific and convenient (but have yet to be made economical).

Microorganisms play a major role in bioconversion and bioremediation, and already there are examples of microbial systems under exploitation for their capacity to metabolise voluminous and recalcitrant materials (e.g. the conversion of cellulose to fuel alcohol and the dissimilation of crude oil in spills). Transformations catalysed by microorganisms are also of great value in other applications including pharmaceutical manufacturing (e.g. the semisynthesis of antibiotics and stereospecific modification of steroids) and the food and drink industry (e.g. acid and alcohol fermentations).

Microbial conversion is a growth area, as shown by a glimpse at the vast quantity of literature produced annually. A great deal of the research undertaken focuses on degradation of substrates and is often followed by manipulation of the basic dissimilatory routes to provide a more specific conversion. This emphasises the importance of fundamental knowledge of the natural degradative capacities and mechanisms. Additionally, it is often the case that knowledge gained in one area of degradation research is highly valuable in other areas. This can apply to such information as the metabolic pathways, the enzymes involved and the methodologies used in investigations.

It is therefore important for researchers to be aware of the wider aspects of the biodegradation of natural and synthetic materials. Of course the number of substrates available for discussion is vast and therefore this book has focused on a current range of the most important chemicals and materials. Within the limits of one volume, it is hoped that the reader will benefit from such an approach and will maintain an outward view on this increasingly important area of microbiology.

W. B. Betts

Contents

Contributors

Dr. A. S. Ball
Department of Biology, University of Essex, Wivenhoe Park, Colchester, Essex CO4 3SQ

Dr. W. B. Betts
Institute for Applied Biology, Department of Biology, University of York, Heslington, York YO1 5DD

Dr. R. K. Dart
Department of Chemistry, University of Technology, Loughborough Leicestershire LE11 3TU

Dr. K. H. Engesser
Institut für Mikrobiologie der Universität Stuttgart
W 7000 Stuttgart, FRG

Dr. Christine S. Evans
Division of Biotechnology, School of Biological and Health Sciences, Polytechnic of Central London, 115 New Cavendish Street, London W1M 8JS

Dr. P. Fischer
Institut für Organische Chemie der Universität Stuttgart
W 7000 Stuttgart, FRG

Dr. X. T. He
Department of Agronomy, Ohio State University, Columbus, Ohio USA

Dr. D. J. Hopper
Department of Biochemistry, University College of Wales, Aberystwyth, Dyfed SY23 3DD

Dr. M. S. A. Leisola
Cultor Ltd, Research Center, 02460 Kantvik, Finland

Mr. B. F. P. Little
Aspects International Ltd., Environmental Consultants, Litchem House,
Bickershaw Lane, Abram, Wigan WN2 5TB

Mr. N. Mackay
Institute for Applied Biology, Department of Biology, University of York,
Heslington, York YO1 5DD

Dr. A. J. McCarthy
Department of Genetics and Microbiology
Life Sciences Building, University of Liverpool, Liverpool L69 3BX

Dr. A. Muheim
Swiss Federal Institute of Technology, Department of Biotechnology, ETH-
Hönggerberg, CH-8093 Zürich, Switzerland

Dr. S. J. Palmer
Viridian Bioprocessing Ltd, 114-116 John Wilson Business Park, Thanet
Way, Whitstable, Kent CT5 3QT

Ms. S. L. Pedlar
Institute for Applied Biology, Department of Biology, University of York,
Heslington, York YO1 5DD

Dr. M. Radosevich
Department of Agronomy, Ohio State University, Columbus, Ohio USA

Dr. H. W. H. Schmidt
Givaudan Forschungsgesellschaft AG, CH-8600Dübendorf, Switzerland

Dr. H. E. Schoemaker
DSM Research, Bio-organic Chemistry Section, PO Box 18, 6160 MD
Geleen, The Netherlands

Dr. G. K. Sims
Environmental Chemistry Laboratory, DowElanco, Midland, Michigan USA

Dr. R. N. Smith
Biodeterioration Centre, Hatfield Polytechnic, Hatfield, Hertfordshire
AL10 9AB

Professor S. J. Traina
Department of Agronomy, Ohio State University, Columbus, Ohio USA

Dr. U. Tuor
Swiss Federal Institute of Technology, Department of Biotechnology, ETH-
Hönggerberg, CH-8093 Zürich, Switzerland

Dr. J. M. Wyatt
Viridian Bioprocessing Ltd, 114-116 John Wilson Business Park, Thanet
Way, Whitstable, Kent CT5 3QT

Chapter 1

Aspects of the Aerobic Degradation of Aromatics by Microorganisms

D. J. Hopper

Introduction

The ability to metabolise aromatic compounds and use them as sole sources of carbon and energy for growth is displayed by many species of bacteria and fungi with some more versatile than others in the range of enzymes and pathways they have at their disposal. To grow on such a compound an organism must be able to break down at least part of the molecule to the simple carbon compounds that are intermediates in central pathways of metabolism. These can then be oxidised to provide energy or can serve as the starting point for biosynthesis of cell constituents. In any particular pathway it may take several successive transformations before the starting material is converted into these central metabolites.

The process can, of course, occur in the presence or absence of oxygen but the feature of aerobic catabolism of aromatic compounds that distinguishes the process from anaerobic mechanisms is the use that is made of the class of enzymes known as oxygenases. These are particularly important in the ring-fission reactions but also are very much involved in the preparation of molecules for ring-fission and examples of this will be given later.

There have been numerous studies of the aerobic metabolism of aromatic compounds over the past few decades and comprehensive reviews of the topic have been published (Gibson 1984; Hagedorn et al. 1988). Many exciting discoveries have been made and continue to be reported but some broad patterns have emerged and these will be briefly reviewed here. The survey will be confined to relatively simple aromatic compounds and illustrated by some work in my laboratory together with other aspects of recent interest.

The key step in the degradation of aromatics is the opening of the stable ring structure of these compounds to give aliphatic intermediates and it has become apparent that there are relatively few types of substrates for ring-fission enzymes. The ring is activated for cleavage by insertion of hydroxyl groups and most substrates have at least two such substituents situated *ortho* or *para* to each other. There are exceptions to this rule where a single hydroxyl group suffices and these include 1-hydroxy-1-naphthoic acid (Kiyohara and Nagao 1977) and 5-chlorosalicylic acid (Crawford *et al.* 1979) but for the great majority of pathways the rule holds good. Some of these ring-fission substrates, catechol (1,2-dihydroxybenzene), protocatechuic acid (3,4-dihydroxybenzoic acid) and gentisic acid (2,5-dihydroxybenzoic acid) for example, are common to pathways for several compounds and serve as focal points towards which a range of different substances are funnelled. This was well illustrated in a review by Chapman (1972) who showed the catabolism of a range of aromatics converging on these substrates and many more examples of pathways with these as ring-fission substrates have been reported since then. Substituted catechols and several other *ortho*- and *para*-dihydroxy compounds have also been recognised as important ring-fission substrates.

This convergence of pathways on common ring-fission substrates makes it convenient to consider the catabolism of any particular compound in three stages, first the preparation of the compound for ring-fission, then the ring-fission reaction itself followed by the conversion of the resulting aliphatic intermediate into central metabolites. It is in the first two stages that the oxygenase reactions, characteristic of aerobic metabolism, are of importance and several examples of these will be given.

Preparation for Ring-fission

To become a substrate for ring-fission any particular compound may simply require ring hydroxylation. Benzene, for example, is converted into catechol and toluene to 3-methylcatechol by dihydroxylation and 4-hydroxybenzoate is converted into protocatechuate by insertion of a single hydroxyl. Alternatively there may have to be considerable modification and perhaps elimination of side-chains before ring-fission occurs. In another pathway for toluene the methyl is oxidized to carboxyl which is removed as carbon dioxide when the ring is hydroxylated.

Oxygenases, both of the monooxygenase type that insert one atom of an oxygen molecule into their substrate and of the dioxygenase type that insert both atoms, have roles in both of these processes (Fig. 1.1). Many aromatic hydrocarbons and benzoic acids are converted into *o*-dihydroxycompounds by simultaneous introduction of two hydroxyl groups catalysed by a dioxygenase, intermediate in this process is the corresponding *cis*-dihydrodiol which is then dehydrogenated to give the catechol. Examples include benzene and toluene as mentioned above. The dioxygenases involved are complex enzymes with more than one interacting protein (Gibson and Subramanian 1984). Where the starting material is already phenolic, it may only need insertion of a single hydroxyl group to achieve the status of a ring-fission substrate. These reactions are catalysed by monooxygenases which are generally less complex then the dihydroxylases. They are usually flavoproteins, some of which have been studied in great detail. Some of these ring hydroxylations, both monooxygenase- and dioxygenase-catalysed, result in the elimination of ring substituents. For example, both salicylate and benzoate are converted into catechol, the former by a flavoprotein monooxygenase and the latter by a dioxygenase.

Monooxygenases are also prominent in the reactions used for modification of ring substituents. For example demethoxylases act by hydroxylation of the methoxyl group to give a hemiacetal which readily splits to a hydroxyl group and formaldehyde. Other ethers may be treated in the same way and a good example is from the degradation of

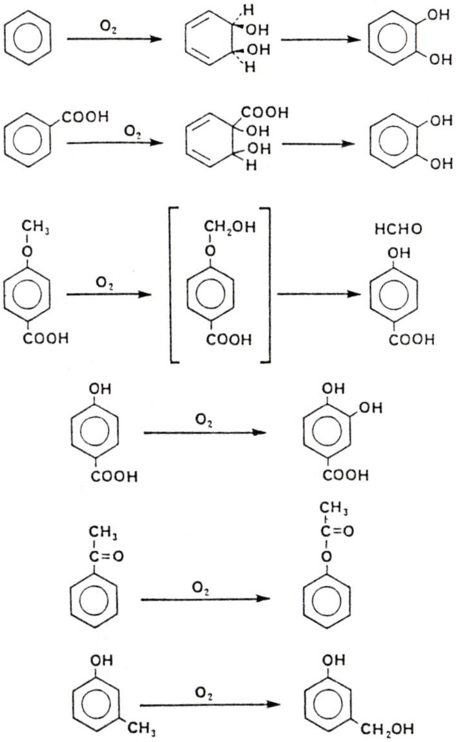

Fig. 1.1. Examples of reactions involving oxygenases in the preparation of aromatic compounds for ring-fission.

the herbicide 2,4-dichlorophenoxyacetic acid where the side-chain is removed as glyoxylic acid to leave 2,4-dichlorophenol. These enzymes, like the ring dihydroxylases, are multiprotein systems, and in this respect they also resemble the alkane hydroxylases which hydroxylate the terminal methyl group of an alkane. Similar complex monooxygenases are used for attack on some of the methyl substituents in aromatic rings although, as will be described later, in some cases a quite different type of enzyme and mechanism is used. Methyl groups may be hydroxylated to the corresponding benzyl alcohol which is then converted by dehydrogenases first to the aldehyde and then to carboxylic acid.

Some of these points can be illustrated from work undertaken in my laboratory on the bacterial metabolism of 4-hydroxyacetophenone which is summarised in the next section.

Degradation of 4-hydroxyacetophenone

Two pathways have been described for the catabolism of 4-hydroxyacetophenone. The first (Fig. 1.2) used by *Pseudomonas putida* JD1 (Darby *et al.* 1987) illustrates a general strategy used by microorganisms to deal with ketones. Oxygen is inserted

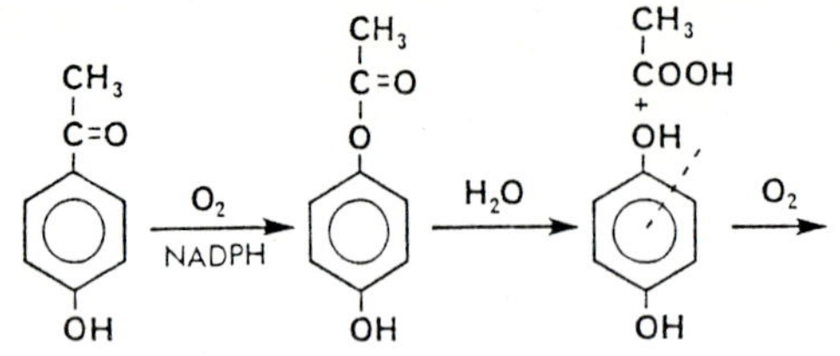

Fig. 1.2. Pathway to the ring-fission substrate for the catabolism of 4-hydroxyacetophenone by *Pseudomonas putida*.

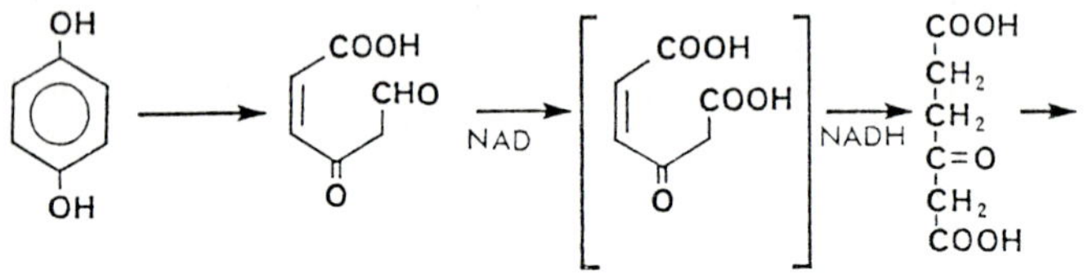

Fig. 1.3. Proposed route for hydroquinone catabolism.

between the ketonic carbon and its neighbour, in an equivalent of the Baeyer-Villiger reaction, to give an ester. The enzyme concerned is a monooxygenase and is an example of this class of enzyme that is not a hydroxylase. As for other monooxygenases there is a requirement for a source of reductant to reduce the second atom of the oxygen molecule to water and in this case NADPH was used. This procedure for dealing with ketones has been most thoroughly investigated in the conversion of alicyclic ketones, such as cyclohexanone, into lactones and the enzymes involved have been purified. They are relatively simple flavoproteins although they do vary with regard to their subunit structures (Trudgill 1984). Acetophenone itself is converted in a similar manner into phenyl acetate. This is the first step in its catabolism in a pathway found in species of *Nocardia* and *Arthrobacter* (Cripps 1975; Cripps *et al.* 1978). The pathway parallels that shown in Figure 1.2 for 4-hydroxyacetophenone but hydrolysis of the ester that is formed yields phenol which is hydroxylated to catechol as the ring-fission substrate. Attempts to purify the acetophenone monooxygenase were unsuccessful because of its instability and it is not known if this too is a flavoprotein. The 4-hydroxyacetophenone monooxygenase from *Pseudomonas putida* JD1 is more stable but has not yet been purified to the point where the involvement of flavin can be demonstrated. Other examples of this procedure for transforming a ketone into an ester or lactone are found in the metabolism of tridecanone (Forney and Markovetz 1969) and progesterone (Rahim and Sih 1966). The resulting esters are readily hydrolysed and that from 4-hydroxyacetophenone, 4-hydroxyphenylacetate, gives hydroquinone and acetic acid.

The hydroquinone, with two hydroxyl groups *para* to each other, is the ring-fission substrate. In contrast to compounds such as catechol or protocatechuate, hydroquinone has been reported as the ring-fission substrate in relatively few pathways and its breakdown to central metabolites has never been described in detail. It is converted by

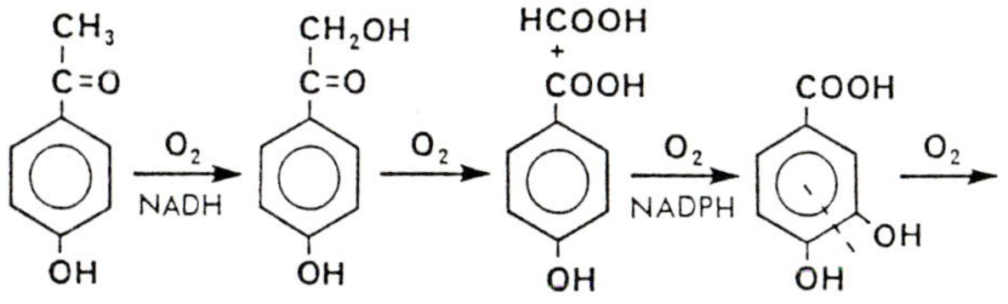

Fig. 1.4. Pathway to the ring-fission substrate for the catabolism of 4-hydroxyacetophenone by an *Alcaligenes* sp.

cell extracts into 3-oxoadipate, an intermediate common with one of the pathways for catechol metabolism and a proposed scheme is shown in Figure 1.3.

The second route for 4-hydroxyacetophenone degradation, this time found in an *Alcaligenes* sp., is rather different (Fig. 1.4) but still involves the use of oxygenases (Hopper *et al.* 1985a). Initial attack by cell extracts requires oxygen and NADH, indicative of a monooxygenase, but rather than formation of an ester it is hydroxylation of the methyl group that occurs. It might be expected that this would be a prelude to oxidation of the methyl to carboxyl to give 4-hydroxybenzoylformate, a compound that is a known intermediate of 4-hydroxymandelate catabolism where it undergoes decarboxylation to 4-hydroxybenzaldehyde. Instead the methyl hydroyxlation is in preparation for cleavage on the side-chain by a dioxygenase to yield formic acid and 4-hydroxybenzoic acid. This enzyme has been purified and appears to consist of four subunits of equal size, each about M_r 20000. Its designation as a dioxygenase has been demonstrated by showing incorporation of oxygen from $^{18}O_2$ into both products (Hopper 1986). The 4-hydroxybenzoate formed from this cleavage is then hydroxylated to give protocatechuic acid as the ring-fission substrate.

Anaerobic Hydroxylases

The role of oxygenases as hydroxylases in the preparation of aromatic compounds for ring-fission has been emphasised in the preceding sections. However, the point should be made that not all hydroxylases are oxygenases. This statement is obvious for anaerobic metabolism, where hydroxylations are still important, but sometimes tends to be overlooked in aerobic processes. In this section our work on anaerobic hydroxylases involved in the degradation of alkylphenols will be summarised and their connection with anaerobic catabolism discussed.

One of the pathways for the catabolism of *p*-cresol (4-methylphenol) involves oxidation of the methyl group to carboxyl. Attack is initiated by hydroxylation of the methyl group to give 4-hydroxybenzyl alcohol and it is the enzyme that catalyses this step, *p*-cresol methylhydroxylase, that is to be described. The enzyme has been purified and characterised from several species of *Pseudomonas* isolated and grown under aerobic conditions (Hopper 1988). All are very similar but the most thoroughly studied is hydroxylase A from *P. putida* NCIB 9869, one of two similar *p*-cresol methylhydroxylases produced by this organism under different growth conditions.

The mechanism involves dehydrogenation of the *p*-cresol, probably with formation of a quinone methide intermediate which is then hydrated to yield the 4-hydroxybenzylalcohol (Fig. 1.5). Thus the incorporated oxygen is derived from water

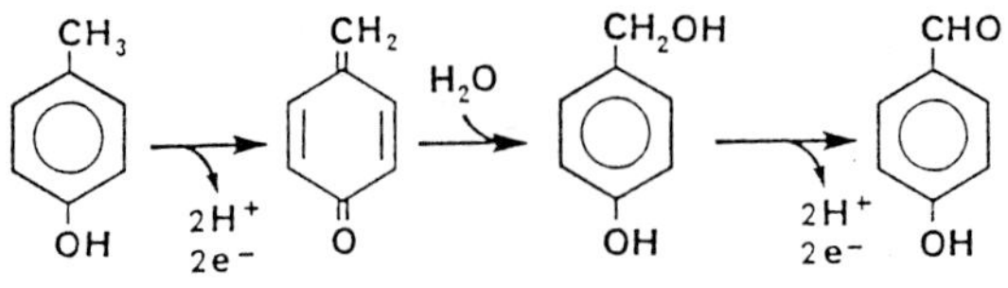

Fig. 1.5. The reaction catalysed by *p*-cresol methylhydroxylase.

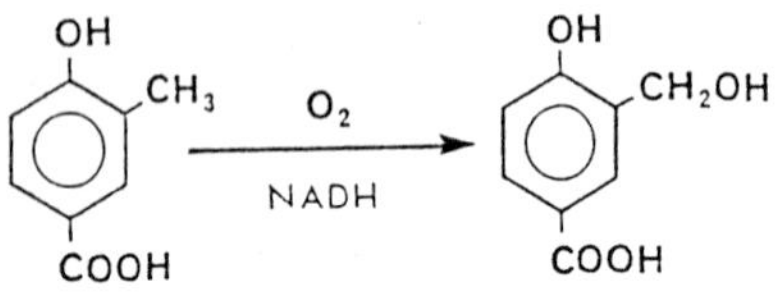

Fig. 1.6. Hydroxylation of an *o*-methylphenol, 4-hydroxy-3-methylbenzoate, by a monooxygenase.

rather than from O_2 and this was demonstrated by use of $H_2^{18}O$ (Hopper 1978). It should be noted that this mechanism requires the correct *para* orientation of the methyl and hydroxyl group in the ring. The *meta* orientation does not lead to a quinone methide and the enzyme for hydroxylation of the methyl groups of *m*-cresol or 3,5-xylenol required O_2 and NADH as for a monooxygenase (Hopper and Chapman 1971). Theoretically a methyl group *ortho* to hydroxyl could form an *o*-quinone methide but in the one example we have investigated this does not appear to happen; the methyl group of 4-hydroxy-3-methylbenzoate is hydroxylated by an enzyme of the monooxygenase type that consists of more than one protein component (Fig. 1.6: El-Mansi and Hopper 1990). One advantage of the mechanism described for *p*-cresol hydroxylation is that it is less energetically demanding on the cell in that there is no requirement for NAD(P)H as would be needed for a monooxygenase.

The *p*-cresol methylhydroxylase has a broad specificity and, provided there is a hydroxyl and a hydrogen-bearing carbon orientated *para* to each other, many substituted compounds are substrates. Thus 4-hydroxybenzylalcohol, the product of the reaction with *p*-cresol, is itself a substrate and is converted into 4-hydroxybenzaldehyde (Fig. 1.5). This activity is not necessarily of physiological importance, however, as the organism also contains an NAD-linked alcohol dehydrogenase active with this substrate.

Regarding the structure of *p*-cresol methylhydroxylase, it is a flavocytochrome c consisting of two flavoprotein subunits of M_r 50000 and two cytochrome c subunits of M_r 9000. The flavin is FAD and is bound covalently to the protein through an 8α-(O-tyrosyl) linkage (McIntire *et al.* 1981). The subunits can be separated for individual examination by isoelectric focussing and on mixing will reconstitute active enzyme (McIntire and Singer 1982). The enzymes that have been characterised from other species are also flavocytochromes with similar subunit structures and many similar properties (Hopper 1988).

As a dehydrogenase the *p*-cresol methylhydroxylase requires an electron acceptor and for assays artificial acceptors such as phenazine methosulphate can serve this purpose.

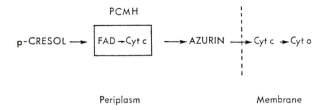

Fig. 1.7. Electron transport route from *p*-cresol methylhydroxylase.

The natural acceptor, however, is probably the small blue copper-containing protein, azurin. This will readily accept electrons from the enzyme and will link *p*-cresol oxidation to a membrane component and thence to oxygen via a cytochrome oxidase (Fig. 1.7: Causer *et al.* 1984). Thus O_2 is only required as the final electron acceptor at the end of an electron-transport chain. Supporting evidence for this role of azurin comes from the fact that both azurin and *p*-cresol methylhydroxylase are found in the periplasm of *P. putida* (Hopper *et al.* 1985b).

Although these enzymes have been purified from organisms grown aerobically and are associated with aerobic pathways for *p*-cresol degradation, the non-participation of O_2 means that such a mechanism could be used for the anaerobic oxidation of the methyl group of *p*-cresol. In connection with this it is interesting to note that there have been several reports in recent years suggesting that the first stage in the anaerobic metabolism of *p*-cresol, under nitrate or sulphate reducing conditions or by methanogenic consortia, is oxidation of the methyl group to carboxyl (Bossert *et al.* 1986; Smolenski and Suflita 1987; Roberts *et al.* 1987). In one of these the fates of the methyl carbons of *p*-cresol and *m*-cresol in a methanogenic consortium are contrasted, with that from the former being lost as carbon dioxide and that from the latter as methane, reflecting perhaps the inability of *m*-cresol to be dehydrogenated to a quinone methide.

Another of the reports described the isolation, from polluted river sediment, of a mixed culture capable of degradation of *p*-cresol anaerobically under denitrifying conditions (Bossert *et al.* 1986; Bossert and Young 1986). The culture consisted of two organisms, designated PC-07 and PB-04, of which PC-07 was able to oxidise *p*-cresol to 4-hydroxybenzoic acid and PB-04 could further degrade this product. Partial purification of the *p*-cresol methylhydroxylase from PC-07 suggested that it too may be a flavocytochrome (Bossert *et al.* 1989) and we have now confirmed this by characterisation of the purified enzyme. Its M_r, subunit structure and kinetic properties are all similar to those found for the enzymes from pseudomonads whereas the organism, PC-07, has been identified as an *Achromobacter* sp. Thus this type of enzyme has been shown to operate in at least one of the anaerobic systems and in this area the distinctions we make between aerobic and anaerobic degradation are not so clear cut.

4-Ethylphenol Catabolism

The degradation of the next higher homologue of *p*-cresol, 4-ethylphenol, is also initiated by hydroxylation of the side-chain in the pathway used by *P. putida* JD1

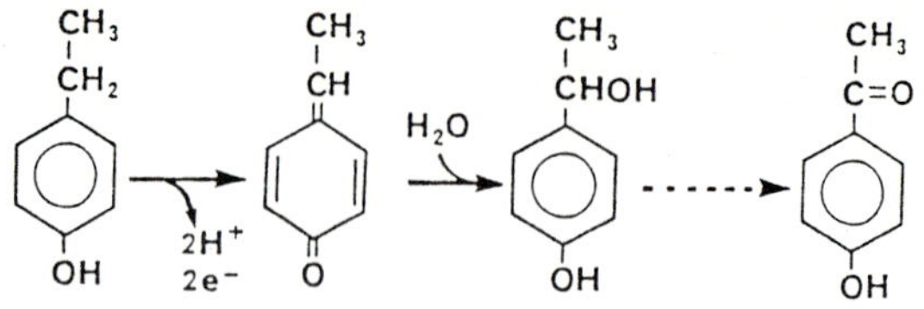

Fig. 1.8. Reactions catalysed by 4-ethylphenol methylenehydroxylase.

(Darby *et al.* 1987). It is the methylene closest to the aromatic ring that is attacked to give 1-(4-hydroxyphenyl)ethanol (Fig. 1.8). This secondary alcohol is then dehydrogenated to the corresponding ketone which leads into the pathway for 4-hydroxyacetophenone involving insertion of oxygen to give an ester (Fig. 1.2) as discussed earlier. The hydroxylase is again of the anaerobic type and has been purified and characterised (Reeve *et al.* 1989). It too is a flavocytochrome and in its M_r, subunit composition, redox potential of its cytochrome and patterns of steady-state kinetics it closely resembles *p*-cresol methylhydroxylase. The main difference is in its specificity; it is much more active than *p*-cresol methylhydroxylase towards alkylphenols with longer-chain alkyl groups. The enzyme will hydroxylate *p*-cresol but its specificity coefficient is 360 fold greater for 4-ethylphenol. Likewise *p*-cresol methylhydroxylase will attack 4-ethylphenol but in its case the specificity coefficient is 115 fold greater in favour of *p*-cresol. If *P. putida* JD1 is grown on *p*-cresol rather then 4-ethylphenol then it synthesises a separate *p*-cresol methylhydroxylase, again of the flavocytochrome type but different from the 4-ethylphenol methylenehydroxylase (Reeve *et al.* 1988).

Another interesting point of difference between the two enzymes is in the stereochemistry of the reaction. As this involves formation of a secondary alcohol the production of one or other of the enantiomers becomes a possibility. With azurin or horse-heart cytochrome c as electron acceptors 4-ethylphenol methylenehydroxylase produces the R(+) isomer in high enantiomeric excess whereas all the *p*-cresol methylhydroxylases, including the one from *P. putida* JD1 itself, give the S(-) isomer (Reeve *et al.* 1990). The alcohol is a substrate for the enzyme and can be converted into 4-hydroxyacetophenone albeit at a much slower rate. Both enantiomers can be dehydrogenated by 4-ethylphenol methylenehydroxylase but curiously it is the S(-) enantiomer, the stereoisomer opposite to the one formed in the first reaction, that is the preferred substrate with an almost seven-fold higher specificity coefficient. Physiologically, however, this step appears to be catalysed by an NAD-linked dehydrogenase.

Homologues of *p*-cresol up to 4-nonylphenol have been shown to be substrates for the 4-ethylphenol methylenehydroxylase and at this chain length measurement of rates becomes affected by the solubility of the substrate. This type of attack with subsequent ester formation and hydroylsis extends the options available to microorganisms for dealing with alkyl substituents. Alternatives are to leave them intact until after ring-fission or to oxidise the terminal methyl group and proceed by ß-oxidation. Even for alkylbenzenes this route via an alkylphenol methylenehydroxylase becomes a possibility if the substrate can first be hydroxylated *para* to the alkyl group. A precedent for such a reaction is seen with the hydroxylation of toluene to give *p*-cresol by *Pseudomonas mendocina* (Gibson 1988).

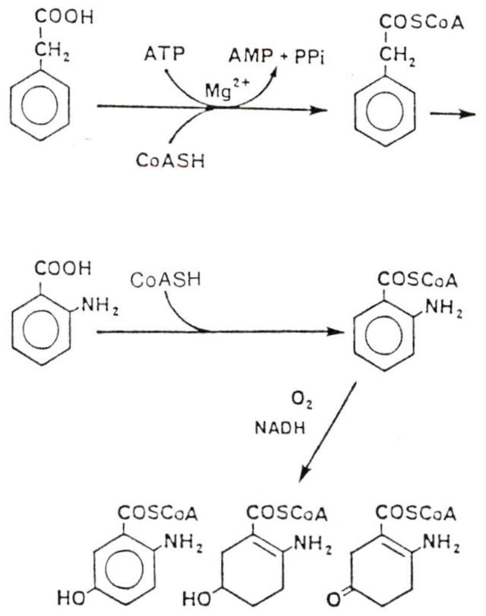

Fig. 1.9. Initial steps in pathways for phenylacetic acid and anthranilic acid.

Metabolism of Phenylacetic Acid

Another area of possible overlap of aerobic and anaerobic mechanisms is in the metabolism of phenylacetic acid. Pathways for the degradation of this compound have been described that include monohydroxyphenylacetic acids as intermediates and homoprotocatechuate or homogentisate as the ring-fission substrate. However, there have been suggestions that in some organisms a different route is used for phenylacetic acid than for the monohydroxyphenylacetic acids. The sequence of this pathway is unknown but some light is thrown onto this puzzle by the recent papers describing the presence of a phenylacetyl-CoA ligase in a strain of *P. putida* grown on phenylacetic acid (Fig. 1.9) (Martinez-Blanco *et al.* 1990a,b). The enzyme was not induced by growth on hydroxyphenylacetic acids nor were these substrates. Moreover 4-hydroxyphenylacetic acid hydroxylase, present at high activity in 4-hydroxyphenylacetic acid-grown cells, was not detectable after growth on phenylacetic acid and the indications are that the phenylacetyl-CoA ligase has a role in the catabolism of phenylacetic acid by a novel pathway.

We too have evidence for the formation of a CoA-ester in the catabolism of phenylacetic acid by a different strain of *Pseudomonas*. This organism does not grow on any of the hydroxyphenylacetic acids but when grown on phenylacetic acid there is some accumulation of 2-hydroxyphenylacetic acid in the medium. However, this compound is probably a side-product and not an intermediate as it is not oxidised by whole cells or by cell extracts that oxidise phenylacetic acid. Some homogentisate oxygenase activity can be detected in cell extracts but not in amounts expected for a key enzyme in a catabolic pathway. No oxidation of other likely ring-fission substrates was observed. Thus the steps of the pathway remain obscure but the link with anaerobic metabolism is in the initial formation of a CoA-ester. Such a reaction is seen for example in the reductive catabolism of benzoic acids that takes place under anaerobic conditions (Hutber and Ribbons 1983; Evans and Fuchs 1988).

Also of relevance here is the recent discovery of a pathway for degradation of anthranilic acid (2-aminobenzoic acid) in which the formation of the CoA-ester is the first step (Fig. 1.9) (Ziegler *et al.* 1987; Ziegler *et al.* 1989). The organism used is a denitrifying *Pseudomonas* strain which can grow on anthranilic acid either aerobically or anaerobically and in both cases appears to proceed by making the CoA-ester of the acid. While formation of the CoA-ester might be expected for the anaerobic pathway this does not occur in the known aerobic pathways for this compound. These involve dihydroxylation of the free acid to give catechol or 2,3-dihydroxybenzoic acid as ring-fission substrates. The next step in the aerobic metabolism of the anthranilyl-CoA is catalysed by a flavoprotein monooxygenase which is unusual in that several products, including 2-amino-5-hydroxybenzyl-CoA, 2-amino-5-hydroxycyclohex-1-enecarboxyl-CoA and 2-amino-5-oxocyclohex-1-enecarboxyl-CoA have been identified (Buder and Fuchs 1989; Langkau *et al.* 1990). The relative amounts depend on the levels of NADPH and it is the last of these compounds that is the probable physiological product. We have further evidence suggestive of an alternative pathway for anthranilic acid. We have isolated a *Pseudomonas* species that grows on this compound but could not detect activity in cell extracts towards any of the expected ring-fission substrates. The possibility of formation of the CoA-ester by this organism has not been investigated.

Ring-fission and Subsequent Pathways

The known pathways for aerobic oxidation of aromatics involve ring-fission by dioxygenase enzymes and the activities of these and the pathways for conversion of the products to central metabolites have been well documented (Bayly and Barbour 1984; Dagley 1989). As mentioned earlier, the compounds catechol and protocatechuic acid are at focal points of a number of pathways and the pathways for their breakdown have attracted extensive study. Cleavage of these *o*-dihydroxyl aromatics occurs either between the two hydroxyl groups or adjacent to one of the hydroxyls. The first is an intradiol cleavage, often referred to as *ortho*-fission, and the latter an extradiol cleavage known as *meta*-fission. The dioxygenase involved is usually specific for one type of cleavage or the other and each leads to quite distinct products and pathways for their subsequent metabolism. Variation in the *meta* pathway allows for the breakdown of substituted catechols. For example, the ring-fission product from catechol itself is an aldehyde which is oxidised to acid and the carboxyl group is lost as carbon dioxide. However, if the catechol is substituted in the 3-position then the ring-fission product is a ketone and therefore cannot be oxidized. When this occurs the substituted carbon is removed in a hydrolytic reaction to give an acid and a product that is the same as from the decarboxylation route. The *meta*-pathway can also cope with substituents in the 4-position resulting in formation of an analogue of acetaldehyde, the product containing that carbon atom in unsubstituted catechol. Many compounds that are hydroxylated to substituted catechols are metabolised in this way (Fig. 1.10).

Protocatechuic acid can also be cleaved by *meta*-fission. A 4,5-dioxygenase produces 4-hydroxy-2-carboxymuconic semialdehyde. Oxidation of the aldehyde to acid proceeds not perhaps as expected, by an aldehyde dehydrogenase, but by formation of a hemiacetal that is dehydrogenated to a lactone which in turn is ring-opened hydrolytically (Fig. 1.11). Hydration and aldolytic cleavage then give pyruvate and

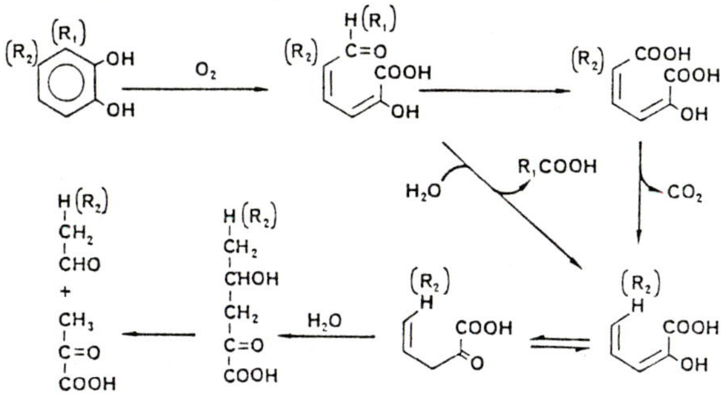

Fig. 1.10. The *meta*-fission pathway showing the fates of unsubstituted catechol and catechols substituted in the 3- (R_1) and 4- (R_2) positions.

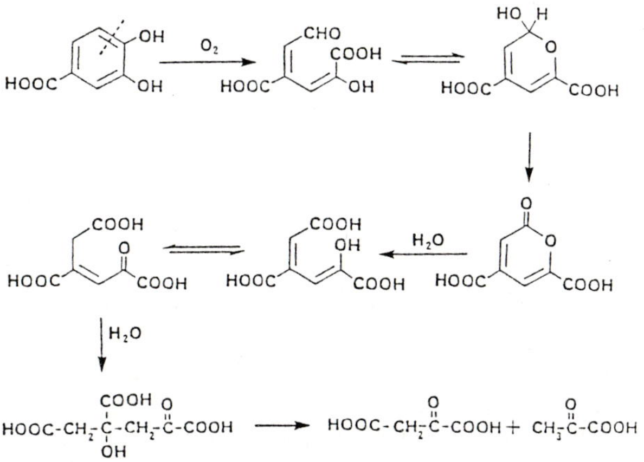

Fig. 1.11. *Meta*-cleavage pathway for protocatechuic acid.

oxaloacetate as products. *Meta*-cleavage by a 2,3-dioxygenase has also been reported and this gives 2-hydroxy-5-carboxymuconic semialdehyde which is decarboxylated to 2-hydroxy-muconic semialdehyde, an intermediate of the *meta*-fission pathway for catechol.

The pathways for *ortho*-fission of catechol and protocatechuic acid in bacteria are shown in Figure. 1.12 and converge at 3-oxoadipate enol-lactone. The same pathway for catechol metabolism is seen in fungi but for protocatechuate it is the ß-carboxymuconolactone that is formed and this is converted in a single step to 3-oxoadipic acid.

It was thought that the *ortho*-pathway was only able to cope with unsubstituted catechols and that substituted catechols would be metabolized via the *meta*-fission route. Although ring-opening of substituted catechols by *ortho*-pathway dioxygenases did occur the γ-methylmuconolactone formed in the next step accumulated as a dead-end product. This was because the lactone was unable to undergo the isomerization which is the next step. This requires the shift of a proton from C-4 to C-2 and with a methyl

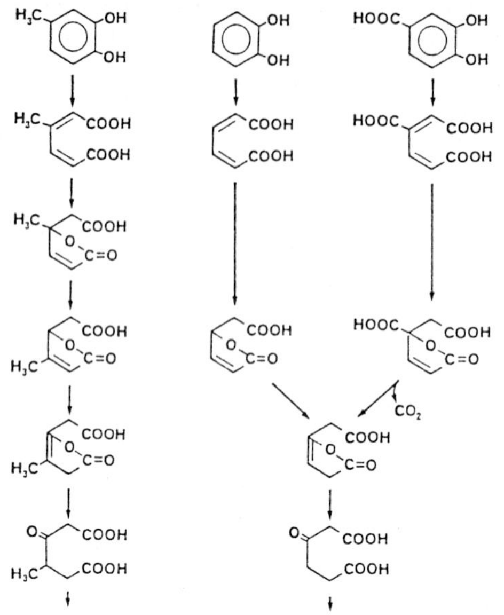

Fig. 1.12. The *ortho*-fission pathway for the bacterial catabolism of catechol and protocatechuic acid with the modification found in nocardioform bacteria for dealing with 4-methylcatechol.

group at C-4 this reaction is blocked. One of the most interesting advances in recent years has been the realisation that the *ortho*-pathway, with modifications, can indeed be utilised for some substituted catechols e.g. 4-Methylcatechol. Fungi are able to achieve this by direct formation of the ß-methylmuconolactone from *cis,cis*-methylmuconic acid which leaves the appropriate carbon unsubstituted (Powlowski and Dagley 1985). Bacteria of the Nocardioform actinomyces, like other bacteria, form the γ-methylmuconolactone but circumvent the problem this poses by producing a 4-methyl-2-enelactone methyl isomerase which converts the γ-muconolactone into the ß-muconolactone (Bruce *et al.* 1989). This intermediate can then be handled by the *ortho*-pathway enzymes to give 4-methyl-3-oxoadipic acid (Fig. 1.12). From the foregoing examples it can be seen that, although the broad outline and in some cases the considerable detail of aerobic catabolism of these simple aromatic compounds has been delineated, interesting and unexpected twists to the story continue to arise and probably remain to be discovered.

References

Bayly RC, Barbour MG (1984) The degradation of aromatic compounds by the meta and gentisate pathways. In: Gibson DT (ed) Microbial degradation of organic compounds. Marcel Dekker Inc, New York, pp 253-294

Bossert ID, Young LY (1986) Anaerobic oxidation of *p*-cresol by a denitrifying bacterium. Appl Environ Microbiol 52:1117-1122

Bossert ID, Rivera MD, Young LY (1986) *p*-cresol biodegradation under denitrifying conditions; isolation of a bacterial coculture. FEMS Microbiol Ecol 38:313-319

Bossert ID, Whited G, Gibson DT, Young LY (1989) Anaerobic oxidation of *p*-cresol mediated by a partially purified methylhydroxylase from a denitrifying bacterium. J Bacteriol 171:2956-2962

Bruce NC, Cain RB, Pieper DH, Engesser K-H (1989) Purification and characterisation of 4-methylmuconolactone methyl-isomerase, a novel enzyme of the modified 3-oxoadipate pathway in nocardioform actinomycetes. Biochem J 262: 303-312

Buder R, Fuchs G (1989) 2-Aminobenzoyl-CoA mono-oxygenase/reductase, a novel type of flavoenzyme. Eur J Biochem 185: 629-635

Buder R, Ziegler K, Fuchs G, Langkau B, Ghisla S (1989) 2-Aminobenzoyl-CoA monooxygenase/reductase, a novel type of flavoenzyme. Eur J Biochem 185: 637-643

Causer MJ, Hopper DJ, McIntire WS, Singer TP (1984) Azurin from *Pseudomonas putida*: an electron acceptor for *p*-cresol methylhydroxylase. Biochem Soc Trans 12: 1131-1132

Chapman PJ (1972) An outline of reaction sequences used for the bacterial degradation of phenolic compounds. In: Chapman PJ, Dagley S (eds) Degradation of synthetic organic molecules in the biosphere. Printing and Publishing Office, National Academy of Sciences, Washington DC, pp 17-55

Crawford RL, Olsen PE, Frick TD (1979) Catabolism of 5-chlorosalicylate by a *Bacillus* isolated from the Mississipi river. Appl Environ Microbiol 38: 379-384

Cripps RE (1975) The microbial metabolism of acetophenone and some chloroacetophenones by an *Arthrobacter* species. Biochem J 152: 233-241

Cripps RE, Trudgill PW, Whateley JJG (1978) The metabolism of 1-phenylethanol and acetophenone by *Nocardia* T5 and an *Arthrobacter* species. Eur J Biochem 8: 175-186

Dagley S (1989) Chemical unity and diversity in bacterial catabolism. In: Poindexter JS, Leadbetter ER (eds) Bacteria in Nature vol 3. Plenum Publishing Corp, New York, pp 259-291

Darby JM, Taylor DG, Hopper DJ (1987) Hydroquinone as the ring-fission substrate in the catabolism of 4-ethylphenol and 4-hydroxyacetophenone by *Pseudomonas putida* JD1. J Gen Microbiol 113: 2137-2146

El-Mansi EMT, Hopper DJ (1990) Resolution of the 4-hydroxy-3-methylbenzoate hydroxylase of *Pseudomonas putida* into two protein components. FEMS Microbiol Letts 66: 147-152

Evan WC, Fuchs G (1988) Anaerobic degradation of aromatic compounds. Ann Rev Microbiol 42: 289-317

Forney FW, Markovetz AJ (1969) An enzyme system for aliphatic methyl ketone oxidation. Biochem Biophys Res Commun 37: 31-38

Gibson DT (1984) Microbial degradation of organic compounds. Marcel Dekker Inc. New York (Microbiology series vol 13)

Gibson DT (1988) Microbial metabolism of aromatic hydrocarbons. In: Hagedorn SR, Hanson RS, Kunz DA (eds) Microbial metabolism and the carbon cycle. Harwood Academic Press, New York, pp 33-58

Gibson DT, Subramanian V (1984) Microbial degradation of aromatic hydroxarbons. In: Gibson DT (ed) Microbial degradation of organic compounds. Marcel Dekker Inc, New York, pp 181-252

Hagedorn SR, Hanson RS, Kunz DA (1988) Microbial metabolism and the carbon cycle. Harwood academic publishers, New York

Hopper DJ (1978) Incorporation of [^{18}O] water in the formation of *p*-hydroxybenzylalcohol by the *p*-cresol methylhydroxylase from *Pseudomonas putida*. Biochem J 175: 345-347

Hopper DJ (1986) Oxygenase properties of the (4-hydroxybenzoyl)-methanol-cleavage enzyme from an *Alcaligenes* sp. Biochem J 239: 469-472

Hopper DJ (1988) Properties of *p*-cresol methylhydroxylases. In: Hagedorn SR, Hanson RS, Kunz DA (eds) Microbial metabolism and the carbon cycle. Harwood Academic Publishers New York, pp 247-258

Hopper DJ, Chapman PJ (1971) Gentisic acid and its 3- and 4-methyl-substituted analogues as intermediates in the bacterial degradation of m-cresol, 3,5-xylenol and 2,5-xylenol. Biochem J 122: 19-28

Hopper DJ, Jones HG, Elmorsi EA, Rhodes-Roberts ME (1985a) The catabolism of 4-hydroxyacetophenone by an *Alcaligenes* sp. J Gen Microbiol 131: 1807-1814

Hopper DJ, Jones MR, Causer MJ (1985b) Periplasmic location of *p*-cresol methylhydroxylase in *Pseudomonas putida*. FEBS Letts 182: 485-488

Hutber GN, Ribbons DW (1983) Involvement of Coenzyme A esters in the metabolism of benzoate and cyclohexanecarboxylate by *Rhodopseudomonas paulstris*. J Gen Microbiol 129: 2413-2420

Kiyohara H, Nagao K (1977) Enzymatic conversion of 1-hydroxy-2-naphthoate in phenanthrene-grown *Aeromonas* sp. S45P1. Agric Biol Chem 41:705-707

Langkau B, Chisla S, Buder R, Ziegler K, Fuchs G (1990) 2-Aminobenzoyl-CoA
    monooxygenase/reductase, a novel type of flavoenzyme. Identification of the reaction products.
    Eur J Biochem 191: 365-371
Martinez-Blanco H, Reglero A, Luengo JM (1990a) Carbon catabolite regulation of phenylacetyl-
    CoA ligase from *Pseudomonas putida*. Biochem Biophys Res Commun 167: 891-897
Martinez-Blanco H, Reglero A, Rodriguez-Aparicio LB, Luengo JM (1990b) Purification and
    biochemical characterization of phenylacetyl-CoA ligase from *Pseudomonas putida*. J Biol Chem
    265: 7084-7090
McIntire W, Singer TP (1982) Resolution of *p*-cresol methylhydroxylase into catalytically active
    subunits and reconstitution of the flavocytochrome. FEBS Letts 143: 316-318
McIntire W, Edmonson DE, Singer TP, Hopper DJ (1981) 8α-O-Tyrosyl-FAD, the prosthetic group
    of bacterial *p*-cresol methylhydroxylase. Biochemistry 20: 3068-3075
Powlowski J, Dagley S (1985) The ß-ketoadipate pathway in *Trichosporon cutaneum* modified for
    methyl-substituted metabolites. J Bacteriol 163: 1126-1135
Rahim MA, Sih CJ (1966) Mechanisms of steroid oxidation by microorganisms. XI Enzymatic
    cleavage of the pregnane side chain. J Biol Chem 241: 3615- 3623
Reeve CD, Moreman AD, Hopper DJ (1988) Alkylphenol hydroxylases in the oxidation of *p*-cresol,
    4-ethylphenol and 4-n-propylphenol by *Pseudomonas putida* JD1. FEMS Microbiol Letts
    52: 251-254
Reeve CD, Carver MA, Hopper DJ (1989) The purification and characterisation of 4-ethylphenol
    methylenehydroxylase, a flavocytochrome from *Pseudomonas putida* JD1. Biochem J
    263:431-437
Reeve CD, Carver MA, Hopper DJ (1990) Stereochemical aspects of the oxidation of 4-ethylphenol
    by the bacterial enzyme 4-ethylphenol methylenehydroxylase. Biochem J 269: 815-819
Roberts DJ, Fedorak PM, Hrudey SE (1987) Comparison of the fates of the methyl carbons of
    m-cresol and *p*-cresol in methanogenic consortia. Can J Microbiol 33: 335-338
Smolenski WJ, Suflita JM (1987) Biodegradation of cresol isomers under anoxic conditions. Appl
    Environ Microbiol 53: 710-716
Trudgill PW (1984) Microbial degradation of the alicyclic ring: structurel relationships and
    metabolic pathways. In: Gibson DT (ed) Microbial degradation of organic compounds. Marcel
    Dekker Inc. New York, pp 131-180
Ziegler K, Braun K, Bockler A, Fuchs G (1987) Studies on the anaerobic degradation of benzoic acid
    and 2-aminobenzoic acid by a denitrifying *Pseudomonas* strain. Arch Microbiol 149: 662-69
Ziegler K, Buder R, Winter J, Fuchs G (1989) Activation of aromatic acids and aerobic
    2-aminobenzoate metabolism in a denitrifying *Pseudomonas* strain. Arch Microbiol 151:171-176

Chapter 2

Degradation of Haloaromatic Compounds

K. H. Engesser and P. Fischer

Economical and Ecological Relevance of Halogenated Aromatic Hydrocarbons (HAHs)

An ever increasing number of halogenated organic compounds has been produced by industry in the last few decades. These compounds are employed as biocides, for synthetic polymers, as solvents, and as synthetic intermediates. Production figures are often incomplete, and total production has frequently to be extrapolated from estimates for individual countries.

Hexachlorobenzene production, for instance, was estimated at about 10 000 tonne yr^{-1} in the 1970s (Rippen and Frank 1986). Total polychlorobenzene production, since its introduction to industrial use, has been calculated at roughly 750 000 tonne (Reineke and Knackmuss 1988). About two thirds of this overall production are accredited to have entered closed processes. Consequently, 250 000 tonne must have been released more or less directly into the environment. Around 1980, world production of pentachlorophenol was reported as 40 000 tonne yr^{-1} most of which can be supposed to have entered into the environment. 1,4-Dichlorobenzene production, at the same time, was estimated at around 100 000 tonne yr^{-1} (Rippen et al. 1984). Total 2,4-dichlorophenol production at the end of the 1970s was calculated in excess of 70 000 tonne yr^{-1} (Behret 1989).

Compounds of this type as a rule are highly persistent against biodegradation and belong, as "recalcitrant" chemicals, to the class of so-called xenobiotics. This term is used to characterise chemical substances which have no or limited structural analogy to natural compounds for which degradation pathways have evolved over billions of years. Xenobiotics frequently have some common features, e.g. high octanol/water partitioning coefficients and low water solubility which makes for a high accumulation ratio in the biosphere (bioaccumulation potential) (Johnson and Kennedy 1973).

Recalcitrant compounds therefore are found accumulated in mammals, especially in fat tissue, animal milk supplies (Frank and Braun 1989), and also in human milk (Collins *et al.* 1982; Ip and Phillips 1989; Skaare and Polder 1990). Highly sophisticated analytical techniques have been developed for the detection of organochlorines at the trace and ultratrace level (Burse *et al.* 1990).

Chlorinated aromatic compounds in many cases display acute or chronic toxicity for humans, with the probability also of mutagenic, cancerogenic (Nesnow *et al.* 1986), and teratogenic effects (Magnus-Francis 1990). Moreover, HAHs frequently are contaminated with highly pernicious polychlorinated dibenzofurans and dibenzodioxins (Hagenmaier 1986). Because of extreme biological effects at very low concentration (Whitlock 1990, Ryan *et al.* 1990, Safe 1990), many HAHs have been included in the list of "Priority Pollutants". This list expresses the public concern about uncontrolled use of these chemicals (Keith and Telliard 1979), and at the same time recognises the tremendous waste disposal problems (Levine and Chitwood 1985).

For a possible microbial clean-up of environmental contamination, one has to differentiate clearly between "point source" and "dispersed" pollution. In the first case, large amounts of chemicals, in high concentration, are present in one location (landfills, waste dumps, industrial effluents, accidental spills). In dispersed pollution, chemical concentration is low but spread over a large area or volume. Different strategies of bioremediation are required for these two types of pollution.

There are also diverse natural sources for HAHs. Marine aquifers, for example, produce a number of brominated compounds (Siuda and DeBernardis 1973, Neidleman and Geigert 1987, Wannstedt *et al.* 1990). The presence of such chloro and bromo compounds, especially in marine environments, has presented a challenge to microorganisms which sometimes develop astonishing degradative capabilities for these halogenated structures.

Biodegradation of HAHs is covered in a number of reviews (Reineke and Knackmuss 1988; Reineke 1986; Ribbons *et al.* 1987; Häggblom 1990; Ghosal *et al.* 1985; Commandeur and Parsons 1990; Rochkind-Dubinsky *et al.* 1986; Leisinger and Brunner 1986; Neilson 1990; Rasul-Chaudry and Chapalamadugu 1991) which concentrate *inter alia* on single classes of HAHs, on ecological aspects, on genetics or on bioremediation techniques. In the present review, special emphasis is placed on the mechanisms by which halide is liberated from organic molecules (Table 2.1).

In sharp contrast to aliphatic halides (Knackmuss 1981), the carbon-halogen bond in aryl halides is not susceptible to hydrolysis by nucleophilic displacement reactions. Frequently, halide elimination is observed only as a secondary process after metabolic transformation of the HAHs to non-aromatic, i.e. aliphatic or olefinic intermediates ("late" elimination). In the course of an alternative mechanism, enzyme-mediated addition of hydroxyl groups or other nucleophiles or of electrophiles (e.g. hydratation, epoxidation, dioxygenation) is followed by elimination of H-Hal ("early" elimination). Reductive halide displacement represents a third mechanistic possibility.

The term "(bio)degradation" will be used in this review only when HAHs are completely mineralised, with stoichiometric release of halide, i.e. synonymous with biomineralisation. In contrast, processes will be characterised as "(bio)transformation" which result in some structural alteration only of the substrate. Frequently, only the disappearance of the substrate is monitored without establishing either the carbon balance or the stoichiometry of the overall reaction. This is likewise subsumed under the term "(bio)transformation" which thus may also cover incomplete metabolisation.

There is reason to assume that such biotransformation processes (also called "cometabolism") represent a major way for the removal of recalcitrant compounds from

Table 2.1. Representative examples for bacterial degradation or transformation of haloarenes

Class of compounds	Bacterial strain/genus	Mech-anism	Reference
1. Halobenzoates			
4-chlorobenzoate	Pseudomonas	H	Klages and Lingens 1980
3-chlorobenzoate	Pseudomonas sp. B13	E	Dorn *et al.* 1974
polyhalobenzoates	Pseudomonas aeruginosa JB2	?	Hickey and Focht 1990
2-chlorobenzoate	Pseudomonas	E	Hartmann *et al.* 1989
3-, 4-, and 3,5-dichlorobenzoate	Pseudomonas	E	Hartmann *et al.* 1979
2-halobenzoates	Pseudomonas putida CLB250	0	Engesser and Schulte 1989
4-chlorophenylacetate	Pseudomonas	0	Klages *et al.* 1981
2,4-dichlorobenzoate	Alcaligenes denitrificans	R/H	van den Tweel *et al.* 1987
4-chlorobenzoate	Nocardia	H	Klages and Lingens 1979
2. Halophenoxyalkanoates (Halo-PAs)			
4-chloro-2-methyl-PA	Pseudomonas	E	Gaunt and Evans 1971a,b
2,4-dichloro- / 4-chloro-2-methyl PA	Alcaligenes eutrophus	E	Pieper *et al.* 1988
3. Halophenols			
monochlorophenols	Pseudomonas	E	Knackmuss and Hellwig 1978
polychlorinated phenols	Rhodococcus	H,R,O	Apajalahti + Salkinoja-S.'87
dichlorophenols	Pseudomonas putida	E	Spain and Gibson 1988
monochlorophenols	Rhodococcus sp. AN117, AN213	E	Janke *et al.* 1989
polychlorinated phenols	Flavobacterium	O?, R	Saber and Crawford 1985
polychlorinated phenols	Mycobacterium	H?, O?, B	Häggblom *et al.* 1988
4. Halobenzenes			
dichloro- and trichlorobenzenes	Pseudomonas	E/O?	van der Meer *et al.* 1991
1,2-dichlorobenzene	Pseudomonas	E	Haigler *et al.* 1988
1,4-dichlorobenzene	Alcaligenes	E	Schraa *et al.* 1986
5. Haloanilines			
monochlorinated anilines	Pseudomonas acidovorans	E	Loidl *et al.* 1990
monochlorinated anilines	Pseudomonas ?	E	Latorre *et al.* 1984
6. Polychlorobiphenyls (PCB)			
PCBs	Alcaligenes/Acinetobacter	(B*)	Furukawa *et al.* 1978
PCBs	Alcaligenes eutrophus	(B*)	Bedard *et al.* 1987
PCBs	Acinetobacter	?	Adriaens and Focht 1990
PCBs	Enrichment cultures	R(B)	Quensen *et al.* 1988
7. Halobiarylethers			
4-fluoro-4'-carboxybi-phenylether	Pseudomonas	(P*)	Engesser *et al.* 1990
chlorinated dibenzofurans	Alcaligenes	?	Parsons *et al.* 1990
8. Miscellaneous			
Diethylsimazine	Rhodococcus corallinus	H	Cook and Hütter 1986
DDT	Aerobacter aerogenes	E/R	Wedemeyer 1967
5-chloro-2-hydroxynicotinic acid	Mycobacterium	E/H?	Tibbles *et al.* 1989b
Chloridazon	Phenylobacterium immobile	(P)	Lingens *et al.* 1985

H = hydrolytic; 0 = oxygenolytic; E = elimination; R = reductive; P = partial degradation; ? = not established unequivocally; (B*) = no dehalogenation observed; (P*) = no dehalogenation observed

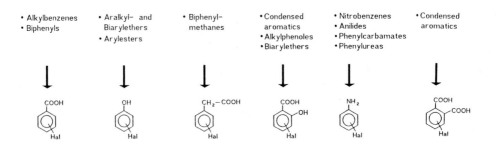

Fig. 2. 1. Central intermediates of haloarene degradation.

the biosphere (Knackmuss 1981). A series of non- or pre-adapted enzymes may transform a substrate stepwise, without energy being derived from the individual reactions. This works only if the co-substrates deliver sufficient energy to maintain the induction and metabolic potential of the active microorganisms. Alternatively, a substrate may be degraded only partially, with the microorganism deriving growth-sustaining energy from these processes, which may be termed "partial degradation".

Channelling of Complex Haloarene Structures into Key Intermediates: the Importance of Model Compounds for Degradation Studies

Among the different haloarenes, produced by industry, there are sometimes extremely toxic compounds such as TCDD (2,3,7,8-tetrachlorodibenzo-p-dioxin), PCP (pentachlorophenol), PCBs (polychlorinated biphenyls), and HCB (hexachlorobenzene). Some HAHs are at the same time highly polar and of high molecular weight (chlorinated and sulfonated lignin components), or very insoluble and toxic (halogenated dibenzofurans and dibenzodioxins). In the "early days" of haloarene degradation research, investigations were therefore confined to readily water-soluble mono- and dihalosubstituted benzoates and phenoxyalkanoates. These substrates are easily degradable, and biochemical studies were consequently speeded up.

Figure 2.1 demonstrates that the degradation of many haloarenes, with great structural variety, may be channelled into a limited number of central intermediates (Dagley 1978). A bouquet of so-called "peripheral" enzymes transforms all kinds of haloarenes into a few mononuclear haloaromatic structures, such as benzoic acids, salicylates, anilines, and phenols. Chloro-substituted phenoxyalkanoates, chloronaphthalines, and chlorobiphenyls, for instance, are transformed by these peripheral sequences. Biodegradation of 4,4'-dichlorobiphenyl affords 4-chlorobenzoate as an essential intermediate (Kimbara *et al.* 1988), closely following the degradation pathway for biphenyl (see Fig. 2.1). Chlorinated benzoic acids are also reported as intermediates of polychlorinated biphenyl (PCB) degradation, independent of chlorine content.

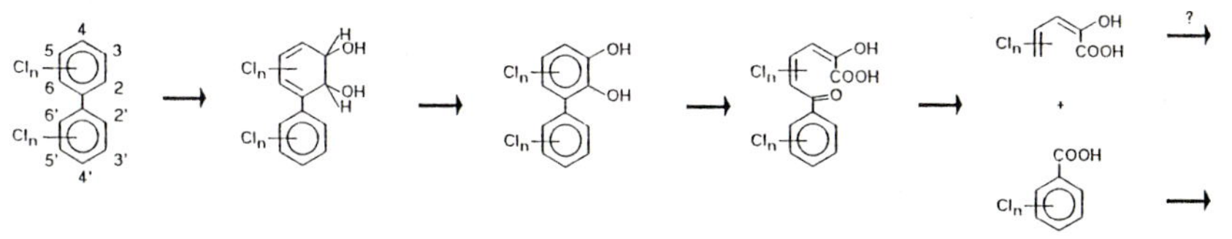

Fig. 2.2. Aerobic degradation of polychlorinated biphenyls by an *Achromobacter* species.

Polychlorinated Biphenyls (PCBs)

Following an early report on the aerobic degradation of polychlorinated biphenyls by an *Achromobacter* species (Ahmed and Focht 1973), an overwhelming amount of information has been presented by many different groups (Ballschmiter *et al.* 1977; Baxter *et al.* 1975; Furukawa and Matsumura 1976; Furukawa *et al.*; 1978, Furukawa *et al.* 1979). The biochemistry of PCB transformation was generally described as analogous to the established pathway of biphenyl catabolism (see Fig. 2.2) (Omori *et al.* 1986; Catelani *et al.* 1971). In a first step, halo-substituted phenylcatechols are formed intermediately by action of biphenyl 2,3-dioxygenases and 2,3-dihydro-2,3-dihydroxybiphenyl dehydrogenases. Subsequent meta-cleavage and hydrolysis of the ring cleavage product gives chloro-substituted benzoates from one phenyl ring and 2-oxo-4-pentenoates, with a varying number of chlorines, from the other (Shields *et al.* 1985; Kimbara *et al.* 1988; Kilpi *et al.* 1988; Adriaens *et al.* 1989). In some cases, (chlorophenyl)glyoxylic acids or chlorinated acetophenones are accumulated, indicating the existence of other marginal biotransformation pathways (Shiaris and Sayler 1982; Bedard *et al.* 1987). From Kanechlor 400^R (a technical PCB mixture of mainly tetrachlorobiphenyls), chlorobenzoates, dihydroxy compounds (supposedly chlorocatechols), and meta-cleavage compounds, all with two to four chlorine substituents, are produced during metabolisation by an *Acinetobacter* species (Furukawa *et al.* 1983). More heavily chlorinated PCBs are metabolised only slightly, with dihydroxypentachlorobiphenyl derivatives being detected as sole metabolites.

Aerobic biotransformation of PCBs via biphenyl-related pathways seems to be subject to some structural restrictions which are mostly due to the prevalent 2,3-dioxygenation mode of cometabolic attack on PCBs:

1 An increasing number of chlorine substituents generally decreases biodegradation rates in aerobic systems; consequently, PCB congeners with more than five chlorines are virtually not transformed (Bedard *et al.* 1987).
2 One unsubstituted ring facilitates biotransformation.
3 One ring at least must have one ortho and the adjacent meta position unsubstituted.

Steric screening by the bulky chlorine atoms renders such PCB congeners, where all ortho and/or meta positions are blocked, not or only slightly biodegradable. As mentioned above, PCBs generally are attacked via 2,3-dioxygenation (Safe 1984). Some microorganisms seem to possess a different set of biphenyl degrading enzymes by which PCB congeners are attacked, unexpectedly, in 3,4-position (Bedard *et al.* 1986). Bacteria of this type (e.g. *Corynebacterium* sp MB1 and *Alcaligenes eutrophus* H850) are able to oxygenate, in addition to lower chlorinated PCBs, even 2,5,2',5'-tetrachloro-, 2,4,5,2',5'-pentachloro- and, albeit slower, 2,4,5,2',4',5'-hexachlorobiphenyl, with unusual metabolites such as chlorinated acetophenones being formed.

All microorganisms, described so far as competent for PCB transformation, do not use PCBs with more than two chlorine substituents as sole source of carbon (Bedard *et al*. 1986; Adriaens *et al*. 1989; Shields *et al*. 1985). The respective transformations thus must be termed cometabolic. For one mixed culture, growing solely on a PCB cocktail containing mostly tetrachlorobiphenyls, it has not been clarified whether the microorganism in fact used the higher chlorinated congeners for growth (Kimbara *et al*. 1988).

If biphenyl is added to facilitate any energy-consuming biotransformation process, PCBs under such relaxed conditions are more susceptible to microbial attack (Focht and Brunner 1985; Brunner *et al*. 1985). For example, after addition of both an *Acinetobacter* strain P6 and biphenyl to PCB-containing soil, up to 27% of labeled PCB was recovered as $^{14}CO_2$. Addition of the microorganism alone, without biphenyl, did not improve biodegradation (Brunner *et al*. 1985). Likewise, degradation of 4-chlorobiphenyl, as a PCB model, was greatly enhanced by addition of the 4-chlorobiphenyl-degrading bacterium *Alcaligenes* A4 (Hill *et al*. 1989). The strain survives sufficiently long in soil to offer the opportunity for its application in bioremediation processes.

In most of the experiments reviewed above, only PCB substrate disappearance was monitored. Due to the very low biotransformation rates (Bedard *et al*. 1987) and the difficulty of measuring chloride in soil matrices, no stoichiometry of chloride release is given as a rule. There are indications, however, of cometabolic chloride release, after meta-cleavage of chloro-substituted phenyl catechols, being a feasible though highly inefficient process (Adriaens and Focht 1990).

The halobenzoates, haloacetophenones or other metabolic intermediates, generated by these cometabolic PCB-degrading processes, should in principle be converted to halocatechols. It cannot be ruled out, however, that other pathways are involved.

Chlorinated N-Heterocycles

Enzymes of biphenyl-degrading organisms have been found to be rather unspecific. Accordingly, heterocyclic biphenyl analogues like Antipyrin and Chloridazon are partially degraded by e.g. *Phenylobacterium immobile* and similar strains since the bacteria can utilise at least one phenyl ring as a source of carbon and energy (Lingens *et al*. 1985). The hete-rocyclic moiety is not degraded at all, and is accumulated quantitatively. Comparative analysis of some 16S-ribosomal nucleic acid partial sequences showed that this microorganism constituted a new genus even though the transformation pathway for the heterocyclic substrates is identical, except for one enzyme, with that of the biphenyl-degrading organisms (Ludwig *et al*. 1984). Intensive

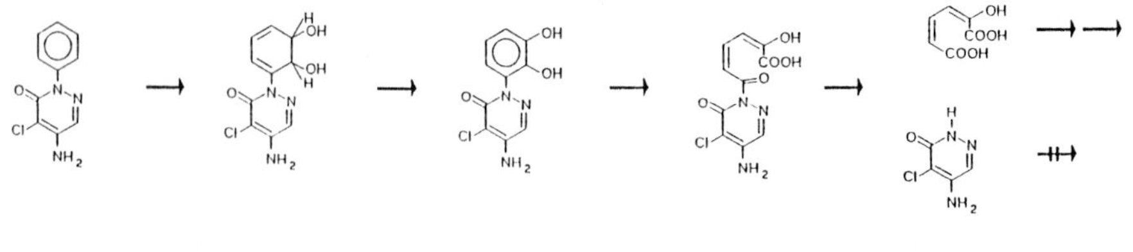

Fig. 2.3. Chlorinated *N*-heterocycle degradation by *Phenylobacterium immobile*.

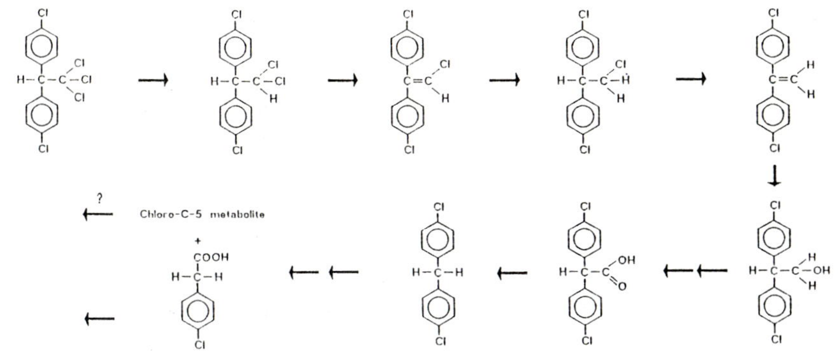

Fig. 2.4. Co-metabolism of DDT by a *Klebsiella (Aerobacter) aerogenes* strain.

characterisation of the N-heterocycle pathway enzymes (see Fig. 2.3) revealed this to be an amidase which releases the C-6 metabolite, 4-oxalocrotonate (2-hydroxymuconate), instead of the C-5 metabolite 2-oxo-4-pentenoate, generated by regular hydrolase activity (Schmitt *et al.* 1984; Sauber *et al.* 1977). These Chloridazon-degrading bacteria also possess a hydrolase-type enzyme, the presence of which could be demonstrated after growth on cinnamic acid (Tittmann *et al.* 1980).

A similar process has been described for the transformation and partial utilisation of 3-chloroquinoline-8-carboxylic acid by *Pseudomonas* spec. EK III. The heterocycle is degraded to the dead-end product 5-chloro-2-hydroxynicotinic acid and pyruvate which serves as the principal carbon source (Tibbles *et al.* 1989a). Another bacterium can utilise this nicotinic acid derivative for growth (see Hydrolytic Displacement of Halogen).

1,1,1-Trichloro-2,2-bis(4-chlorophenyl)ethane   (DDT)

DDT was transformed cometabolically (see Fig. 2.4) by a *Klebsiella aerogenes (Aerobacter aerogenes)* strain, *via* reductive dechlorination, to 1,1-dichloro-2,2-bis (4-chlorophenyl)ethene (DDD). In a second step, HCl is eliminated from the DDD and the double bond hydrogenated. The 1-chloro-2,2-bis(4-chlorophenyl)ethane thus formed finally yields 4,4'-dichlorobenzophenone and 4,4'-dichlorodiphenylmethane (Wedemeyer 1967). Other authors have shown these metabolites to be cometabolised, by a diphenylmethane-degrading *Hydrogenomonas* strain, to 4-chlorophenylacetate (Focht and Alexander 1970, Focht and Alexander 1971) which already has been demonstrated to be smoothly degradable (see Oxygenolytic Elimination of Halogen).

In a combined anaerobic/aerobic process, this *Hydrogenomonas* strain was found to first dechlorinate the DDT side chain and, in a second stage, metabolise the 4,4'-dichlorodiphenylmethane to a (4-chlorophenyl)acetate and chlorinated ring cleavage products (see Fig. 2.4). DDT was later also reported to be degraded very slowly in a similar experiment with a *Pseudomonas aeruginosa* strain. With lactate as co-substrate, the trichloromethyl moiety was claimed to be transformed to a carboxyl group under anaerobic or microaerophilic conditions (Golovleva and Skryabin 1981), followed by decarboxylation and reductive dechlorination of both rings. The resulting

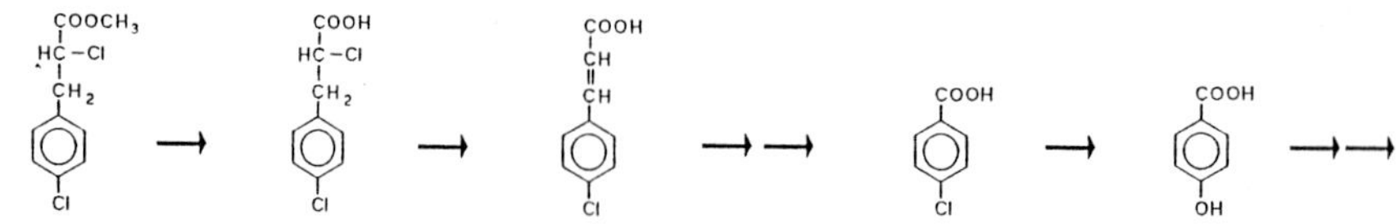

Fig. 2.5. Degradation of the herbicide Bidisin.

biphenylmethane was proposed as source of carbon and energy under aerobic conditions (Golovleva and Skryabin 1981). In some cases, reductive removal of chlorine precedes metabolism by aerobic microorganisms. This will be dealt with separately (see Liberation of Halide by Reductive Mechanisms).

Bidisin

Degradation of the herbicide Bidisin, methyl 2-chloro-3-(4-chlorophenyl)propionate), demonstrates strikingly how a complex structure is channeled into the established catabolic pathway for a basic structure (in this case 4-chlorobenzoate). After hydrolysis of the ester function, the aliphatic chlorine is eliminated, yielding 4-chlorocinnamate (see Fig.2.5). 4-Chlorobenzoate is formed in the ensuing steps according to the regular fatty acid oxidation pathway. This intermediate undergoes hydrolytic dechlorination to 4-hydroxybenzoate (see Hydrolytic Displacement of Halogen) which in turn is smoothly degraded (Köcher et al. 1976).

Chloronaphthalines

Knowledge concerning degradation of chloronaphthalines is scarce. Chlorosalicylates have been shown to be intermediates in the transformation of 1- and 2-chloronaphthaline (Morris and Barnsley 1982) and 1,4-dichloronaphthaline (Durham and Stewart 1987). Metabolic sequences dissimilating naphthalene via salicylate obviously are responsible for these reactions which, however, do not sustain growth of the organisms (see also Dehalogenation of Halocatechols after Meta-Cleavage).

Halogenated Biarylethers

As indicated above, little is known about degradation pathways for halogenated biarylethers (Rast et al. DBP 1990). Turnover even of the heavily chlorinated 2,3,7,8-tetrachlorodibenzo-p-dioxin was reported although no products of these (generally very slow) processes were characterised (see for example Quensen and Matsumura 1983). This is partially due to the sometimes highly dangerous properties of halogenated biaryl ethers, and to their very limited solubility. Quite recently, degradation of a model compound, 4-carboxy-4'-fluorodiphenyl ether, was described (Engesser et al. 1990a), 4-fluorophenol being found to accumulate quantitatively in the growth medium (see Fig. 2.6).

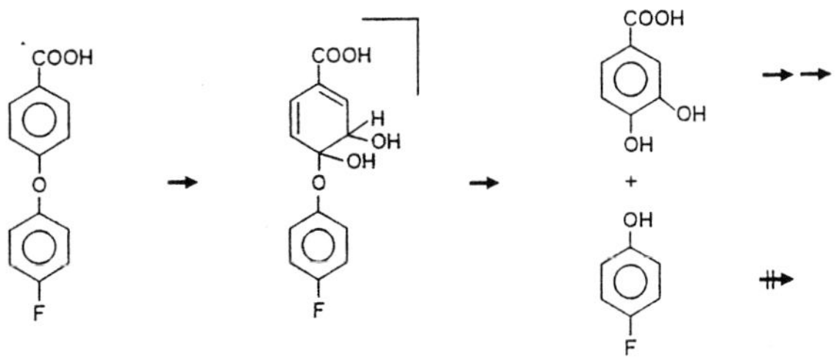

Fig. 2.6. Degradation of a model halogenated biarylether, 4-carboxy-4'-fluorodiphenyl ether.

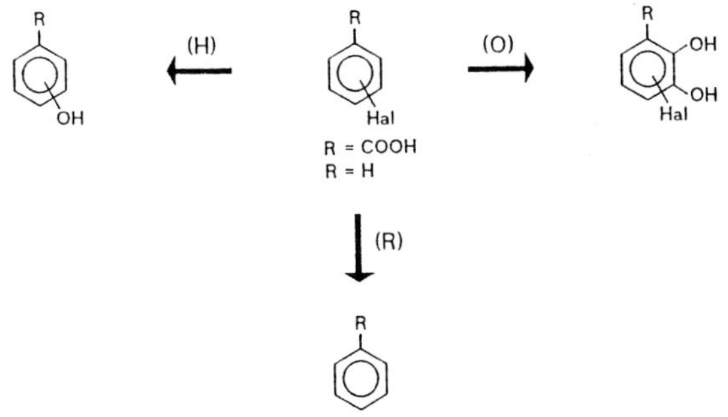

Fig. 2.7. Three routes for the degradation of mononuclear benzene derivatives.

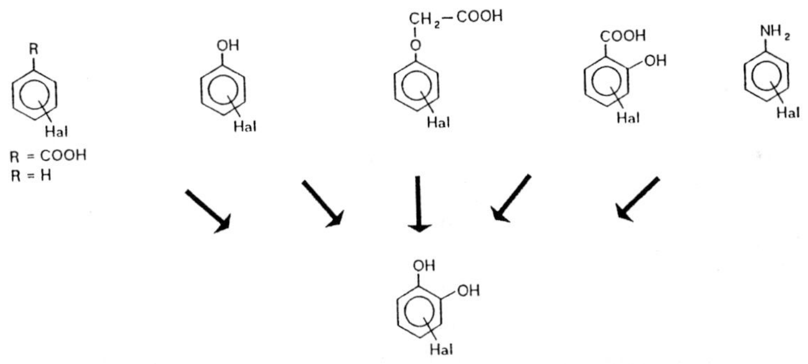

Fig. 2.8. Precursors for the halocatechol branch of mononuclear benzene degradation.

Chlorocatechols as Central Intermediates in Metabolisation of Chlorinated Aromatic Structures

As shown above, many complex haloaromatic structures are reduced to the limited number of basic mononuclear structures collated in Figure 2.1. Further metabolisation of these benzene derivatives proceeds along three different routes (see Fig. 2.7):

1 "hydrolytic" or monooxygenolytic displacement of halide yielding monohydroxy
   benzene structures (Horvath 1971);
2 reductive liberation of halide (Tweel *et al.* 1987);
3 dioxygenation and subsequent dehydrogenation to halo-substituted
   dihydroxybenzenes (halocatechols).

For the halocatechol branch, the diversity of the respective "halocatechol precursors" is
shown in Figure 2.8.

This mechanistic strategy has been established for chlorobenzoates (Chatterjee *et al.*
1981; Hartmann *et al.* 1989; Hartmann *et al.* 1979; Don *et al.* 1985; Hickey and Focht
1990; Haller and Finn 1979; Horvath and Alexander 1970; Reineke and Knackmuss
1978a,b) as well as for fluorobenzoates (Engesser *et al.* 1990b; Hughes 1965; Vora *et
al.* 1988; Horvath and Flathman 1976; Harper and Blakley 1971; Clarke *et al.* 1975;
Ali *et al.* 1962). In general, the principle of converging pathways allows for one
metabolic sequence to operate on substrates as different structurally as halobenzoates,
haloacetophenones (Higson and Focht 1990b), halophenoxyalkanoates, haloanilines,
halophenols, and halobenzenes.

3-Chlorobenzoate

A 3-chlorobenzoate(3CB)-utilising bacterium, *Pseudomonas* sp. B13, was isolated in
1974 after pre-enrichment with benzoate (Dorn *et al.* 1974). Of all the isomeric
monohalobenzoates, this organism utilises only 3-chloro- and 3-bromobenzoate and,
after adaptation, 4-fluorobenzoate. Halosubstituted cyclohexadienediol carboxylic acids
are formed in an initial dioxygenation step which are dehydrogenated enzymatically to a
mixture of 3- and 4-chlorocatechol or 4-fluorocatechol in the degradation, respectively,
of 3-chloro- and 4-fluorobenzoate (Reineke and Knackmuss 1978a,b; Dorn and
Knackmuss 1978a,b).

(Chlorophenoxy)alkanoates

Studies on the biodegradation of (2,4-dichlorophenoxy)acetate (2,4-D) and (2-methyl-4-
chlorophenoxy)acetate (MCPA) likewise showed chlorocatechols as central
intermediates for all strains investigated so far. In the first step, the aryl alkyl ether
bond is labilised by action of a monooxygenase. The hemiacetals thus generated are
chemically unstable, and rearrange to phenols and glyoxylate or homologous α-keto
acids (Loos *et al.* 1967a,b,c; Bollag *et al.* 1967; Tiedje and Alexander 1969; Evans *et
al.* 1971a,b; Gaunt and Evans 1961; Gamar and Gaunt 1971). These substituted
phenols are subject to a second monohydroxylation reaction yielding catechols (Bollag
et al. 1968; Gaunt and Evans 1971a,b). One representative enzyme for this process, a
2,4-dichlorophenol hydroxylase, has been purified and characterised as highly specific
for chlorophenols (Beadle and Smith 1982; Liu and Chapman 1984). Phenol, on the
other hand, is not a substrate for this enzyme.

A direct reductive ether cleavage, not in accord with this general reaction scheme, has
been described for the transformation of phenoxyalkanoates with long aliphatic chains
(MacRae and Alexander 1963) as well as of (2,4,5-trichlorophenoxy)acetate (2,4,5-T)
(Mikesell and Boyd 1985). Hydroxylation of the aromatic nucleus prior to ether
cleavage was recognised to yield non-degradable products (Faulkner and Woodcock

1964; Evans et al. 1971a). An *Aspergillus niger* species was found to totally degrade 2,4-D with elimination of chloride before cleavage of the ether bond (Shailubhai et al. 1983).

As mentioned above, chlorophenols are subject to monohydroxylation yielding chlorocatechols. This transformation can be effected by unspecific phenol hydroxylases (Knackmuss and Hellwig 1978) as well as by highly specialised chlorophenol hydroxylases. Among these, the enzyme coded on the plasmid pJP4 has been shown to strictly prefer 2,4-dichloro- and 2-methyl-4-chlorophenol over monochlorophenols, phenol not being transformed at all (Liu and Chapman 1984; Pieper et al. 1988). The respective enzyme from an *Acinetobacter* behaved essentially similar. Phenols, although not transformed, acted as uncoupling agents, i.e. caused H_2O_2 production from NAD(P)H (Beadle and Smith 1982). The phenomenon of preferential attack of chlorinated compounds over the natural substrate is encountered to a lesser degree also in chlorocatechol degradation.

Chloroanilines

Chlorinated anilines are transformed to chlorocatechols in a one-step reaction, two hydroxyl groups being inserted geminal and ortho to the amino function by an aniline dioxygenase. The unstable hemi-aminal thus formed eliminates NH_3 yielding catechols (Bachofer et al. 1975; Janke et al. 1984). Isomeric halocatechols are produced in varying percentage, depending on the strain employed, from unsymmetrically substituted anilines (Reber et al. 1979; Schukat et al. 1983; Zeyer et al. 1985; Ihn et al. 1989; Janke et al. 1989; Surovtseva et al. 1980; Surovtseva et al. 1986; Latorre et al. 1984; Loidl et al. 1990), as in the case of unsymmetrically substituted halobenzoates (Engesser et al. 1990b). Thus, 2- and 4-chloroaniline are transformed, respectively, to 3-chloro- and 4-chlorocatechol only. From 3-chloroaniline, 4-chlorocatechol is formed preferentially.

Chlorosalicylates

Chlorosalicylates, like chlorophenols, can be monooxygenated yielding chlorocatechols (Rubio et al. 1986a). Chlorosalicylate-degrading organisms have been constructed by introducing genes encoding a salicylate 1-hydroxylase into a strain with chlorocatechol degrading capacity. Turnover rates vary considerably between the different isomeric chlorosalicylates, with the 3-chloro isomer being the most difficult to degrade (Rubio et al. 1986a,b). Degradation of 3,6-dichloro-2-methoxybenzoic acid (Dicamba) via 3,6-dichlorosalicylate was reported, though without any details on the further metabolisation of the halosalicylate.

A *Bacillus brevi* strain, originally described to degrade 5-chlorosalicylate, was reported to also dissimilate 3,5-dichlorosalicylate (Krueger et al. 1989), 5-chlorosalicylate being proposed as the substrate of a ring-cleaving gentisate 1,2-dioxygenase. This would constitute one of the very few cases of direct ring cleavage of chlorosubstituted monohydroxy arenes (not dihydroxyarenes or catechols) (Crawford et al. 1979). The fact that the 5-chlorosalicylate-degrading *Bacillus* dissimilates only 3,5-, but not 3,6-dichlorosalicylate indicates that this compound is not degraded via ring cleavage of 3,6-dichlorosalicylate. Rather, transformation of the substrate to a catechol by action of a salicylate monohydroxylase precedes degradation.

Halobenzenes

These are metabolised frequently by dioxygenases yielding halo-substituted dienediols which in turn are dehydrogenated to halocatechols (Reineke and Knackmuss 1984; Sperl and Harvey 1988; Gibson *et al.* 1968). Di- and trihalobenzenes have also been described to be metabolised *via* halocatechols (Bont *et al.* 1986; Meer *et al.* 1991; Spain and Nishino 1987; Schraa *et al.* 1986; Oltmanns *et al.* 1988). Even *o*-dichlorobenzene which is hardly attacked by most haloarene degraders is metabolised by a *Pseudomonas* strain *via* initial dioxygenase attack (Haigler *et al.* 1988). Chlorotoluenes were reported to be degraded despite two mutually "incompatible" substituents on the same aromatic nucleus (see Degradation of Mixtures of Halo and Alkyl Arenes). Degradation of *p*-chlorotoluene followed the normal chlorobenzene metabolism route, i.e. 2,3-dihydroxylation and formation of both chloro- and methyl-substituted catechols. Subsequently, chlorine is eliminated from the respective muconic acid derivative after cycloisomerisation while the methyl substituent is retained in a methyl-substituted dienelactone (Haigler and Spain 1989). 2,6-Dichlorotoluene degradation was once claimed for a landfill-isolate *via* a catechol pathway (Vandenbergh *et al.* 1981) but this preliminary report was not followed up.

The alternative reductive dehalogenation mechanism is discussed later (see Liberation of Halide by Reductive Mechanisms).

Biochemistry of Halocatechol Degradation

4-Fluorocatechol

Catechol is degraded in many bacteria along the well-established ortho or 3-oxoadipate pathway (Ornston and Stanier 1966; Ornston 1966). A catechol 1,2-dioxygenase generates *cis,cis*-muconic acid. This is cycloisomerised to (+)-muconolactone and muconoenollactone which in turn is hydrolyzed to 3-oxoadipate. This is degraded finally to acetyl-CoA and succinate (Fig.2.9).

This mechanism was found to be effective, however, only for the catabolism of 4-fluorocatechol (Clarke *et al.* 1975; Engesser *et al.* 1990b; Engesser *et al.* 1980; Schreiber *et al.* 1980) which is cleaved, in contrast to other halocatechols, by regular catechol 1,2-dioxygenases at sufficiently high rates to allow growth on 4-fluorobenzoate (Dorn and Knackmuss 1978b; Schreiber *et al.* 1980). Ring cleavage of halocatechols generally forms the bottleneck of haloarene degradation via ortho pathways. The astonishing reactivity of 4-fluorocatechol can be rationalised in terms of the strong mesomeric electron release of the parafluorine substituent (Engesser *et al.* 1988). For all other halocatechols, the inductive electron-withdrawing effect of the halogen drastically decreases reaction rates of the regular oxygen-dependent ortho-pyrocatechases (Dorn and Knackmuss 1978b).

Ortho-cleavage of 4-fluorocatechol yields 3-fluoromuconate which can be smoothly cycloisomerised to 4-fluoromuconolactone (Harper and Blakley 1971). This lactone which, under physiological conditions, is chemically reasonably stable, may be transformed enzymatically by regular enollactone hydrolases to maleylacetate with concomitant formation of fluoride (Schlömann *et al.* 1990a,b). This pathway is likely to operate also in the Gram-negative strain FLB300 which showed high maleylacetate reductase activity (Engesser *et al.* 1990b). The reductive step, catalyzed by this enzyme,

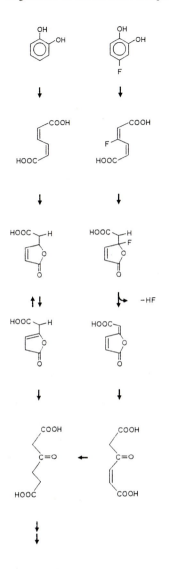

Fig. 2.9. Degradation of catechol and fluorocatechol via the "ortho" pathway.

has the 4-fluorolactone degradation converging with the normal 3-oxoadipate pathway. For dissimilation of 4-fluorocatechol *via* the ortho pathway, only one additional enzyme is required over that already present in strains degrading catechol *via* the 3-oxoadipate pathway (see Fig. 2.9). It should be mentioned, however, that in many strains degradation of 4-fluorolactone appears much more complex both as to the enzymes involved and to stability and structure of the transformation products (Schlömann *et al.* 1990a,b).

No productive, i.e. growth-sustaining degradation process, for 3-fluorocatechol has been described so far. Either this substrate is hardly transformed at all, or the 2-fluoromuconic acid intermediate is resistant against the cycloisomerases of all bacterial sources tested (Engesser *et al.* 1980; Schmidt and Knackmuss 1980; Schmidt *et al.* 1980).3-Fluorocatechol thus represents a typical non-biodegradable haloaromatic compound.

Very recently, anaerobic consortia were described to reductively dechlorinate polychlorocatechols to lesser chlorinated derivatives (Allard *et al.* 1991) (see Liberation of Halide by Reductive Mechanisms). The metabolism of Fluorocatechols, however, was not investigated.

Specialised Enzymes for Halocatechol Catabolism: Three Reasons for Non-biodegradability

As mentioned above, the simple degradative mechanism for 4-fluorocatechol does not work for 4-chlorocatechol. Firstly, the chlorine substituent severely retards ring cleavage by regular ortho pyrocatechase (Dorn and Knackmuss 1978b; Engesser *et al.* 1988). Cycloisomerisation of 3- and especially 2-chloromuconic acid (see also Fig. 2.10) is severely retarded as well since conventional enzymes convert substituted muconic acids only very slowly because of steric hindrance by the rather bulky chlorine and methyl substituents. This illustrates the second major constraint of haloarene catabolism by regular, non-specialised enzymes which often lack the unspecificity to cope with bulky substrates.

The product of 3-chloromuconate cycloisomerisation, unlike 4-fluoromuconolactone (Harper and Blakley 1971; Schlömann *et al.* 1990b), is chemically unstable and eliminates halide, thus forming a doubly unsaturated lactone (dienelactone) in the final degradative step (Schmidt and Knackmuss 1980). This dienelactone is a dead-end product for which no enzymatic activity is present in any particular bacterium not specialised for halocatechol degradation. Cometabolic degradation of haloarenes thus suffers from a third constraint, the formation of dead-end products.

Halocatechol Degradation via Specialised Ortho Pathway Enzymes

Halocatechols are intermediates in the degradation of halobenzoates, halobenzenes, haloanilines, halophenols, and other halogenated arenes. These intermediates are effectively degraded by many strains (Dorn *et al.* 1974; Bollag *et al.* 1968; Pieper *et al.* 1988; Ditzelmüller *et al.* 1989; Horvath *et al.* 1990; Don *et al.* 1985; Evans *et al.* 1971a,b). Specialised catechol 1,2-dioxygenases generally attack mono- or dihalogenated catechols, in preference over catechol (Dorn and Knackmuss 1978a,b; Pieper *et al.* 1988), in an intradiol fashion with formation of substituted muconic acids. Of the various isomeric dichlorocatechols, only 3,5- and 3,6-dichlorocatechol are transformed at excellent rates to, respectively, 2,4- and 2,5-dichloromuconic acid (Pieper *et al.* 1988; Hartmann *et al.* 1979; Bont *et al.* 1986; Spain and Nishino 1987; Schraa *et al.* 1986). Dioxygenation of 3,4- and 4,5-dichlorocatechols proceeds even slower than with catechol (Pieper *et al.* 1988; Ditzelmüller *et al.* 1989; Schraa *et al.* 1986; Loidl *et al.* 1990). Further metabolism of the corresponding chloromuconic acids seems to be severely impeded as well. At high biomass concentrations, however, release of chloride indicated a slow albeit productive metabolism (Pieper 1986; Furukawa *et al.* 1979).

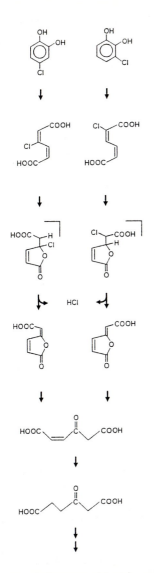

Fig. 2.10. Degradation of chlorocatechols involving cycloisomerisation and spontaneous elimination of hydrogen chloride.

Chlorinated muconic acids are cycloisomerised by more or less specialised chloromuconate cycloisomerases (Schmidt and Knackmuss 1980). Some highly specialised enzymes transform only 2,4-dichloro- and 3-chloromuconic acid at high rates, with 2-chloro- and unsubstituted muconic acid being attacked rather slowly (Pieper et al. 1988; Kuhm et al. 1990).

As shown in Figure 2.10, cycloisomerisation of 2-chloro-*cis, cis*-muconate affords an unstable butenolide which was proposed to form a doubly unsaturated lactone, *trans*-4-carboxymethylenebut-2-ene-4-olide (*trans*-dienelactone), by spontaneous anti-elimination of hydrogen chloride. Cycloisomerisation of the corresponding 3-chloro-*cis, cis*-muconic acid, upon HCl elimination, yielded the *cis*-4-carboxymethylenebut-2-en-4-olide (*cis*-dienelactone) (Schmidt and Knackmuss 1980; Bollag *et al.* 1968).

This is the first halide liberation step in the course of the ortho pathway. At this point, the degradation pathways of catechol and of the halo analogues are branching mechanistically. Only on the 3-oxoadipate level (see below and Fig. 2.9), the two degradation pathways converge again. The chlorocatechol-related pathways have been shown in some cases, however, to have evolved from the enzymes of regular ortho pathways.

Different muconate cycloisomerases, e.g. chloromuconate cycloisomerase from *Pseudomonas putida* (pAC27) and dichloromuconate cycloisomerase of *Alcaligenes eutrophus* JMP134, were shown to be closely related (Yeh *et al.* 1982; Aldrich *et al.* 1987; Ghosal and You 1988), and may even have evolved from common ancestors. This clearly demonstrates nature to be able to cope with new challenges by evolving new activities from pre-existing though inefficient entities. All these enzymes were concluded to follow the same mechanistic pathway, liberating halide from an enzyme-bonded anionic intermediate instead of eliminating HCl from the free chloro-substituted cycloisomerisation product (Schlömann *et al.* 1990b). Nevertheless, these enzymes should not be mistaken with true halidohydrolases which actively remove halide by substitution with either hydroxide or glutathione (Goldman *et al.* 1968).

Enzymes hydrolyzing these dienelactones are termed dienelactone hydrolases. They have been described for many organisms and seem to play an important role in the degradation not only of chloro-, but also of fluoro- and bromoarenes. One enzyme has been purified to homogeneity and characterised by X-ray diffraction (Ngai *et al.* 1987; Pathak and Ollis 1990; Pathak *et al.* 1988).

The products of these reactions are maleylacetate or its ß-chloro derivative (from 3- and 3,5-dichlorocatechol, respectively). Maleylacetates are readily transformed, by a maleylacetate reductase (MAR), to 3-oxo- or ß-ketoadipates whence this pathway was named. The point at which the second chlorine is removed has not yet been established unequivocally. From experiments with an *Arthrobacter* strain which likewise transforms chlorosuccinate to succinate (Duxburry *et al.* 1970), it was deduced that chloromaleylacetate is reduced to 2-chloro-4-oxoadipate followed by hydrolysis to acetyl-CoA and chlorosuccinate which in turn yields succinate. Accordingly, ring-labeled (2,4-dichlorophenoxy)acetate was metabolised to succinate (Tiedje *et al.* 1969). A maleylacetate reductase from a different source was later shown to dehalogenate (ß-chloromaleyl)acetate to chloride and 3-oxoadipate, thereby excluding chlorosuccinate as an intermediate in 3,5-dichlorocatechol degradation. The authors reported that chloromaleylacetate reduction required twice as much NADH as maleylacetate turnover. They concluded that the product of maleylacetate reductase action, chloro-substituted ß-ketoadipate, spontaneously eliminated chloride to maleylacetate which in a second step was reduced to 3-oxoadipate. There remains some doubt as to this mechanism since no purified enzymes were employed. It is doubtful, for instance, whether 2-chloro-4-oxoadipate in fact is sufficiently unstable to spontaneously eliminate chloride, forming maleylacetate. Nevertheless, chlorocatechol degradation can be considered as clearly established from the work on 3-chlorobenzoate and (2,4-dichlorophenoxy)acetate degradation in the last 25 years.

The pathways, detailed above, allow for metabolisation of mono- and dihalo catechols. There is no indication, however, that the enzymes involved can productively metabolise tri- or even more heavily substituted halocatechols. Polychlorinated aromatic substrates with ≥ 3 chlorine atoms per ring therefore must be metabolised *via* different routes. Two exceptions to this rule have recently been proposed. For 1,2,4-trichlorobenzene (1,2,4-TCB), aerobic transformation *via* 3,4,6-trichlorocatechol and subsequent metabolisation along a specialised ortho pathway was suggested (Meer *et al.* 1991). The authors could not exclude the possibility of initial oxygenolytic chloride release (see Oxygenolytic Elimination of Halogen), and did not present any evidence on what happened to the third chlorine of the 1,2,4-TCB substrate. Likewise, aerobic degradation of 1,2,4,5-tetrachlorobenzene has been reported to proceed *via* chlorocatechols (Springer and Rast 1988; Wittich *et al.* 1989). Once again, one cannot exclude initial dechlorination prior to ring cleavage *via* 3,5,6-trichlorocatechol as an intermediate.

Degradation of Mixtures of Halo and Alkyl Arenes

The metabolism of halocatechols *via* so-called meta pathways as a rule is unproductive, resulting in production of dead-end metabolites, slow and non-stoichiometric liberation of halide, and inactivation of the key enzymes, the catechol-2,3-dioxygenases (Bartels *et al.* 1984; Engesser *et al.* 1989a) (for the only exception reported so far, see Dehalogenation of Halocatechols after Meta-Cleavage). This situation still holds today despite many efforts (Engesser KH, unpublished results; Pfeiffer F, personal communication). Alkylcatechols, on the other hand, are generally degraded by enzymes of the meta pathway. Metabolism via ortho-cleavage as a rule leads to accumulation of methyllactones as dead-end metabolites (Engesser *et al.* 1989a). Mixtures of halo- and alkylcatechols therefore cannot be degraded quantitatively since the pathways for these two substrates are mutually incompatible. All efforts have failed so far to isolate bacteria which can productively degrade halocatechols *via* meta pathways, i.e. not in a cometabolic manner. A new selection technique was therefore developed to identify microorganisms with modified ortho pathways. From enrichment experiments with methyllactones, methylcatechol-degrading organisms were isolated which, preferentially or even exclusively, utilise ortho pathways for complete mineralisation of halo and alkyl arene mixtures. The meta-cleaving enzyme was inactivated by transposon insertion to avoid misrouting of halocatechols. Alternatively, enzymes of the methylcatechol ortho pathway were cloned into strains, free of meta pathways (Engesser *et al.* 1989a).

This goes to show that non-biodegradability of otherwise easily metabolisable compounds may also be due to misrouting of substrates. Very recently, a *Pseudomonas* strain was described to degrade a mixture of chlorobenzene and toluene (Pettigrew *et al.* 1991). Chloro- and methylcatechols were found to be accumulated in the culture medium; this did not happen with a mutant of this strain which had been blocked in the gene encoding the meta-pyrocatechase enzyme. Both methyl- and chlorocatechol were metabolised *via* an ortho pathway.

Oxygenolytic Elimination of Halogen

It has been shown in the chapters above that metabolism of haloarenes *via* halocatechols and subsequent ortho cleavage is a useful tool in microbial degradation of these compounds. Such ortho-cleaving routes are restricted, however, to mono- and disubstituted halocatechols. Even these compounds may be rendered slowly

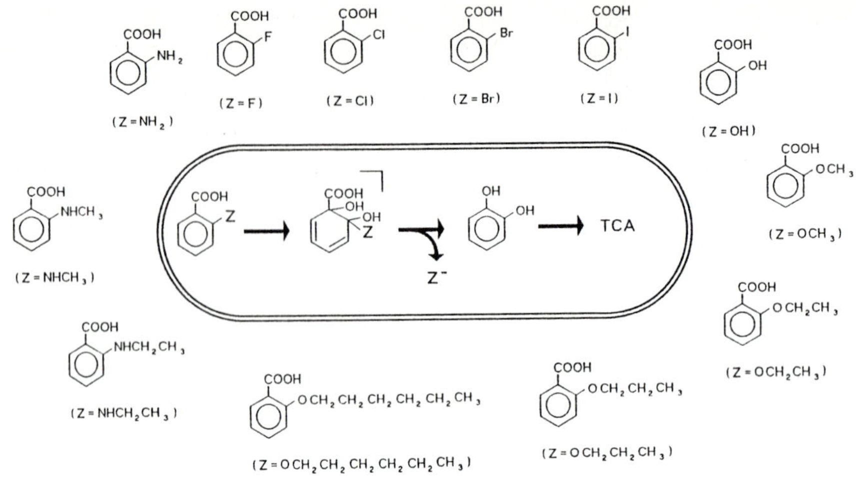

Fig. 2.11. Degradation of various aromatic substrates by initial dioxygenation in *Pseudomonas putida* CLB 250.

biodegradable by unfavourable substitution patterns, e.g. vicinal dihalo substitution. Biomineralisation therefore is greatly facilitated if some mechanism exists by which halo substituents are eliminated at an early metabolic stage.

2-Fluoro- and 2-chlorobenzoate are frequently employed as model substrates for oxygenolytic substituent removal. Dioxygenase attack yields geminal halohydroxy compounds which spontaneously rearomatise to unsubstituted catechol, with concomitant liberation of halide (Engesser *et al.* 1980; Hickey and Focht 1990; Engesser and Schulte 1989; Vora *et al.* 1988). This oxygenolytic mechanism apparently also works for 2-bromo- and, after some mutation, for 2-iodobenzoate (Engesser and Schulte 1989). The halogen-free catechols thus formed are further metabolised along ortho pathways. The 1,2-dioxygenation mechanism was established unequivocally by analysis of the 2-methylbenzoate cometabolism products. For degradation of 2-chlorobenzoate by *Pseudomonas* sp. strain B300, however, oxygenolytic elimination of halide was not confirmed with certainty, and a degradation pathway *via* 3-chlorocatechol could not be definitely excluded (Sylvestre *et al.* 1989).

Interestingly, the 2-chlorobenzoate-degrading enzyme system in *Pseudomonas* sp. CLB 250 (Engesser and Schulte 1989) proved to be functional also for various other 2-substituted benzoates with substituents which may be eliminated as anions (see Fig. 2.11), e.g. alkoxy, amino, and alkylamino groups. Dioxygenases thus could be demonstrated to effectively cleave ether molecules. This capacity was extended even to the degradation of halogenated dibenzofurans and dibenzodioxins (see Strategies for Degradation of Chlorinated Dibenzofurans and Dibenzodioxins).

Fluoride elimination from 3,5-difluoro-4-hydroxybenzoate, with accumulation of 5-fluoro-3,4-dihydroxybenzoate (5-fluoroprotocatechuate), was effected by the monooxygenating 4-hydroxybenzoate-3-hydroxylase of *Pseudomonas fluorescens* (Husain *et al.* 1980). Dehalogenation of 3-substituted fluorobenzenes by a toluene dioxygenase has recently been reported (Renganathan 1989); this rather unspecific enzyme at the same time produced varying amounts of fluorocatechols, however, depending on the size of the substituent in 3-position.

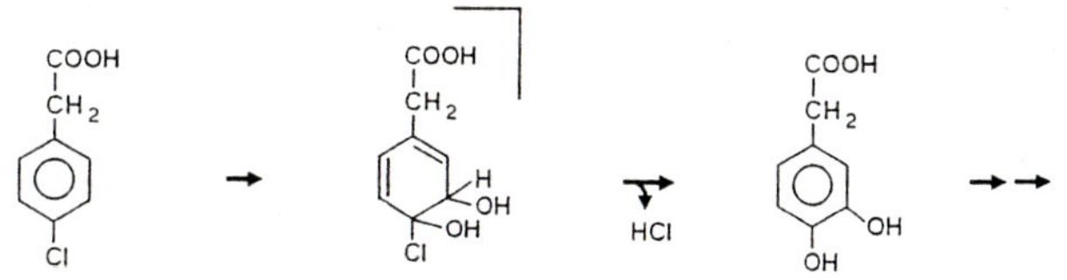

Fig. 2.12. Degradation of 4-chlorophenyl acetate by a *Pseudomonas* species strain CBS 3.

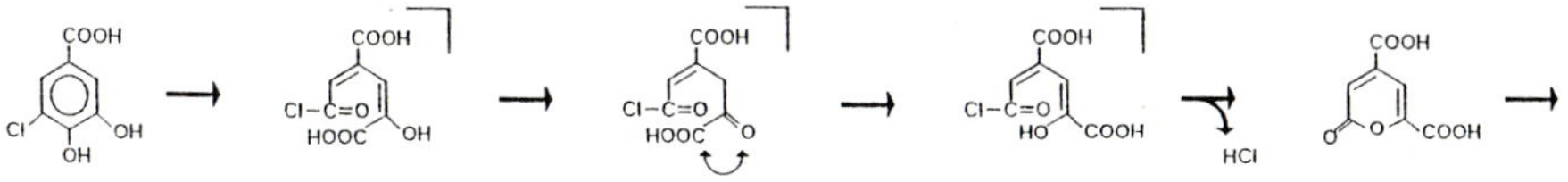

Fig. 2.13. Bacterial dehalogenation of 5-chlorovanillate.

A *Pseudomonas* sp. strain CBS3 has been suggested to dioxygenate 4-halophenyl acetates to unstable *cis*-dihydrodiols (Klages *et al.* 1981; Markus *et al.* 1984) which, after rearomatisation and elimination of halide, afforded homoprotocatechuate (see Fig. 2.12). The two enzyme components catalyzing the dehalogenation were purified, and the reaction was demonstrated to require NADH and Fe^{2+}. No final proof for a dioxygenation mechanism was presented, however, e.g. by product analysis of unproductive alkyl-analogue turnover or by employing mixtures of $^{18}O_2/^{16}O_2$. The homoprotocatechuate formed is metabolised *via* another meta pathway.

Dehalogenation of Halocatechols after Meta Cleavage: the 5-Chlorovanillate Case

In the course of the bacterial catabolism of lignin model compounds, 5-methoxyvanillate was transformed into 5-methoxyprotocatechuate, and the methoxy substituent then removed in the course of the dioxygenation catalyzed by a protocatechuate 4,5-dioxygenase (Kersten *et al.* 1985). Surprisingly, the chlorine in 5-chlorovanillate is removed analoguously after ring cleavage of 5-chloroprotocatechuate (see Fig. 2.13), with a pyrone being formed (2-pyrone-4,6-dicarboxylate). Dehalogenation seems to be gratuitous in this case; it may offer a tool, though, for the evolution of new dehalogenating enzymes from ether-cleaving oxygenases. There are indications, on the other hand, that chloride is eliminated from 4-chlorobenzoate in the first metabolic step of a 4-carboxybiphenyl ether-cleaving dioxygenase (Engesser *et al.* 1990a). As yet, the productive meta-cleavage of halocatechol derivatives, described above, has rarely been found in nature, and seems to be restricted to ortho-halosubstituted catechols.

Consequently, 30% only of the organic halogen was released as halide (measured reliably by a halogen electrode) in the course of cometabolism of the 4-halocatechols produced from 4-chloro- and 4-fluorobenzoate by *Pseudomonas putida* mt-2. A chlorinated semialdehyde was characterised extensively, and the proximal mode of ring cleavage established unequivocally for 4-halocatechols (Schacht *et al.* submitted for publication). Slow cometabolic degradation *via* meta pathway was claimed for 4-chlorocatechol derived from 4-chlorophenol, with 85% of the stoichiometric amount of halide reputedly being released. Halide detection was based on a spot test, though, and could not be reproduced in our laboratory with the original strain. Also, no ring-cleavage products were characterised (Janke and Fritsche 1979).

Chloro-substituted products of chlorocatechol ring cleavage accumulated in the culture broth during degradation of 1- and 2-chloronaphthalin (Morris and Barnsley 1982). The authors speculated about the toxicity of these compounds without any firm structural data. No growth was observed with chloronaphthalenes, and chloride release was not measured.

Despite many efforts, a productive, i.e. growth-sustaining metabolism of halogenated catechols *via* meta pathways has not been verified so far. Cometabolic liberation of halide, however, may occur to varying extent.

Strategies for Degradation of Chlorinated Dibenzofurans and Dibenzodioxins

Chlorinated dibenzofurans and dibenzodioxins are among the most pernicious chemicals. Up to now, no single microorganism has been found which was able to degrade higher chlorinated dibenzofurans or dibenzodioxins. In devising a strategy for rendering these recalcitrant molecules biodegradable, it is essential to dissect the tricyclic compounds into individual structural elements such as the biarylether linkage and the vicinal dichloro-substitution pattern. Some knowledge has been accumulated in the last few years on the degradation of 1,2-dichloroarenes (Meer *et al.* 1991; Haigler *et al.* 1988; Allard *et al.* 1991). Little information is found in the literature on degradation of biaryl ethers in general, and of cyclic biaryl ethers in particular. Efforts have been concentrated, therefore, on the microbial, especially bacterial degradation of biaryl ethers. Once the two isolated problems have been resolved, the single degradative capabilities must be combined either in a single strain or in a mixed culture; this has been shown a useful tool in biodegradation (Engesser *et al.* 1989a).

As described above, few competent model systems existed for the dioxygenolytic cleavage even of alkyl aryl ethers (Kersten *et al.* 1982), and none for diaryl ethers (Engesser and Schulte 1989). In the meantime, dioxygenolytic ether cleavage surprisingly has been realised even with cyclic biarylethers. Degradation of 3- and 4-carboxybiphenylether (CBPE) (Wittich 1990; Engesser *et al.* 1990a) is triggered by initial 1,2-dioxygenation, shown by isolation and unequivocal characterisation of dead-end products of ether analogues (Engesser *et al.* 1990a). Dioxygenase attack on aryl ether bonds yields chemically labile hemiacetals which, in the case of CBPE, decompose to protocatechuate and phenol both of which are easily biodegradable. This clearly demonstrates the superiority of an early cleavage of those bonds, constituting the xenobiotic structure, over cleavage at a later stage.

Dibenzofuran- and dibenzodioxin-attacking bacteria have been described quite recently (Engesser *et al.* 1989b; Fortnagel *et al.* 1990). A detailed investigation of the DBF metabolism revealed initial dioxygenolytic cleavage of the aryl ether bond once again to be the crucial step in the overall degradation (Engesser *et al.* 1989b). The product of dibenzofuran ether cleavage, 3-(2-hydroxyphenyl)catechol (HPC), was shown to suffer

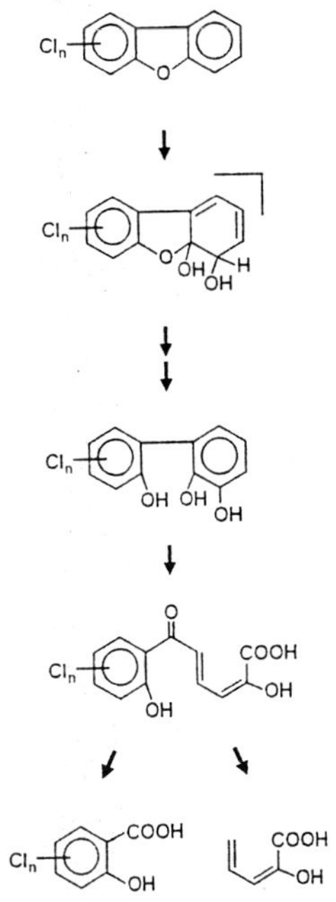

Fig. 2.14. Degradation of chlorinated dibenzofuran ethers by bacteria.

meta cleavage (Strubel *et al.* 1991). In an ensuing step, hydrolase activity produces salicylate and 2-oxo-4-pentenoate, with the same pathway being proposed for chlorinated analogues (Fig. 2.14). Unsubstituted salicylate is metabolised *via* catechol which then is cleaved in meta fashion and subsequently degraded by enzymes of the meta pathway; the same mechanism holds for the oxopentenoate metabolite. Recently, oxidation of 2-chloro- and 2,8-dichloro-DBF has been claimed (Parsons *et al.* 1990) without, however, establishing the biochemistry of the process.

Even though degradation of dibenzodioxin and its chlorinated analogues is complicated by the second ether bond, organisms have been described which effectively transform the parent compound (Harms *et al.* 1990). Mono-, di-, and, to a limited extent, trihalogenated DBDs were already shown to be metabolised substantially by several bacterial species, pre-grown on dibenzofuran. No products, however, were given (Rast *et al.* DBP 1989). There clearly is a pressing need for research in this field in order to identify bacteria which are able to effectively degrade dibenzodioxins and finally the chloro derivatives. The extremely limited "bioavailibility" of these compounds may have to be overcome by applying two-phase systems.

Hydrolytic Displacement of Halogen

Chlorobenzoates

Hydrolytic liberation of halide, at an early stage of the overall metabolism, greatly enhances the biodegradability of the target compounds, as in the case of the oxygenolytic removal of halosubstituents. Such hydrolytic dechlorination was first shown with an *Aspergillus niger* strain transforming 2-chloro- to (2-hydroxyphenoxy)acetate (Faulkner and Woodcock 1961). Later, degradation of 3-chlorobenzoate *via* 3-hydroxy- and 3,6-dihydroxybenzoate (gentisate) was described (Johnston *et al.* 1972), which definitely proceeded without any chlorocatechol production. The stoichiometry of 3-hydroxybenzoate excretion and substrate turnover was not determined, however, and the proposed hydrolytic mechanism of chloride substitution could not be established unequivocally.

In the following period, many different cases of hydrolytic halogen removal were presented. In one case, hydrolytic liberation of halide from 4-chlorobenzoate was reported even for alkalophilic conditions (Shimao *et al.* 1989). Besides 4-fluorobenzoate (Oltmanns *et al.* 1989), 4-chlorobenzoate was frequently employed as substrate; it is dechlorinated by various *Arthrobacter* (Ruisinger *et al.* 1976; Marks *et al.* 1984b), *Nocardia* (Klages and Lingens 1979), *Pseudomonas* (Klages and Lingens 1980), *Acinetobacter* (Adriaens *et al.* 1989; Adriaens and Focht 1991), and *Alcaligenes* species (Tweel *et al.* 1986). If, in the degradation by *Alcaligenes*, oxygen concentration was reduced to 1.2 % of the normal saturation concentration, accumulation of 4-hydroxybenzoate was observed which the authors had suggested as the direct product of hydrolysis. No definite proof was given, though, for the hydrolytic and non-oxygenolytic nature of halide liberation, e.g. by ^{18}O-labeling experiments. In all the transformations described so far, 4-hydroxybenzoate was metabolised first to 3,4-dihydroxybenzoate which then was degraded along either ortho (Klages and Lingens 1980) or meta pathways (Ruisinger *et al.* 1976; Klages and Lingens 1979).

Incorporation of ^{18}OH, from ^{18}O-labeled H_2O, definitely proves that dehalogenation proceeds as a hydrolytic process (Müller *et al.* 1984; Marks *et al.* 1984a). No ^{18}O label was incorporated into the 4-hydroxybenzoate formed in a negative control experiment under incubation with $^{18}O_2$ gas (Marks *et al.* 1984a). The enzyme from *Pseudomonas* CBS3 (Klages and Lingens 1980) in crude extracts was found to be activated by Mn^{2+} and Co^{2+}. In contrast to the enzyme from *Arthrobacter*, 4-fluorobenzoate could not be converted (Thiele *et al.* 1987). The polar or even ionic carboxyl group seems to be requisite for substrate binding (Thiele *et al.* 1988) since methyl 4-chlorobenzoate was not a substrate. Cloning experiments at first seemed to indicate that more than one gene was involved in 4-chlorobenzoate hydrolysis (Savard *et al.* 1986); recently, it was demonstrated that, in a first step, the 4-chlorobenzoate is transformed to the CoA ester which is the effective substrate for the action of a regular molecular-weight hydrolase (Löffler *et al.* 1991). The key step accordingly is a nucleophilic attack at the chloro-substituted C-4 carbon atom of the 4-chlorobenzoate CoA-ester (see Fig. 2.15).

A recent report (Adriaens and Focht 1991) on the mechanism of hydrolysis of the aryl chloro bond, based on results of the 3,4-dichlorobenzoate transformation by an *Acinetobacter* strain 4-CB1, may be interpreted in favour of an addition-elimination mechanism (see Fig. 2.16). In a first step, the para-Cl is replaced by OH. Water then is added in 3,4-position followed by elimination of HCl. Subsequent enzymatic processes

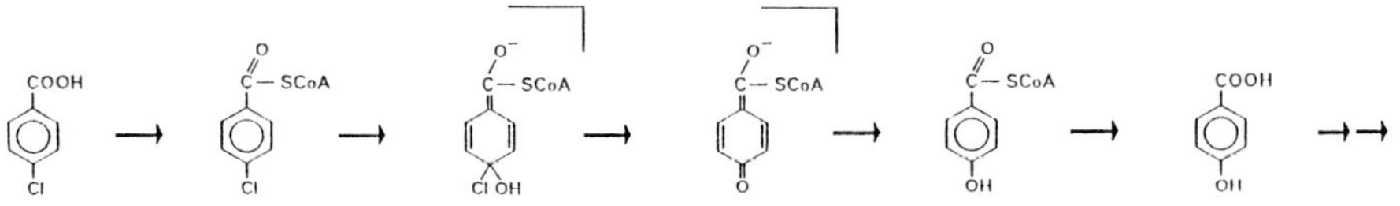

Fig. 2.15. Chloroarene dehalogenation mechanism involving nucleophilic attack at the chloro-substituted C1 atom.

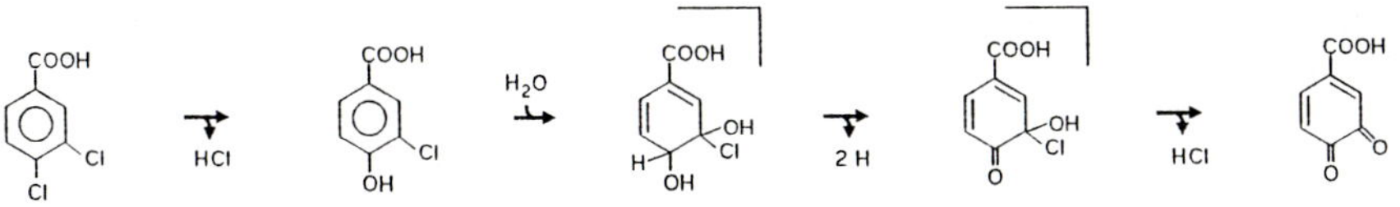

Fig. 2.16. Addition-elimination mechanism for the hydrolysis of the aryl chloro bonds in 3, 4-dichlorobenzoate.

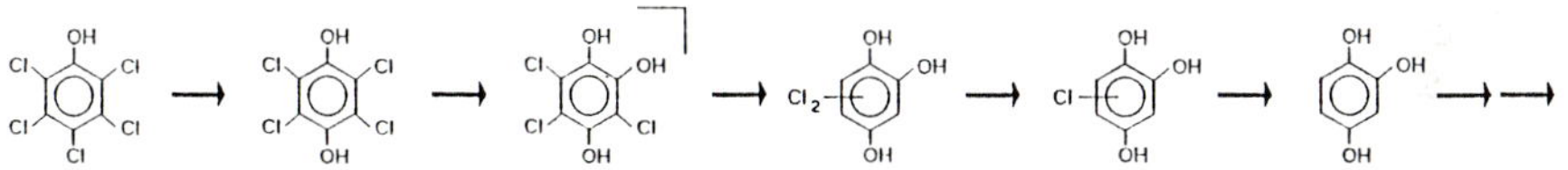

Fig. 2.17. Hydrolytic degradation of pentachlorophenol involving two substitition and three reductive dehalogenation steps.

yield 4-carboxy-*o*-quinone which may be the product of anaerobic cometabolism of 3,4-dichlorobenzoate by the 4-chlorobenzoate-grown cells. No matter which enzymatic mechanism actually prevails, the aromatic π system of the chloroarene substrate has to be broken up prior to hydrolysis of the carbon-halogen bond.

A combination of reductive and hydrolytic attack was reported for 2,4-dichlorobenzoate (Zaitsev and Karasevich 1985; Tweel *et al.* 1987), the initial product of reductive dechlorination, 4-chlorobenzoate, being metabolised *via* hydrolytic halide replacement (see Liberation of Halide by Reductive Mechanisms). For a *Pseudomonas aeruginosa* strain, recently reported to dehalogenate 2-bromobenzoate, hydrolytic displacement of halogen is indicated by accumulation of salicylate in oxygen-depleted cells (Higson and Focht 1990a).

Pentachlorophenol (PCP

For hydrolytic pentachlorophenol (PCP) degradation (Häggblom *et al.* 1989; Apajalahti and Salkinoja-Salonen 1987), initial substitution of chlorine by OH to 2,3,5,6-tetrachlorohydroquinone was proposed, a second substitution step yielding 3,5,6-trichloro-1,2,4-trihydroxybenzene (see Fig. 2.17). Further degradation proceeded *via* three reductive dehalogenation steps (see Liberation of Halide by Reductive Mechanisms). The hypothesis that the *p*-chlorine substituent is displaced hydrolytically not only in pentachlorophenol but also in 2,3,4,5- and 2,3,4,6-tetrachlorophenol, seems to be confirmed by labeling experiments with $H_2^{18}O$ for which ^{18}O-labelled hydroquinone intermediates were established (Apajalahti and Salkinoja-Salonen 1987). However, the hydrolytic displacement reaction worked only in the presence of NADH; additionally, at least traces of oxygen were required. This prompted other researchers to carefully re-examine the first dechlorination step in the *Arthrobacter* strain ATCC 33790 (Schenk *et al.* 1989; Schenk *et al.* 1990). Labeling experiments with $H_2^{18}O$ and $^{18}O_2$, as possible oxygen donors, revealed that para-^{18}OH groups were introduced only when the enzyme extract was incubated with $NADH/O_2$ as ^{18}OH equivalents. However, since the ^{18}OH label was also non-enzymatically incorporated into tetrachlorohydroquinone from $H_2^{18}O$, no differentiation is possible between hydrolytic and oxygenolytic removal of halogene. These results, i.e. the requirement for oxygen and a reduced pyridine dinucleotide being present, allow the assumption that the first step in PCP degradation is an oxygenolytic attack also for the *Rhodococcus* strain (see Apajalahti and Salkinoja-Salonen 1987). Interestingly, PCP degradation potential seems to be rather wide-spread, having been demonstrated for many bacteria (Rott *et al.* 1979; Saber and Crawford 1985; Suzuki 1977; Watanabe 1973; Liu *et al.* 1981; Klecka and Maier 1985; Pignatello *et al.* 1983). A *Flavobacterium* sp. has been demonstrated to also attack triiodophenols after growth on PCP (Xun and Orser 1991).

N-Heterocycles

s-Triazines which are widely used as herbicides have been described to be biodegradable in both aerobic and anaerobic systems (Cook and Hütter 1981; Jessee *et al.* 1983). These compounds, just as some chlorinated derivatives like 6-amino-2-chloro-4-ethylamino-1,3,5-triazine, serve as source of nitrogen. Since the transformation was carried out anaerobically in cell extracts, the authors concluded the dehalogenation to follow a hydrolytic mechanism. Degradation was triggered by removal of the chlorine substituent, yielding 2-amino-4-ethylamino-1,3,5-triazine-6(5H)-one. Two dehalogenases have been proposed which differ in specificity towards the two alkyl-amino functions in these triazine agrochemicals (Cook and Hütter 1986). The subject of s-triazine degradation is covered in an excellent review (Cook 1987).

In the breakdown of 5-chloro-2-hydroxynicotinic acid, a dead-end product of 3-chloroquinoline-8-carboxylic acid partial degradation (see Channelling of Complex Haloarene Structures into Key Intermediates), chloro-substituted maleic or fumaric acid were proposed as intermediates which in turn are subject to hydrolytic dehalogenation (Tibbles *et al.* 1989b).

Liberation of Halide by Reductive Mechanisms

Molecular oxygen was initially considered to be essential for the activation of arenes by hydroxylation. Non-activated benzene derivatives, with three or more halogen substituents, would be expected, from simple mechanistic considerations, to be more or less non-biodegradable by enzymes which employed an electrophilic hydroxylation mechanism. Unexpectedly, polyhalophenols were found to still be degraded in aerobic systems, most probably by action of monooxygenating enzymes. This seemed to invalidate the "dogma" that heavily chloro-substituted arenes are not subject to aerobic microbial attack. One might argue, however, that the electrophilic displacement of the first chlorine substituent in polyhalophenols is facilitated by the mesomeric effect of a para-hydroxyl group. This is exemplified e.g. by the formation of tetrachloro-p-hydroquinone from pentachlorophenol discussed above (Häggblom *et al.* 1989; Apajalahti and Salkinoja-Salonen 1987).

Still more surprisingly, dioxygenolytic liberation of chloride from tetrachlorobenzenes was claimed in two cases (Springer and Rast 1988; Wittich *et al.* 1989). These substrates are deactivated towards electrophilic attack by four chlorines without the remedy of an activating OH-substituent. The situation is problematical, though, only as long as an electrophilic mechanism of hydroxylation is assumed; for a possible attack by radical species, these objections would no longer hold.

Dehalogenation of an aromatic nucleus was reported even in the absence of oxygen (Ide *et al.* 1972; Kuwatsuka and Igarashi 1975; Murthy *et al.* 1979). Accumulation of lesser chlorinated phenols like 2,3,5- and 2,4,5-tri-, 3,4-di- and 3-chlorophenol from pentachlorophenol indicated a reductive mechanism of chlorine removal without additional hydroxylation steps. Many reductive dehalogenation reactions have been described since these early reports, e.g. for pesticides such as techlofthalam (Kirkpatrick *et al.* 1981), thiobencarb (Moon and Kuwatsuka 1984), chlornitrofen (Yamada and Suzuki 1983), 2,4,5,6-tetrachloroisophthalonitrile (Sato and Tanaka 1987), and diuron (Attaway *et al.* 1982; Stepp *et al.* 1985). Partial metabolism was observed in many cases, with only one chlorine atom being removed and lesser chlorinated metabolites being accumulated.

Polyhalophenols are metabolised, after initial attack presumably by monohydroxylases (Apajalahti and Salkinoja-Salonen 1987), by hydrolytic as well as reductive processes, with complete liberation of the organic halogen as halide. A cell free extract of a *Rhodococcus* species (Häggblom *et al.* 1989) was found to catalyze formation of 1,2,4-trihydroxybenzene from 2,3,5,6-tetrachlorohydroquinone (see Fig. 2.16), following a reductive mechanism. This same mechanism seems to operate in the degradation of 2,3,5,6-tetra-, 2,3,6- as well as 2,4,6-tri-, and 2,6-dichlorophenol by a *Flavobacterium* species isolated with pentachlorophenol as a selection substrate. The dehalogenation enzymes preferentially dehalogenate 2,6-disubstituted halophenols (Steiert *et al.* 1987).

Purely reductive dechlorination systems have been described in addition to the combined action of hydrolytic/oxygenolytic on one, and reductive dechlorination systems, on the other hand. Partial dechlorination of pentachlorophenol to lesser chlorinated phenols was found to depend on pre-enrichment with monochlorophenols (Mikesell and Boyd 1986). A combination of these enrichment cultures could be demonstrated to totally dehalogenate pentachlorophenol, with some formation of methane. For pentachlorophenol, uniformly labeled with ^{14}C, 70% of the radioactive carbon was recovered in form of $^{14}CO_2$ and $^{14}CH_4$.

Aquatic sediments were found to liberate halogen from mono- and dichlorophenols (Sharak-Genthner *et al.* 1989a), 4-chlorophenol generally being degraded with the slowest rate. Degradation of 3- and 4-chlorobenzoate in some cases was nitrate-dependent, suggesting nitrate respiration as the energy-providing process (Sharak-Genthner *et al.* 1989b). A 2-chlorophenol-mineralising anaerobic mixed culture was isolated from sewage sludge which dehalogenated also 2-bromo- and 2,6-dichlorophenol reductively. 2,4-Dichlorophenol in this system was transformed only to 4-chlorophenol which once again proved to be hardly degradable under anaerobic conditions (Dietrich and Winter 1990). Recently, however, 2,4-dichlorophenol was

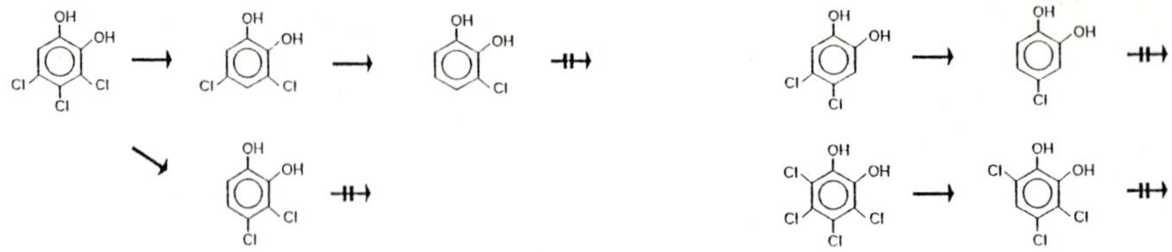

Fig. 2.18. Anaerobic dechlorination of chlorinated catechols.

demonstrated to be totally dechlorinated *via* 4-chlorophenol and phenol; this finally was carboxylated to benzoate (Zhang and Wiegel 1990).

A 2,4-dibromophenol-degrading consortium was described, without commenting on the energetics of the dehalogenation step (King 1988), which consists of dehalogenating organisms and sulfate-reducing bacteria. The latter did not directly attack the halophenol but rather utilised the dehalogenated phenol.

Quite recently, a rare case of anaerobic dechlorination was reported for chlorinated catechols, i.e. 1,2-dihydroxybenzenes (Allard *et al.* 1991). Cultures enriched with vanillins, catechin, and phloroglucinol as substrates exhibited dechlorinating activity with chloro catechols. The process is highly specific, yielding, for example, exclusively 3-chlorocatechol from 3,4,5-trichlorocatechol. Chloride removal was observed also with other isomeric chlorocatechols as shown in Figure 2.18.

Anaerobic transformation of 3-bromo-4-hydroxybenzaldehyde to 4-hydroxybenzoate and, ultimately, phenol has been described to be catalyzed by cultures enriched from sediments (Neilson *et al.* 1988).

A rare case of phototrophic metabolism of 3-chlorobenzoate (3CB) was recorded for *Rhodopseudomonas palustris* WS17 (Kamal and Campbell-Wyndham 1990). Of the radioactive label from 3-chlorobenzoate, 75 % was incorporated into the biomass, 25% being liberated as $^{14}CO_2$. The authors claimed chloride release to occur during reductive degradation of the cosubstrate, benzoate, without presenting any detailed evidence, however, for this pathway.

Biotransformation of polyhalogenated biphenyls probably represents the most important instance of reductive dehalogenation. As described above (see Channelling of Complex Haloarene Structures into Key Intermediates), aerobic metabolism of polychlorinated biphenyls (PCBs) frequently leads to accumulation of chlorinated intermediates which may be bound chemically to soil components (Brunner *et al.* 1985) thus feigning total degradation. Intensive dehalogenation, prior to aerobic metabolism, would render PCBs much more susceptible to total breakdown into CO_2 and chloride, the ultimate goal of biodegradation. Sediments from the Hudson River, New York, were investigated for anaerobic degradation potential towards PCBs. Mono- and di-chlorinated biphenyls were degraded most efficiently, biphenyls with four or more chloro substituents were not. Trihalogenated biphenyls were transformed only when the chlorine substituents were scattered over both rings; 2,3-dichloro substitution, for example, strongly reduced transformation rates (Chen *et al.* 1988).

Other investigators found, however, that even Arochlor 1260[R], with an average of six chlorine atoms per molecule, was attacked in Hudson river sediments. Since different patterns of lesser chlorinated PCBs were formed, different microbial consortia seemed to participate in these transformations. Dehalogenation reactions were clearly biological, no significant chemical reduction taking place (Brown (jr.) *et al.* 1987). In a separate investigation, dechlorination of Arochlor 1242[R] was demonstrated at a

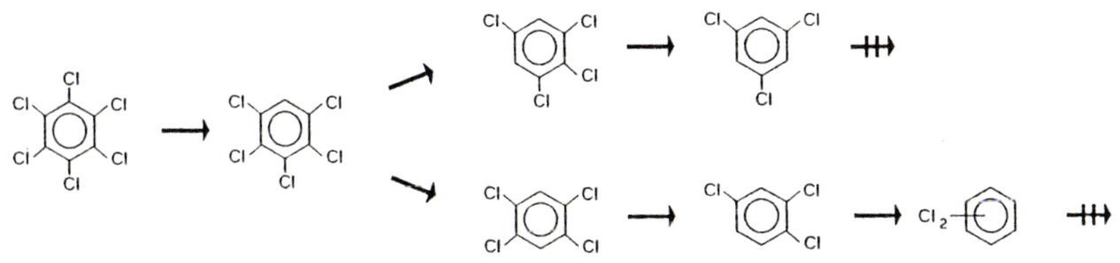

Fig. 2.19. Reductive dechlorination of hexachlorobenzene.

concentration of as high as 700 mgl^{-1} sediment. Within 16 weeks, half of the organic chlorine was metabolised, with the percentage of mono- and dichloro biphenyls increasing from 9% to 88%. The para and meta chlorines were displaced preferentially (Quensen (III) *et al.* 1988). Arochlor^{R}1260, in contrast, proved to be more recalcitrant, and in laboratory degradation experiments required far longer adaptation times. After one year, only 15% of the meta and para chlorines had been removed. Lesser chlorinated biphenyls again proved to be very susceptible to reductive dechlorination in these systems (Quensen(III) *et al.* 1990).

Reductive dechlorination by microorganisms has been described also for hexachlorobenzene (Fig. 2.19). The final products, 1,3,5-tri- and isomeric dichlorobenzenes, were not transformed further; penta- and tetrachlorobenzenes, however, were accumulated only transiently (Fathepure *et al.* 1988). Different organisms, in soil columns, were shown to reductively dechlorinate tri- and dichlorobenzenes to chlorobenzene as the final metabolite (Bosma *et al.* 1988). These dechlorination reactions seem to be mediated by rather unspecialised enzymes since bacteria of many different species, isolated from intestine and not previously exposed to haloarenes, were able to catalyze dechlorination of 1,2,4-trichlorobenzene to chlorobenzene (Tsuchiya and Yamaha 1984). As enzymatic reactions, these dehalogenations still show considerable specificity. Another hexachlorobenzene-degrading consortium was shown to accumulate 1,2,3- and 1,2,4-tri- as well as 1,3- and 1,2-dichlorobenzene (Mousa and Rogers 1990). Partial dechlorination of hexachlorobenzene by glutathione addition has been demonstrated for mammals, penta- and tetrachlorobenzene being formed besides 2,3,5,6-tetrachlorophenylmethylmercaptan (Renner and Nguyen 1984).

Halosubstituted anilines have also been described to be dehalogenated reductively. For example, 2,4- and 3,4-dichloroaniline are transformed to monochloroanilines. These dichloroaniline-transforming cultures degrade 3,4-dichlorophenol without any lag phase; thus, cross acclimation seems to have taken place between phenol- and aniline-transformation processes (Struijs and Rogers 1989). 2,3,4,5-Tetrachloroaniline was reductively dechlorinated to 2,3,5-tri- and 3,5-dichloroaniline (Kuhn and Suflita 1989) (Fig. 2.20); the principle that chlorine substituents in ortho or para position to an electron-releasing group are removed preferentially, seems to hold also for anilines.

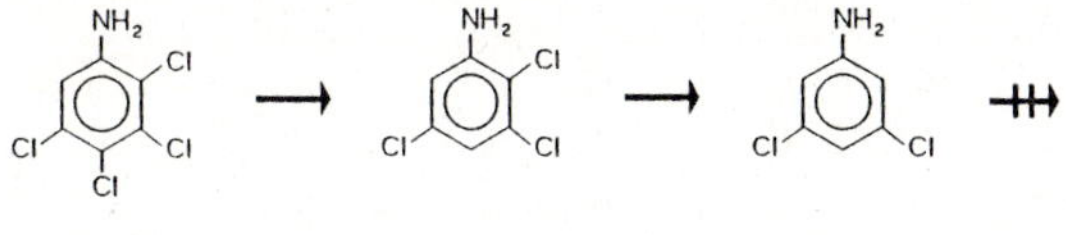

Fig. 2.20. Reductive dehalogenation of chlorosubstituted anilines.

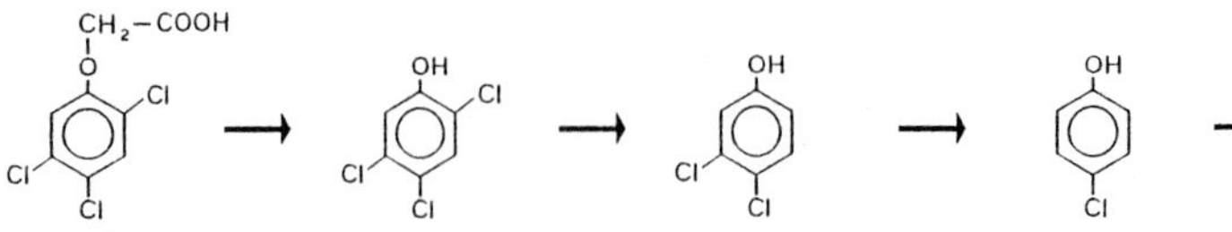

Fig. 2.21. Cleavage of the aryl alkyl ether bond and subsequent reductive dechlorination of chlorinated phenoxyacetate.

In pond sediments, reductive dechlorination of Diuron^R (3,4-dichlorophenyl-1,1-dimethylurea) in 4-position yielded 3-chlorophenyl-1,1-dimethylurea in stoichiometric amount (Attaway *et al.* 1982). Structurally related herbicides also suffer reductive dehalogenation (Stepp *et al.* 1985).

Chlorinated phenoxyacetates were demonstrated to be reductively dechlorinated after cleavage of the aryl alkyl ether bond. A 3-chlorobenzoate-enriched consortium selectively substituted the para-chlorine in 2,4,5-T (2,4,5-trichlorophenoxyacetate), yielding (2,5-dichlorophenoxy)acetate (Suflita *et al.* 1984). 2,4,5-T, after cleavage of the ether bond and removal of the ortho chlorine, was transformed to 3,4-dichlorophenol in anaerobic sewage sludge. Further removal of the meta chlorine resulted in the accumulation of 4-chlorophenol which could not be degraded further (Mikesell and Boyd 1985) (see Fig. 2.21).

A 3- and 4-chlorobenzoate-degrading consortium was found to degrade the halobenzoates anaerobically, inevitably requiring nitrate. The authors speculated about a reductive dechlorination of halobenzoates to benzoate which in turn was proposed to be degraded with nitrate as an electron acceptor (Sharak-Genthner *et al.* 1989a).

A reductive dechlorination of DDT (1,1,1-trichloro-2,2-bis(4-chlorophenyl)ethane) was reported to be catalyzed by a *Pseudomonas aeruginosa* strain (see Channelling of Complex Haloarene Structures into Key Intermediates).

There is only scattered knowledge on the mechanism of reductive dechlorination reactions despite their tremendous potential for bioremediation of contaminated sites. One crucial question is whether the microorganisms can derive energy from the dehalogenating reaction and thus may be kept in pure culture.

The best studied model system is the dehalogenation of 3-halo-substituted benzoates (Suflita *et al.* 1982; Horowitz *et al.* 1983). For a 3-chlorobenzoate-degrading consortium, the individual organisms were separated, and a strain DCB-1 was recognised as principal dechlorinating organism (Shelton and Tiedje 1984). It could be shown from thermodynamic calculations that the reductive dechlorination step in strain DCB-1 is exergonic, supplying energy to the cell by a novel type of chemotrophic mode of growth (Dolfing 1990; Mohn and Tiedje 1990).

Degradation of 2-fluorobenzoate by benzoate-dissimilating, denitrifying bacteria was reported (Schennen *et al.* 1985). When cells were grown anaerobically on benzoate, they transformed 2-fluorobenzoate without any lag period, under concomitant defluorination. A benzoyl-CoA-synthetase, the key enzyme especially of anaerobic benzoate degradation, was demonstrated to be active also towards 2-fluorobenzoate. The authors speculated about fortuitous elimination of fluoride from reduced intermediates, no clear-cut evidence, however, being presented for the reductive nature of the defluorination mechanism. This holds also for the anaerobic defluorination of 2- and 4-fluorobenzoate, catalyzed by other denitrifying bacteria (Taylor *et al.* 1979).

In general, however, the exact mechanism of reductive dechlorination remains uncertain. The reaction may, for one, proceed in form of direct substitution by hydride.

Alternatively, a two-step process may be envisaged, e.g. by substitution of halogen by a hydroxyl group which would have to be followed by reductive dehydroxylation. The fact that reductive dehalogenation is an energy-yielding process would eventually be met also by an intermediate dehydroxylation step which from calculations was estimated to be an energy-conserving reaction (Szewzyk *et al.* 1985). An especially attractive mechanism would follow the addition-elimination process analoguous to that discussed for the hydrolytic removal of halogen by haloarene hydrolases (see Hydrolytic Displacement of Halogen and Figure 2.16) (Adriaens and Focht 1991)). Further in-depth investigations are definitely necessary to clarify this issue. Although the first step in reductive transformation of benzene derivatives generally is strongly endergonic (Evans and Fuchs 1988), the overall reaction may be exergonic due to the elimination of halide.

Conclusions

An important application of HAH biodegradation is bioremediation, i.e. the clean-up of polluted environmental compartments by microbiological methods. On-site trials have shown pentachlorophenol (PCP) to be amenable to biodegradation, with PCP concentration being reduced from 200 mg kg^{-1} to 15 mg kg^{-1} soil upon addition of a *Rhodococcus* species (Valo and Salkinoja-Salonen 1986). Soil contaminated with 2,4,5-T (2,4,5-trichlorophenoxyacetate) was decontaminated after supplementation with a *Pseudomonas* strain, the herbicide concentration being reduced from an initial 20 g kg^{-1} to 1-2 g kg^{-1} soil (Kilbane *et al.* 1983). In these cases, organisms were available which derived energy from the biodegradation processes. Transformation of polychlorinated biphenyls (PCBs), in contrast, seems not to yield energy, and thus does not sustain growth. To overcome this limitation, unsubstituted biphenyl was added to soil heavily contaminated with PCBs. Thus, the cometabolic transformation potential was enhanced considerably although still no total degradation was observed (Brunner *et al.* 1985).

The generally very lipophilic HAHs tend to be absorbed on soil particles (Sabljic 1989). Therefore, the "bioavailability", i.e. the accessibility of these substrates for microorganisms otherwise very competent for degradation, is severely reduced. Addition of emulsifiers or of organic phases (Viney and Bewley 1990; Brink and Tramper 1985) may greatly improve degradation efficiency (Harvey *et al.* 1990). Alternative microorganisms were described producing their own bioemulsifiers (Ramsay *et al.* 1988; Morgan and Watkinson 1989). Research on and application of bioremediation techniques is nicely covered by a recent review (Morgan and Watkinson 1989).

Biodegradation can effectively aid in clean-up of contaminated soils and aquifers. To overcome its limitations, microbiology, biochemistry, chemistry, genetics, and process engineering must collaborate in developing microorganisms with improved degradative capacities when natural evolution does not produce the desired activities.

Acknowledgement

We thank H-J Knackmuss for many fruitful discussions during preparation of this review. The help of H Runge with aquisition of literature is greatfully acknowledged as is that of C Kauffmann in typing the manuscript.

References

Adriaens P, Focht DD (1991) Cometabolism of 3,4-dichlorobenzoate by *Acinetobacter* sp. strain 4-CB1. Appl Environ Microbiol 57(1):173-179

Adriaens P, Kohler H-PE, Kohler-Staub D, Focht DD (1989) Bacterial dehalogenation of chlorobenzoates and coculture biodegradation of 4,4'-dichlorobiphenyl. Appl Environ Microbiol 55(4):887-892

Adriaens P, Focht DD (1990) Continuous coculture degradation of selected polychlorinated biphenyl congeners by *Acinetobacter* spp. in an aerobic reactor system. Environ Sci Technol 24(7):1042-1049

Ahmed M, Focht DD (1973) Degradation of polychlorinated biphenyls by two species of *Achromobacter*. Can J Microbiol 19:47-52

Aldrich TL, Frantz B, Gill JF, Kilbane JJ, Chakrabarty AM (1987) Cloning and complete nucleotide sequence determination of the catB gene encoding cis,cis-muconate lactonising enzyme. Gene 52:185-195

Ali DA, Callely AG, Hayes M (1962) Ability of a vibrio grown on benzoate to oxidise para-fluorobenzoate. Nature 196:194-195

Allard A-S, Hynning P-A, Lindgren C, Remberger M, Neilson AH (1991) Dechlorination of chlorocatechols by stable enrichment cultures of anaerobic bacteria. Appl Environ Microbiol 57(1):77-84

Apajalahti JHA, Salkinoja-Salonen MS (1987) Dechlorination and para-hydroxylation of polychlorinated phenols by *Rhodococcus chlorophenolicus*. J Bacteriol 169(2):675-681

Attaway HH, Camper ND, Paynter MJB (1982) Anaerobic microbial degradation of Diuron by pond sediment. Pest Biochem Physiol 17:96-101

Bachofer R, Lingens F, Schäfer W (1975) Conversion of aniline into pyrocatechol by a *Nocardia* sp.: incorporation of oxygen-18. FEBS Lett 50:288-290

Ballschmiter K, Unglert KC, Neu HT (1977) Abbau von chlorierten Aromaten: Mikrobiologischer Abbau der polychlorierten Biphenyle(PCB).III. Chlorierte Benzoesäuren als Metabolite der PCB.. Chemosphere 1:51-56

Bartels I, Knackmuss H-J, Reineke W (1984) Suicide inactivation of catechol 2,3-dioxygenase from *Pseudomonas putida* mt-2 by 3-halocatechol. Appl Environ Microbiol 47:500-505

Baxter RA, Gilbert PE, Lidgett RA, Mainprize JH, Vodden HA (1975) The degradation of polychlorinated biphenyls by microorganisms. Sci Total Environ 4:53-61

Beadle CA, Smith ARW (1982) The purification and properties of 2,4-dichlorphenol hydroxylase from a strain of *Acinetobacter* species. Eur J Microbiol 123:323-332

Bedard DL, Unterman R, Bopp LH, Brennan MJ, Haberl ML, Johnson C (1986) Rapid assay for screening and characterising microorganisms for the ability to degrade polychlorinated biphenyls. Appl Environ Microbiol 51(4):761-768

Bedard DL, Haberl ML, May RJ, Brennan MJ (1987) Evidence for novel mechanisms of polychlorinated biphenyl metabolism in *Alcaligenes eutrophus* H850. Appl Environ Microbiol 53(5):1103-1112

Behret H (1989) Eintrag in die Umwelt bei Herstellung, Verarbeitung, Verwendung und Abfallbeseitigung. In: 2,4-Dichlor phenol. Beratergremium für umweltrelevante, Altstoffe (ed) vol 4, VCH Verlagsgesellschaft, Weinheim, pp 8-19

Bollag J-M, Helling CS, Alexander M (1967) Metabolism of 4-chloro-2-methylphenoxyacetic acid by soil bacteria. Appl Microbiol 15:1393-1398

Bollag J-M, Helling CS, Alexander M (1968) 2,4-D metabolism. Enzymatic hydroxylation of chlorinated phenols. J Agric Food Chem 16:826-828

Bont Jan AMde, Vorage Marc JAW, Hartmans Sybe, Tweel Will JJvan den (1986) Microbial degradation of 1,3-dichlorobenzene. Appl Environ Microbiol 52(4):677-680

Bosma TNP, Meer JR van der, Schraa G, Tros ME, Zehnder AJB (1988) Reductive dechlorination of all trichloro- and dichlorobenzene isomers. FEMS Microbiol Ecol 53:223-229

Brink LES, Tramper J (1985) Optimisation of organic solvent in multiphase biocatalysis. Biotechnol Bioeng 27:1258-1269

Brown(jr.) JF, Bedard DL, Brennan MJ, Carnahan JC, Feng H, Wagner RE (1987) Polychlorinated biphenyl dechlorination in aquatic sediments. Science 236:709-712

Brunner W, Sutherland FH, Focht DD (1985) Enhanced biodegradation of polychlorinated biphenyls in soil by analog enrichment and bacterial inoculation. J Environ Qual 14(3):324-328

Burse VW, Head SL, Korver MP, McClure PC, Donahue JF, Needham LL (1990) Determination of selected organochlorine pesticides and polychlorinated biphenyls in human serum. J Anal Toxicol 14(5/6):137-142

Catelani D, Sorlini C, Treccani V (1971) The metabolism of biphenyl by *Pseudomonas putida*. Experientia 27:1173-1174

Chatterjee DK, Kellog ST, Hamada S, Chakrabarty AM (1981) Plasmid specifying total degradation of chlorinated benzoic acids. J Bacteriol 146:639-646

Chen M, Hong CS, Bush B, Rhee G-Y (1988) Anaerobic biodegradation of polychlorinated biphenyls by bacteria from Hudson river sediments. Ecotoxicol Environ Safety 16:95-105

Clarke KF, Callely AG, Livingstone A, Fewson CA (1975) Metabolism of monofluorobenzoates by *Acinetobacter calcoaceticus* N.C.I.B. 8250. Biochim Biophys Acta 404:169-179

Collins GB, Holmes DC, Hoodless RA (1982) Organochlorine pesticide residues in human milk in Great Britain, 1979-80. Human Toxicol 1:425-431

Commandeur LCM, Parsons JR (1990) Degradation of halogenated aromatic compounds. Biodegradation 1:207-220

Cook AM (1987) Biodegradation of s-triazine xenobiotics. FEMS Microbiol Rev 46:93-116

Cook AM, Hütter R (1981) s-Triazines as nitrogen sources for bacteria. J Agric Food Chem 29:1135-1143

Cook AM, Hütter R (1986) Ring dechlorination of deethylsimazine by hydrolases from *Rhodococcus corallinus*. FEMS Microbiol Lett 34:335-338

Crawford Ronald L, Olson PE, Frick TD (1979) Catabolism of 5-chlorosalicylate by a *Bacillus* isolated from the Mississippi river. Appl Environ Microbiol 38(3):379-384

Dagley S (1978) Pathways for the utilisation of organic growth substrates. In: Gunsalus LC (ed) The Bacteria, Vol. VI Bacterial Diversity, vol 5, Academic Press Inc., New York, pp 305-388

Dietrich G, Winter J (1990) Anaerobic degradation of chlorophenol by an enrichment culture. Appl Microbiol Biotechnol 34:253-258

Ditzelmüller G, Loidl M, Streichsbier F (1989) Isolation and characterisation of a 2,4-dichlorophenoxyacetic acid-degrading soil bacterium. Appl Microbiol Biotechnol 31:93-96

Dolfing Jan (1990) Reductive dechlorination of 3-chlorobenzoate is coupled to ATP production and growth in an anaerobic bacterium, strain DCB-1. Arch Microbiol 153:264-266

Don RH, Weightman AJ, Knackmuss H-J, Timmis KN (1985) Transposon mutagenesis and cloning analysis of the pathways for degradation of 2,4-dichlorophenoxyacetic acid and 3-chlorobenzoate in *Alcaligenes eutrophus* JMP134(pJP4). J Bacteriol 161:85-90

Dorn E, Knackmuss H-J (1978a) Chemical structure and biodegradability of halogenated compounds. Two catechol 1,2-dioxygenases from a 3-chlorobenzoate-grown pseudomonad. Biochem J 174:73-84

Dorn E, Knackmuss H-J (1978b) Chemical structure and biodegradability of halogenated aromatic compounds. Substituent effects on 1,2-dioxygenation of catechol. Biochem J 174:85-94

Dorn E, Hellwig M, Reineke W, Knackmuss H-J (1974) Isolation and characterisation of a 3-chlorobenzoate degrading pseudomonad. Arch Microbiol 99:61-70

Durham Don R, Stewart David B (1987) Recruitment of naphthalene dissimilatory enzymes for the oxidation of 1,4-dichloronaphthalene to 3,6-dichlorosalicylate, a precursor for the herbicide Dicamba. J Bacteriol 169(6):2889-2892

Duxburry JM, Tiedje JM, Alexander M, Dawson JE (1970) 2,4-D metabolism: enzymatic conversion of chloromaleylacetic acid to succinic acid. J Agric Food Chem 18:199-201

Engesser K-H, Schulte P (1989) Degradation of 2-bromo-, 2-chloro- and 2-fluorobenzoate by *Pseudomonas putida* CLB250. FEMS Microbiol Lett 60:143-148

Engesser K-H, Schmidt E, Knackmuss H-J (1980) Adaptation of *Alcaligenes eutrophus* B9 and *Pseudomonas* sp. B13 to 2-fluorobenzoate as growth substrate. Appl Environ Microbiol 39:68-73

Engesser K-H, Cain RB, Knackmuss H-J (1988) Bacterial metabolism of side chain fluorinated aromatics: cometabolism of 3-trifluoromethyl(TFM)benzoate by *Pseudomonas putida* (arvilla) mt2 and *Rhodococcus rubropertinctus* N657. Arch Microbiol 149:188-197

Engesser KH, Pieper DH, Rojo F, Timmis KN, Knackmuss H-J (1989a) Simultaneous degradation of chloro- and methylaromatics via ortho pathway by genetically engineered bacteria and natural soil isolates. In: Hattori T, Ishida Y, Maruyama Y, Morita RY, Uchida A (eds) Recent advances in microbial ecology, Japan Scientific Societies Press, Tokyo, pp 622-626

Engesser KH, Strubel V, Christoglou K, Fischer P, Rast HG (1989b) Dioxygenolytic cleavage of aryl ether bonds: 1,10-dihydro-1,10-dihydroxyfluoren-9-one, a novel arene dihydrodiol as evidence for angular dioxygenation of dibenzofuran. FEMS Microbiol Lett 65:205-210

Engesser KH, Fietz W, Fischer P, Schulte P, Knackmuss H-J (1990a) Dioxygenolytic cleavage of aryl ether bonds: 1,2-Dihydro-1,2-dihydroxy-4-carboxybenzophenone as evidence for initial 1,2-dioxygenation in 3- and 4-carboxy biphenylether degradation. FEMS Microbiol Lett 69:317-322

Engesser KH, Auling G, Busse J, Knackmuss H-J (1990b) 3-Fluorobenzoate enriched bacterial strain FLB 300 degrades benzoate and all three isomeric monofluorobenzoates. Arch Microbiol 153:193-199

Evans WC, Smith BSW, Fernley HN, Davis JI (1971a) Bacterial metabolism of 2,4-dichlorophenoxyacetate. Biochem J 122:543-551

Evans WC, Smith BSW, Moss P, Fernley HN (1971b) Bacterial metabolism of 4-chlorophenoxyacetate. Biochem J 122:509-517

Evans WCh, Fuchs G (1988) Anaerobic degradation of aromatic compounds. Ann Rev Microbiol 42:289-317

Fathepure BZ, Tiedje JM, Boyd SA (1988) Reductive dechlorination of hexachlorobenzene to tri- and dichlorobenzenes in anaerobic sewage sludge. Appl Environ Microbiol 54:327-330

Faulkner JK, Woodcock D (1961) Fungal detoxication. V. Metabolism of o- and p-chlorophenoxyacetic acids by Aspergillus niger. J chem Soc:5397-5400

Faulkner JK, Woodcock D (1964) Metabolism of 2,4-dichlorophenoxyacetic acid (2,4-D) by Aspergillus niger. Nature 203:865

Focht DD, Alexander M (1970) Bacterial degradation of diphenylmethane, a DDT model substrate. Appl Microbiol 20:608-611

Focht DD, Alexander M (1971) Aerobic cometabolism of DDT analogues by Hydrogenomonas sp. J Agric Food Chem 19:20-22

Focht DD, Brunner W (1985) Kinetics of biphenyl and polychlorinated biphenyl metabolism in soil. Appl Environ Microbiol 50(4):1058-1063

Fortnagel P, Harms H, Wittich R-M, Krohn S, Meyer H, Sinnwell V, Wilkes H, Francke W (1990) Metabolism of dibenzofuran by Pseudomonas sp. strain HH69 and the mixed culture HH27. Appl Environ Microbiol 56(4):1148-1156

Frank R, Braun HE (1989) PCB and DDE residues in milk supplies of Ontario, Canada 1985-1986. Bull Environ Contam Toxicol 42:666-669

Frommer W, Kanne R, Neupert M, Rast H-G, Springer W, Tillman W (1990) Mikrobieller Abbau von mehrfach halogenierten Aromaten. Patent application No 90105412.2 Bayer AG (applicant)

Furukawa K, Matsumura F (1976) Microbial metabolism of polychlorinated biphenyls. Studies on the relative degradability of polychlorinated biphenyl components by Alcaligenes sp.. J Agric Food Chem 24:251-256

Furukawa K, Matsumura F, Tonomura K (1978) Alcaligenes and Acinetobacter strains capable of degrading polychlorinated biphenyls. Agric Biol Chem 42:543-548

Furukawa K, Tomizuka N, Kamibayashi A (1979) Effect of chlorine substitution on the bacterial metabolism of various polychlorinated biphenyls. Appl Environ Microbiol 38:301-310

Furukawa K, Tomizuka N, Kamibayashi A (1983) Metabolic breakdown of Kanechlors (polychlorobiphenyls) and their products by Acinetobacter sp.. Appl Environ Microbiol 46(1):140-145

Gamar Y, Gaunt JK (1971) Bacterial metabolism of 4-chloro-2-methylphenoxyacetate: formation of glyoxylate by side-chain cleavage. Biochem J 122:527-531

Gaunt JK, Evans WC (1961) Metabolism of 4-chloro-2-methylphenoxyacetic acid by a soil microorganism. Biochem J 79:25-26

Gaunt JK, Evans WC (1971a) Metabolism of 4-chloro-2-methylphenoxyacetate by a soil pseudomonad. Preliminary evidence for the metabolic pathway. Biochem J 122:519-526

Gaunt JK, Evans WC (1971b) Metabolism of 4-chloro-2-methylphenoxyacetate by a soil pseudomonad Ring-fission, lactonising and delactonising enzymes. Biochem J 122:533-542

Ghosal D, You I-S (1988) Nucleotide homology and organisation of chlorocatechol oxidation genes of plasmids pJP4 and pAC27. Mol Gen Genet 211:113-120

Ghosal D, You I-S, Chatterjee DK, Chakrabarty AM (1985) Microbial degradation of halogenated compounds. Science 228(4696):135-142

Gibson DT, Koch JR, Schuld CL, Kallio RE (1968) Oxidative degradation of aromatic hydrocarbons by microorganisms. II. Metabolism of halogenated aromatic hydrocarbons. Biochemistry 7:3795-3802

Goldman P, Milne GWA, Keister DB (1968) Carbon-halogen bond cleavage. III. Studies on bacterial halidohydrolases. J Biol Chem 243:428-434

Golovleva LA, Skryabin GK (1981) Microbial degradation of DDT. In: Leisinger T, Hütter R, Cook AM, Nüesch J (eds) Microbial degradation of xenobiotics and recalcitrant compounds, vol FEMS Symposium No. 12, Academic Press, New York, pp 287-291

Hagenmaier H (1986) Determination of 2,3,7,8-tetrachlorodibenzo-p-dioxin in commercial chlorophenols and related products. Fresenius Z Anal Chem 325:603-606

Häggblom MM (1990) Mechanisms of bacterial degradation and transformation of chlorinated monoaromatic compounds. J Basic Microbiol 30(2):115-141

Häggblom MM, Nohynek LJ, Salkinoja-Salonen MS (1988) Degradation and o-methylation of chlorinated phenolic compounds by *Rhodococcus* and *Mycobacterium* strains. Appl Environ Microbiol 54: 3043-3052

Häggblom MM, Janke D, Salkinoja-Salonen MS (1989) Hydroxylation and dechlorination of tetrachlorohydroquinone by *Rhodococcus* sp. strain CP-2 cell extracts. Appl Environ Microbiol 55(2):516-519

Haigler BE, Spain JC (1989) Degradation of p-chlorotoluene by a mutant strain of *Pseudomonas* sp. strain JS6. Appl Environ Microbiol 55:372-379

Haigler BE, Nishino SF, Spain JC (1988) Degradation of 1,2-dichlorobenzene by a *Pseudomonas* sp. Appl Environ Microbiol 54:294-301

Haller HD, Finn RK (1979) Biodegradation of 3-chlorobenzoate and formation of black colour in the presence and absence of benzoate. European J Appl Microbiol 8:191-205

Harms H, Wittich R-M, Sinnwell V, Meyer H, Fortnagel P, Francke W (1990) Transformation of dibenzo-p-dioxin by *Pseudomonas* sp. strain HH69. Appl Environ Microbiol 56:1157-1159

Harper DB, Blakley ER (1971) The metabolism of p-fluorobenzoic acid by a *Pseudomonas* sp.. Can J Microbiol 17:1015-1023

Hartmann J, Reineke W, Knackmuss H-J (1979) Metabolism of 3-chloro-, 4-chloro-, and 3,5-dichlorobenzoate by a pseudomonad. Appl Environ Microbiol 37:421-428

Hartmann J, Engelberts K, Nordhaus B, Schmidt E, Reineke W (1989) Degradation of 2-chlorobenzoate by in vivo constructed hybrid pseudomonads. FEMS Microbiol Lett 61:17-22

Harvey S, Elashvili I, Valdes JJ, Kamely D, Chakrabarty AM (1990) Enhanced removal of Exxon Valdez spilled oil from Alaskan gravel by a microbial surfactant. Bio-Technology 8(3):228-230

Hickey WJ, Focht DD (1990) Degradation of mono-, di-, and trihalogenated benzoic acids by *Pseudomonas aeruginosa* JB2. Appl Environ Microbiol 56(12):3842-3850

Higson FK, Focht DD (1990a) Degradation of 2-bromobenzoic acid by a strain of *Pseudomonas aeruginosa*. Appl Environ Microbiol 56(6):1615-1619

Higson FK, Focht DD (1990b) Bacterial degradation of ring-chlorinated acetophenones. Appl Environ Microbiol 56(12):3678-3685

Hill DL, Phelps TJ, Palumbo AV, White DC, Strandberg GW, Donaldson TL (1989) Bioremediation of polychlorinated biphenyls: Degradation capabilities in field lysimeters. Appl Biochem Biotechnol 20/21:223-243

Horowitz A, Suflita JM, Tiedje JM (1983) Reductive dehalogenation of halobenzoates by anaerobic lake sediment microorganisms. Appl Environ Microbiol 45(5):1459-1465

Horvath M, Ditzelmüller G, Loidl M, Streichsbier F (1990) Isolation and characterisation of a 2-(2,4-dichlorophenoxy) propionic acid-degrading soil bacterium. Appl Microbiol Biotechnol 33:213-216

Horvath RS, Alexander M (1970) Cometabolism of m-chlorobenzoate by an *Arthrobacter*. Appl Microbiol 20(2):254-258

Horvath RS, Flathman P (1976) Co-metabolism of fluorobenzoates by natural microbial populations. Appl Environ Microbiol 31(6):889-891

Horvath RS (1971) Cometabolism of the herbicide 2,3,6-trichlorobenzoate. J Agric Food Chem 19(2):291-293

Hughes DE (1965) The metabolism of halogen-substituted benzoic acids by *Pseudomonas fluorescens*. Biochem J 96:181-188

Husain M, Entsch B, Ballou DP, Massey V, Chapman P (1980) Fluoride elimination from substrates in hydroxylation reactions catalyzed by p-hydroxybenzoate hydroxylase. J Biol Chem 255(9):4189-4197

Ide A, Niki Y, Sakamoto F Watanabe I, Watanabe H (1972) Decomposition of pentachlorophenol in paddy soil. Agric Biol Chem 36(11):1937-1944

Ihn W, Janke D, Tresselt D (1989) Critical steps in degradation of chloroaromatics by Rhodococci III. Isolation and identification of accumulating intermediates and dead-end products. J Basic Microbiol 29:291-297

Ip HMH, Phillips DJH (1989) Organochlorine chemicals in human breast milk in Hong Kong. Arch Environ Contam Toxicol 18(4):490-494

Janke D, Fritsche W (1979) Dechlorierung von 4-Chlorphenol nach extradioler Ringspaltung durch *Pseudomonas putida*. Z allg Mikrobiol 19(2):139-141

Janke D, Baskunov BP, Nefedova MYu, Zyakun AM, Golovleva LA (1984) Incorporation of $^{18}O_2$ during cometabolic degradation of 3-chloroaniline by *Rhodococcus* sp. An 117. Z allg Mikrobiol 24:253-259

Janke D, Ihn W, Tresselt D (1989) Critical steps in degradation of chloroaromatics by Rhodococci IV. Detailed kinetics of substrate removal and product formation by resting pre-adapted cells. J Basic Microbiol 29(5):305-314

Jessee JA, Benoit RE, Hendricks AC, Allen GC, Neal JL (1983) Anaerobic degradation of cyanuric acid, cysteine, and Atrazin by a facultative anaerobic bacterium. Appl Environ Microbiol 45(1):97-102

Johnson BT, Kennedy JO (1973) Biomagnification of p,p'-DDT and methoxychlor by bacteria. Appl Microbiol 26(1):66-71

Johnston HW, Briggs GG, Alexander M (1972) Metabolism of 3-chlorobenzoic acid by a pseudomonad. Soil Biol Biochem 4:187-190

Kamal Varsha S, Campbell-Wyndham R (1990) Anaerobic phototrophic metabolism of 3-chlorobenzoate by *Rhodopseudomonas palustris* WS17. Appl Environ Microbiol 56(12):3871-3873

Keith LH, Telliard WA (1979) Priority pollutants. Environ Sci Technol 13(4):416-423

Kersten PJ, Dagley S, Whittaker JW, Arciero DM, Lipscomb JD (1982) 2-Pyrone-4,6-dicarboxylic acid, a catabolite of gallic acids in *Pseudomonas species*. J Bacteriol 152(3):1154-1162

Kersten PJ, Chapman PJ, Dagley S (1985) Enzymatic release of halogens or methanol from substituted protocatechuic acids. J Bacteriol 162:693-697

Kilbane JJ, Chatterjee DK, Chakrabarty AM (1983) Detoxification of 2,4,5-trichlorophenoxyacetic acid from contaminated soil by *Pseudomonas cepacia*. Appl Environ Microbiol 45:1697-1700

Kilpi S, Himberg K, Yrjälä K, Backström V (1988) The degradation of biphenyl and chlorobiphenyls by mixed bacterial cultures. FEMS Microbiol Lett 53:19-26

Kimbara K, Hashimoto T, Fukuda M, Koana T, Takagi M, Oishi M, Yano K (1988) Isolation and characterisation of a mixed culture that degrades polychlorinated biphenyls. Agric Biol Chem 52(11):2885-2891

King GM (1988) Dehalogenation in marine sediments containing natural sources of halophenols. Appl Environ Microbiol 54(12):3079-3085

Kirkpatrick D, Biggs SR, Conway B, Finn CM, Hawkins DR, Honda T, Ishida Mi, Powell GP (1981) Metabolism of N-(2,3-dichlorophenyl)-3,4,5,6-tetrachlorophthalamic acid (Techlofthalam) in paddy soil and rice. J Agric Food Chem 29:1149-1153

Klages U, Lingens F (1979) Degradation of 4-chlorobenzoic acid by a *Nocardia* species. FEMS Microbiol Lett 6:201-203

Klages U, Lingens F (1980) Degradation of 4-chlorobenzoic acid by a *Pseudomonas* sp.. Zbl Bakt Hyg, Abt OrigC1 1:215-223

Klages U, Markus A, Lingens F (1981) Degradation of 4-chlorophenylacetic acid by a *Pseudomonas* species. J Bacteriol 146:64-68

Klecka GM, Maier WJ (1985) Kinetics of microbial growth on pentachlorophenol. Appl Environ Microbiol 49(1):46-53

Knackmuss H-J (1981) Degradation of halogenated and sulfonated hydrocarbons. In: Leisinger T, Hütter R, Cook AM, Nüesch J (eds) Microbial degradation of xenobiotics and recalcitrant compounds, Academic Press, London, pp 189-212

Knackmuss H-J, Hellwig M (1978) Utilisation and cooxidation of chlorinated phenols by *Pseudomonas* sp. B13. Arch Microbiol 117:1-7

Köcher H, Lingens F, Koch W (1976) Untersuchungen zum Abbau des Herbisids Chlorphenpropmethyl im Boden und durch Mikroorganismen. Weed Res 16:93-100

Krueger James P, Butz Robert G, Atallah Yousef H, Cork Douglas J (1989) Isolation and identification of microorganisms for the degradation of Dicamba. J Agric Food Chem 37:534-538

Kuhm A, Schlömann M, Knackmuss H-J, Pieper D (1990) Purification and characterisation of dichloromuconate cycloisomerase from *Alcaligenes eutrophus* JMP 134. Biochem J 266:877-883

Kuhn EP, Suflita JM (1989) Sequential reductive dehalogenation of chloroanilines by microorganisms from a methanogenic aquifer. Environ Sci Technol 23:848-852

Kuwatsuka S, Igarashi M (1975) Degradation of PCP in soils II. The relationship between the degradation of PCP and the properties of soils, and the identification of the degradation products of PCP. Soil Sci Plant Nutr 21(4):405-414

Latorre J, Reineke W, Knackmuss H-J (1984) Microbial metabolism of chloroanilines: enhanced evolution by natural genetic exchange. Arch Microbiol 140:159-164

Leisinger T, Brunner W (1986) Poorly degradable substances. In: Rehm H-J, Reed G (eds) Biotechnology, vol 8, chapter 14, VCH Verlagsgesellschaft, Weinheim, pp 475-513

Levine R, Chitwood DD (1985) Public health investigations of hazardous organic chemical waste disposal in the United States. Environ Health Perspect 62:415-422

Lingens F, Blecher R, Blecher H, Blobel F, Eberspächer J, Fröhner C, Görisch H, Görisch H, Layh G (1985) *Phenylobacterium immobile* gen. nov., sp. nov., a Gram-negative bacterium that degrades the herbicide Chloridazon. Int J Sys Bacteriol 35(1):26-39

Liu D, Thomson K, Strachan WMJ (1981) Biodegradation of pentachlorophenol in a simulated aquatic environment. Bull Environm Contam Toxicol 26:85-90

Liu T, Chapman PJ (1984) Purification and properties of a plasmid-encoded 2,4-dichlorophenol hydroxylase . FEBS Lett 173:314-318

Löffler F, Müller R, Lingens F (1991) A novel mechanism for an enzymatic dehalogenation reaction. Abstr Annu Meet VAAM March,18-21, 1991, Freiburg, FRG; published in: Bioforum 14(1/2):P164,p64

Loidl M, Hinteregger C, Ditzelmüller G, Ferschl A, Streichsbier F (1990) Degradation of aniline and monochlorinated anilines by soil-born *Pseudomonas acidovorans* strains. Arch Microbiol 155:56-61

Loos MA, Roberts RN, Alexander M (1967a) Phenols as intermediates in the decomposition of phenoxyacetates by an Arthrobacter species. Can J Microbiol 13:679-690

Loos MA, Roberts RN, Alexander M (1967b) Formation of 2,4-dichlorophenol and 2,4-dichloroanisole from 2,4-dichlorophenoxyacetate by *Arthrobacter* sp.. Can J Microbiol 13:691-699

Loos MA, Bollag J-M, Alexander M (1967c) Phenoxyacetate herbicide detoxification by bacterial enzymes. J Agric Food Chem 15:858-860

Ludwig W, Eberspächer J, Lingens F, Stackebrandt E (1984) 16 S ribosomal RNA studies on the relationship of a Chloridazon-degrading Gram-negative eubacterium. System Appl Microbiol 5:241-246

MacRae K, Alexander M (1963) Metabolism of phenoxyalkyl carboxylic acids by a *Flavobacterium* species. J Bacteriol 86:1231-1235

Magnus-Francis B (1990) Relative teratogenicity of Nitrofen analogs in mice: Unchlorinated, monochlorinated, and dichlorinated-phenyl ethers. Teratology 41:443-451

Marks TS, Wait R, Smith ARW, Quirk AV (1984a) The origin of the oxygen incorporated during the dehalogenation/ hydroxylation of 4-chlorobenzoate by an *Arthrobacter* sp.. Biochem Biophys Res Commun 124(2):669-674

Marks TS, Smith ARW, Quirk AV (1984b) Degradation of 4-chlorobenzoic acid by *Arthrobacter* sp. Appl Environ Microbiol 48:1020-1025

Markus A, Klages U, Krauss S, Lingens F (1984) Oxidation and dehalogenation of 4-chlorophenylacetate by a two-component enzyme system from *Pseudomonas* sp. strain CBS3. J Bacteriol 160:618-621

Meer JR van der, Neerven AR, Vries EJ, Vos WM, Zehnder AJB (1991) Cloning and characterisation of plasmid-encoded genes for the degradation of 1,2-dichloro-, 1,4-dichloro-, and 1,2,4-trichlorobenzene of *Pseudomonas* sp. strain P51. J Bacteriol 173(1):6-15

Mikesell MD, Boyd SA (1986) Complete reductive dechlorination and mineralisation of pentachlorophenol by anaerobic microorganisms. Appl Environ Microbiol 52:861-865

Mikesell MD, Boyd SA (1985) Reductive Dechlorination of the pesticides 2,4-D, 2,4,5-T, and pentachlorophenol in anaerobic sludges. J Environ Qual 14(3):337-340

Mohn WW, Tiedje JM (1990) Strain DCB-1 conserves energy for growth from reductive dechlorination coupled to formate oxidation. Arch Microbiol 153:267-271

Moon YH, Kuwatsuka S (1984) Properties and conditions of soils causing the dechlorination of the herbicide benthiocarb (thiobencarb) in flooded soils. J Pest Sci 9:745-754

Morgan P, Watkinson RJ (1989) Microbiological methods for the cleanup of soil and ground water contaminated with halogenated organic compounds. FEMS Microbiol Rev 63:277-300

Morris CM, Barnsley EA (1982) The cometabolism of 1- and 2-chloronaphthalene by pseudomonads. Can J Microbiol 28(1):73-79

Mousa MA, Rogers JE (1990) Dechlorination of hexachlorobenzene in two freshwater pond sediments under methanogenic conditions. Abstr Ann Meet Amer Soc Microbiol Q-45:296

Müller R, Thiele Jürgen, Klages Uwe, Lingens Franz (1984) Incorporation of (^{18}O)Water into 4-hydroxybenzoic acid in the reaction of 4-chlorobenzoate dehalogenase from *Pseudomonas* spec. CBS 3. Biochem Biophys Res Commun 124(1):178-182

Murthy NBK, Kaufman DD, Fries GF (1979) Degradation of pentachlorophenol (PCP) in aerobic and anaerobic soil. J Environ Sci Health 14(1):1-14

Neidleman SL, Geigert J (1987) Biological halogenation: roles in nature, potential in industry. Endeavour 11(1):5-15

Neilson AH (1990) The biodegradation of halogenated organic compounds. J Appl Bacteriol 69:445-470

Neilson AH, Allard A-S, Hynning P-A, Remberger M (1988) Transformations of halogenated aromatic aldehydes by metabolically stable anaerobic enrichment cultures. Appl Environ Microbiol 54(9):2226-2236

Nesnow S, Argus M, Bergman H, Chu K, Frith C, Helmes T, McGaughy R, Ray V, Slaga TJ, Tennant R, Weisburger E (1986) Chemical carcinogens. A review and analysis of the literature of selected chemicals and the establishment of the Gene-Tox Carcinogen Data Base. Mutation Res 185:1-195

Ngai K-L, Schlömann M, Knackmuss H-J, Ornston LN (1987) Dienelactone hydrolase from *Pseudomonas* sp. strain B13. J Bacteriol 169(2):699-703

Oltmanns RH, Rast HG, Reineke W (1988) Degradation of 1,4-dichlorobenzene by enriched and constructed bacteria. Appl Microbiol Biotechnol 28:609-616

Oltmanns RH, Müller R, Otto MK, Lingens F (1989) Evidence for a new pathway in the bacterial degradation of 4-fluorobenzoate. Appl Environ Microbiol 55(10):2499-2504

Omori T, Sugimura K, Ishigooka H, Minoda Y (1986) Purification and some properties of a 2-hydroxy-6-oxo-6-phenylhexa-2,4-dienoic acid hydrolyzing enzyme from *Pseudomonas cruciviae* S93 B1 involved in the degradation of biphenyl. Agric Biol Chem 50(4):931-937

Ornston LN (1966) The conversion of catechol and protocatechuate to ß-ketoadipate by *Pseudomonas putida* III. Enzymes of the catechol pathway. J Biol Chem 241:3795-3799

Ornston LN, Stanier RY (1966) The conversion of catechol and protocatechuate to ß-ketoadipate by *Pseudomonas putida* I. Biochemistry. J Biol Chem 241:3776-3786

Parsons JR, Ratsak C, Siekerman C (1990) Biodegradation of chlorinated dibenzofurans by an Alcaligenes strain. In: Hutzinger O, Fiedler O (eds) Organohalogen compounds. Proc. Dioxin '90-EPRI Seminar, vol Vol 1, Ecoinforma Press, Bayreuth, pp 377-380

Pathak D, Ollis D (1990) Refined structure of dienelactone hydrolase at 1.8 A. J Mol Biol 214(2):497-425

Pathak D, Ngai K-L, Ollis D (1988) X-ray crystallographic structure of dienelactone hydrolase at 2.8 A. J Mol Biol 204:435-445

Pettigrew CA, Haigler BE, Spain JC (1991) Simultaneous biodegradation of chlorobenzene and toluene by a *Pseudomonas* strain . Appl Environ Microbiol 57(1):157-162

Pieper DH, Reineke W, Engesser KH, Knackmuss H-J (1988) Metabolism of 2,4-dichlorophenoxyacetic acid, 4-chloro-2-methylphenoxyacetic acid and 2-methylphenoxyacetic acid by *Alcaligenes eutrophus* JMP 134. Arch Microbiol 150:95-102

Pieper D (1986) Metabolismus von substituierten Phenoxyacetaten, Phenolen und Benzoaten durch *Alcaligenes eutrophus* JMP 134 und Derivate. PhD thesis University of Stuttgart, FRG:202-203

Pignatello Joseph J, Martinson Michael M, Steiert John J, Carlson Robert E, Crawford Ronald L (1983) Biodegradation and photolysis of pentachlorophenol in artificial freshwater streams. Appl Environ Microbiol 46(5):1024-1031

Quensen (III) JF, Matsumura F (1983) Oxidative degradation of 2,3,7,8-tetrachlorodibenzo-p-dioxin by microorganisms. Environ Toxicol Chem 2:261-268

Quensen (III) JF, Tiedje JM, Boyd SA (1988) Reductive dechlorination of polychlorinated biphenyls by anaerobic microorganisms from sediments. Science 242:752-754

Quensen (III) JF, Boyd SA, Tiedje JM (1990) Dechlorination of four commercial polychlorinated biphenyl mixtures(Aroclors) by anaerobic microorganisms from sediments. Appl Environ Microbiol 56(8):2360-2369

Ramsay B, McCarthy J, Guerra-Santos L, Kappeli O, Fiechter A, Margaritis A (1988) Biosurfactant production and diauxic growth of Rhodococcus auranthiacus when using n-alkanes as the carbon source. Can J Microbiol 34:1209-1212

Rasul-Chaudry G, Chapalamadugu S (1991) Biodegradation of halogenated organic compounds. Microbiol Rev 55(1):59-79

Reber H, Helm V, Karanth NGK (1979) Comparative studies on the metabolism of aniline and chloroanilines by *Pseudomonas multivorans* strain An 1. Eur J Appl Microbiol 7:181-189

Reineke W (1986) Construction of bacterial strains with novel degradative capabilities for chloroaromatics. J Basic Microbiol 26(9):551-567

Reineke W, Knackmuss H-J (1978a) Chemical structure and biodegradability of halogenated compounds. Substituent effects on dehydrogenation of 3,5-cyclohexadiene-1,2-diol-1-carboxylic acid. Biochim Biophys Acta 542:424-429

Reineke W, Knackmuss H-J (1978b) Chemical structure and biodegradability of halogenated aromatic compounds. Sustituent effects on 1,2-dioxygenation of benzoic acids. Biochim Biophys Acta 542:412-423

Reineke W, Knackmuss H-J (1984) Microbial metabolism of haloaromatics: Isolation and properties of a chlorobenzene- degrading bacterium. Appl Environ Microbiol 47:395-402

Reineke W, Knackmuss H-J (1988) Microbial degradation of haloaromatics. Ann Rev Microbiol 42:263-287

Renganathan V (1989) Possible involvment of toluene 2,3-dioxygenase in defluorination of 3-fluoro-substituted benzenes by toluene-degrading Pseudomonas sp. strain T-12. Appl Environ Microbiol 55(2):330-334

Renner G, Nguyen Phuc-Trung (1984) Mechanisms of the reductive denitration of pentachloronitrobenzene(PCNB) and the reductive dechlorination of hexachlorobenzene(HCB). Xenobiotica 14(9):705-710

Ribbons DW, Cass AEG, Rossiter JT, Taylor SJC, Woodland MP (1987) Biotransformations of fluoroaromatic compounds. J Fluorine Chem 37:299-326

Rippen G, Frank R (1986) Estimation of hexachlorobenzene pathways from the technosphere into the environment. In: Morris CR, Cabral JRP (eds) Hexachlorobenzene: Proceedings of an international symposium, Oxford University Press, Oxford, pp 45-52

Rippen G, Klopffer W, Frische R, Gunther K (1984) The environmental model segment approach for estimating potential environmental concentrations. Ecotoxicol Environ Safety 8:363-377

Rochkind-Dubinsky ML, Sayler GS, Blackburn JW (1986) Microbial decomposition of chlorinated aromatic compounds, vol Microbiology series, chapter 18, Marcel Dekker Inc, New York and Basel

Rott B, Nitz S, Korte F (1979) Microbial decomposition of sodium pentachlorophenolate. J Agric Food Chem 27:306-310

Rubio MA, Engesser K-H, Knackmuss H-J (1986a) Microbial metabolism of chlorosalycylates: accelerated evolution by natural genetic exchange. Arch Microbiol 145:116-122

Rubio MA, Engesser K-H, Knackmuss H-J (1986b) Microbial metabolism of chlorosalicylates: effect of prolonged subcultivation on constructed strains. Arch Microbiol 145:123-125

Ruisinger S, Klages U, Lingens F (1976) Abbau der 4-Chlorbenzoesäure durch eine Arthrobacter-Species. Arch Microbiol 110:253-256

Ryan J, Gasiewicz TA, Brown(jr.) JF (1990) Human body burden of polychlorinated dibenzofurans associated with toxicity based on the Yusho and Yucheng incidents. Fundamental Appl Toxicol 15:722-731

Saber DL, Crawford RL (1985) Isolation and characterisation of Flavobacterium strains that degrade pentachlorophenol. Appl Environ Microbiol 50:1512-1518

Sabljic A (1989) Quantitative modeling of soil sorption for xenobiotic chemicals. Environ Health Perspect 83:179-190

Safe SH (1984) Microbial degradation of organic compounds. In: Gibson DT (ed), vol 13 Microbial degradation of polychlorinated biphenyls, Marcel Dekker, Inc, New York pp 361-369

Safe S (1990) Polychlorinated biphenyls (PCBs), dibenzo-p-dioxins(PCDDs), dibenzofurans(PCDFs), and related compounds: environmental and mechanistic considerations which support the development of toxic equivalency factors (TEFs). Crit Rev Toxicol 21(1):51-88

Sato K, Tanaka H (1987) Degradation and metabolism of a fungicide, 2,4,5,6-tetra-chloroisophthalonitrile (TPN) in soil. Biol Fertil Soils 3:205-209

Sauber K, Fröhner C, Rosenberg G, Eberspächer J, Lingens F (1977) Purification and properties of a Pyrazon dioxygenase from Pyrazon-degrading bacteria. Eur J Biochem 74:89-97

Savard P, Peloquin L, Sylvestre M (1986) Cloning of Pseudomonas sp. strain CBS3 genes specifying dehalogenation of 4-chlorobenzoate. J Bacteriol 168(1):81-85

Schacht S, Engesser K-H, Dorn E, Knackmuss H-J (1991) Biodegradation of 4-halosubstituted benzoates via meta-cleavage pathway: Characterisation of unproductive metabolism by Pseudomonas putida mt-2 (Submitted for publication to Arch. Microbiol)

Schenk T, Müller R, Mörsberger F, Otto MK, Lingens F (1989) Enzymatic Dehalogenation of pentachlorophenol by extracts from Arthrobacter sp. strain ATCC 33790. J Bacteriol 171(10):5487-5491

Schenk T, Müller R, Lingens F (1990) Mechanism of enzymatic dehalogenation of pentachlorophenol by Arthrobacter sp. strain ATCC 33790. J Bacteriol 172(12):7272-7274

Schennen U, Braun K, Knackmuss H-J (1985) Anaerobic degradation of 2-fluorobenzoate by benzoate-degrading, denitrifying bacteria. J Bacteriol 161(1):321-325

Schlömann M, Schmidt E, Knackmuss H-J (1990a) Different types of dienelactone hydrolase in 4-fluorobenzoate-utilising bacteria. J Bacteriol 172(9):5112-5118

Schlömann M, Fischer P, Schmidt E, Knackmuss H-J (1990b) Enzymatic formation, stability, and spontaneous reactions of 4-fluoromuconolactone, a metabolite of the bacterial degradation of 4-fluorobenzoate. J Bacteriol 172(9):5119-5129

Schmidt E, Knackmuss H-J (1980) Chemical structure and biodegradability of halogenated aromatic compounds.Conversion of chlorinated muconic acids into maleoylacetic acid. Biochem J 192:339-347

Schmidt E, Remberg G, Knackmuss H-J (1980) Chemical structure and biodegradability of halogenated aromatic compounds. Halogenated muconic acids as intermediates. Biochem J 192:331-337

Schmitt S, Müller R, Wegst W, Lingens F (1984) Chloridazon-catechol dioxygenases, a distinct group of meta-cleaving enzymes. Hoppe-Seyler's Z Physiol Chem 365:143-150

Schraa G, Boone ML, Jetten MSM, Neerven AR, Colberg PJ, Zehnder AJB (1986) Degradation of 1,4-dichlorobenzene by *Alcaligenes* sp. strain A175. Appl Environ Microbiol 52(6):1374-1381

Schreiber A, Hellwig M, Dorn E, Reineke W, Knackmuss H-J (1980) Critical reactions in fluorobenzoic acid degradation by *Pseudomonas* sp. B13. Appl Environ Microbiol 39:58-67

Schukat B, Janke D, Krebs D, Fritsche W (1983) Cometabolic degradation of 2- and 3-chloroaniline because of glucose metabolism by *Rhodococcus* sp. An 117. Curr Microbiol 9:81-86

Shailubhai K, Sahasrabudhe SR, Vora KA, Modi VV (1983) Degradation of chlorinated derivatives of phenoxyacetic acid and benzoic acid by *Aspergillus niger*. FEMS Microbiol Lett 18:279-282

Sharak-Genthner BR, Allen-Price II W, Pritchard PH (1989a) Characterisation of anaerobic dechlorinating consortia derived from aquatic sediments. Appl Environ Microbiol 55(6):1472-1476

Sharak-Genthner BR, Allen-Price II W, Pritchard PH (1989b) Anaerobic degradation of chloroaromatic compounds in aquatic sediments under a variety of enrichment conditions. Appl Environ Microbiol 55(6):1466-1471

Shelton DR, Tiedje JM (1984) Isolation and partial characterisation of bacteria in an anaerobic consortium that mineralises 3-chlorobenzoic acid. Appl Environ Microbiol 48(4):840-848

Shiaris MP, Sayler GS (1982) Biotransformation of PCB by natural assemblages of freshwater microorganisms. Environ Sci Technol 16:367-369

Shields MS, Hooper SW, Sayler GS (1985) Plasmid-mediated mineralisation of 4-chlorobiphenyl. J Bacteriol 163(3):882-889

Shimao M, Onishi S, Mizumori S, Kato N, Sakazawa C (1989) Degradation of 4-chlorobenzoate by facultatively alkalophilic *Arthrobacter* sp. strain SB8. Appl Environ Microbiol 55(2):478-482

Siuda JF, DeBernardis JF (1973) Naturally occuring halogenated compounds. Lloydia 36:107-143

Skaare JU, Polder A (1990) Polychlorinated biphenyls and organochlorine pesticides in milk of Norwegian women during lactation. Arch Environ Contam Toxicol 19:640-645

Spain JC, Nishino SF (1987) Degradation of 1,4-dichlorobenzene by a *Pseudomonas* sp.. Appl Environ Microbiol 53(5):1010-1019

Spain JC, Gibson DT (1988) Oxidation of substituted phenols by *Pseudomonas putida* F1 and *Pseudomonas* sp strain JS6. Appl Environ Microbiol 54: 1399-11404

Sperl GT, Harvey J (1988) Microbial adaptation to bromobenzene in a chemostat. Curr Microbiol 17:99-103

Springer W, Rast HG (1988) Biologischer Abbau mehrfach halogenierter mono- und polyzyklischer Aromaten gwf Wasser/Abwasser 129 (1):70-75

Steiert JG, Pignatello JJ, Crawford RL (1987) Degradation of chlorinated phenols by a pentachlorophenol-degrading bacterium. Appl Environ Microbiol 53:907-910

Stepp TD, Camper ND, Paynter MJB (1985) Anaerobic microbial degradation of selected 3,4-dihalogenated aromatic compounds. Pest Biochem Physiol 23:256-260

Strubel V, Engesser KH, Fischer p, Knackmuss H-J (1991) 3-(2-Hydroxyphenyl) catechol as substrate for proximal meta ring cleavage in dibenzofuran degradation by *Brevibacterium* sp strain DPO 1361. J Bacteriol 173(6): 1932-1937

Struijs J, Rogers JE (1989) Reductive dehalogenation of dichloroanilines by anaerobic microorganisms in fresh and dichlorophenol-acclimated pond sediment. Appl Environ Microbiol 55(10):2527-2531

Suflita JM, Horowitz A, Shelton DR, Tiedje JM (1982) Dehalogenation: a novel pathway for the anaerobic biodegradation of haloaromatic compounds. Science 218:1115-1117

Suflita JM, Stout J, Tiedje JM (1984) Dechlorination of (2,4,5-trichlorophenoxy)acetic acid by anaerobic microorganisms. J Agric Food Chem 32:218

Surovtseva EG, Volnova AI, Shatskaya TYa (1980) Degradation of monochlorosubstituted anilines by *Alcaligenes faecalis*. Mikrobiologiya 49:351-354

Surovtseva EG, Ivoilov VS, Karasevich YuN (1986) Metabolism of chlorinated anilines by Pseudomonas diminuta. Mikrobiologiya 55:591-595

Suzuki T (1977) Metabolism of pentachlorophenol by a soil microbe . J Environ Sci Health 12:113-127

Sylvestre M, Mailhiot K, Ahmad D, Masse R (1989) Isolation and preliminary characterisation of a 2-chlorobenzoate degrading Pseudomonas. Can J Microbiol 35:439-443

Szewzyk U, Szewzyk R, Schink B (1985) Methanogenic degradation of hydroquinone and catechol via reductive dehydroxylation to phenol. FEMS Microbiol Ecol 31:79-87

Taylor BF, Hearn WL, Pincus S (1979) Metabolism of monofluoro- and monochlorobenzoates by a denitrifying bacterium. Arch Microbiol 122:301-306

Thiele J, Müller R, Lingens F (1987) Initial characterisation of 4-chlorobenzoate dehalogenase from Pseudomonas sp. CBS3. FEMS Microbiol Lett 41:115-119

Thiele J, Müller R, Lingens F (1988) Enzymatic dehalogenation of 4-chlorobenzoate by 4-chlorobenzoate dehalogenase from Pseudomonas sp. CBS3 in organic solvents. Appl Microbiol Biotechnol 27:577-580

Tibbles PE, Müller R, Lingens F (1989a) Microbial metabolism of quinoline and related compounds III. Degradation of 3-chloroquinoline-8-carboxylic acid by Pseudomonas spec. EK III. Biol Chem Hoppe-Seyler 370:1191-1196

Tibbles PE, Müller R, Lingens F (1989b) Degradation of 5-chloro-2-hydroxynicotinic acid by Mycobacterium sp. BA. Biol Chem Hoppe-Seyler 370:601-606

Tiedje JM, Alexander M (1969) Enzymatic cleavage of the ether bond of 2,4-dichlorophenoxyacetate. J Agric Food Chem 17:1080-1084

Tiedje JM, Duxburry JM, Alexander M, Dawson JE (1969) 2,4-D metabolism: Pathway of degradation of chlorocatechols by Arthrobacter sp. J Agric Food Chem 17:1021-1026

Tittmann U, Wegst W, Blecher R, Lingens F (1980) Abbau von trans-Zimtsäure durch Chloridazon-abbauende Bakterien. Zbl Bakt Hyg I Abt Orig C1:124-132

Tsuchiya Toshie, Yamaha Tsutomu (1984) Reductive dechlorination of 1,2,4-trichlorobenzene by Staphylococcus epidermidis isolated from intestinal contents of rats. Agric Biol Chem 48(6):1545-1550

Tweel WJJ van den, Burg N, Kok JB, de Bont JAM (1986) Bioformation of 4-hydroxybenzoate from 4-chlorobenzoate by Alcaligenes denitrificans NTB-1. Appl Microbiol Biotechnol 25:289-294

Tweel WJJ van den, Kok JB, de Bont JAM (1987) Reductive dechlorination of 2,4-dichlorobenzoate to 4-chlorobenzoate and hydrolytic dehalogenation of 4-chloro-, 4-bromo-, and 4-iodobenzoate by Alcaligenes denitrificans NTB-1. Appl Environ Microbiol 53(4):810-815

Valo R, Salkinoja-Salonen M (1986) Bioreclamation of chlorophenol-contaminated soil by composting. Appl Microbiol Biotechnol 25:68-75

Vandenbergh PA, Olsen RH, Colaruotolo JF (1981) Isolation and genetic characterisation of bacteria that degrade chloroaromatic compounds. Appl Environ Microbiol 42(4):737-739

Viney I, Bewley RJF (1990) Preliminary studies on the development of a microbiological treatment for polychlorinated biphenyls. Arch Environ Contam Toxicol 19:789-796

Vora KA, Singh C, Modi VV (1988) Degradation of 2-fluorobenzoate by a pseudomonad. Curr Microbiol 17:249-254

Wannstedt C, Rotella D, Siuda JF (1990) Chloroperoxidase mediated halogenation of phenols. Bull Environ Contam Toxicol 44:282-287

Watanabe I (1973) Isolation of pentachlorophenol decomposing bacteria from soil. Soil Sci Plant Nutr 19:109-116

Wedemeyer G (1967) Dechlorination of 1,1,1-trichloro-2,2-bis(p-chlorophenyl)ethane by Aerobacter aerogenes. Appl Microbiol 15:569-574

Whitlock JP (1990) Genetic and molecular aspects of 2,3,7,8-tetrachlorodibenzo-p-dioxin action. Ann Rev Pharmacol Toxicol 30:251-277

Wittich R-M, Sander P, Fortnagel P (1989) Aerobic degradation of 1,2,4-trichlorobenzene (1,2,4-TCB) and 1,2,4,5-tetra-chlorobenzene (1,2,4,5-TeCB) by pure cultures of soil bacteria (Abstr. Annu. Meet. Germ. Soc. Microbiol., P243). forum mikrobiologie(1-2):100

Wittich R-M. Schmidt S, Fortnagel P (1990) Bacterial degradation of 3- and 4-carboxybiphenyl ether by Pseudomonas sp. NSS2 FEMS Microbiol Lett 67,157-160

Xun L, Orser CS (1991) Biodegradation of triiodophenol by cell-free extracts of a pentachlorophenol-degrading Flavobacterium sp.. Biochem Biophys Res Commun 174(1):43-48

Yamada T, Suzuki T (1983) Occurence of reductive dechlorination products in the paddy field soil treated with CNP (Chlornitrofen). J Pest Sci 8(4):437-443

Yeh W-K, Shih C, Ornston LN (1982) Overlapping evolutionary affinities revealed by comparison of amino acid compositions. Proc Natl Acad Sci USA 79:3794-3797

Zaitsev GM, Karasevich YuN (1985) Preparatory metabolism of 4-chlorobenzoic and 2,4-dichlorobenzoic acids in Corynebacterium sepedonicum. Mikrobiologiya 54(3):356-359

Zeyer J, Wasserfallen A, Timmis KN (1985) Microbial mineralisation of ring-substituted anilines through an ortho-cleavage pathway. Appl Environ Microbiol 50(2):447-453

Zhang X, Wiegel J (1990) Sequential anaerobic degradation of 2,4-dichlorophenol in freshwater sediments. Appl Environ Microbiol 56(4):1119-1127

Chapter 3

Biodeterioration of Fuels

R. N. Smith

Introduction

The biodeterioration of hydrocarbons only occurs when water is present, the active deteriogens growing either at the oil-water interface or in the aqueous phase. It is primarily trophic biodeterioration in which the hydrocarbon is used as a carbon and energy source and as such is synonymous with biodegradation. The only difference is that biodeterioration is biodegradation in the wrong place. Thus microbial degradation of fuel in the wing tanks of an aircraft is biodeterioration but the same process occurring in an oil slick is biodegradation. Biodegradation of hydrocarbons is a strictly aerobic process and degradation cannot occur under anaerobic conditions. This is because hydrocarbons, unlike carbohydrates, contain no oxygen. Hence those processes which take place during the fermentation of glucose, whereby the oxidised product following energy release itself becomes the ultimate hydrogen and electron acceptor to form alcohol, cannot occur. Paradoxically, this does not mean that biodeterioration will not take place under anaerobic conditions; trophic degradation can and does occur providing an alternative electron acceptor such as nitrate or sulphate is present. Whilst primary deterioration is trophic there may be secondary forms of spoilage which arise from microbial growth such as the migration of water droplets into the fuel, the accumulation of microbial slimes in the fuel and souring by hydrogen sulphide produced by the sulphate reducing bacteria.

Hydrocarbons have always been present in the environment in small amounts as a result of natural seepage, where oil fields lay close to the surface, and from plant and animal products. Song et al. (1986) isolated a range of hydrocarbon-degrading organisms from a soil for which there was no history of contamination by mineral oils. However, increased numbers of hydrocarbon degrading organisms are regularly found in soils where oil pollution occurs (Song and Bartha 1990) and higher frequencies of bacteria containing plasmids for hydrocarbon degradation have been found in such environments (Okpokwasili *et al.* 1986). The propensity of the soil microflora for biodegrading hydrocarbons is such that it forms the basis of "Landfarming", a procedure for the disposal of refinery and other petroleum wastes. In this process the waste hydrocarbons are incorporated into the soil where they are broken down by the soil microflora. This has the advantage of lower start-up and operating costs than alternative methods of disposal such as incineration (Gradet and Short 1980). The elimination of oil pollutants can be enhanced by adding fertilisers and tilling the soil to maintain conditions which favour the proliferation of the natural microbial community (Aamand *et al.* 1989; Lapinskas 1989; Song, Wang and Bartha 1990). There is also evidence that the presence of hydrocarbons leads to an increased incidence of bacteria containing plasmids for hydrocarbon degradation (Okpokwasili *et al.* 1986). Thus the biodeterioration of hydrocarbon fuels can be considered to be the normal reaction of the soil and aquatic microflora to a carbon source and whenever hydrocarbons are stored over a water bottom microbial deterioration can be anticipated.

The selective process which occurs in polluted soils and natural waters will also occur in fuel tanks and the susceptibility of any particular hydrocarbon to microbial degradation will depend upon its molecular structure and physical properties. However, microbial growth and biodegradation can only occur in an aqueous environment and so the major impediment to the biodegradation of hydrocarbons is their hydrophobicity and insolubility in water. The contents of a fuel tank invariably contain both an oil and an aqueous phase but the biodegradation of hydrocarbons is restricted to the aqueous phase, with the deteriogens often concentrated at the oil-water interface. This aqueous phase may occur as droplets suspended in the fuel, or on tank walls, or as a distinct water bottom.

Any carbon compound which can be oxidised should be biodegradable and as a general rule we can say that if a material is combustible it will be biodegradable and the rate of biodegradation will depend on the molecular structure. Middle distillate fuels are particularly susceptible to microbial spoilage (Ratledge 1978); they are composed predominantly of alkanes with a chain length between C12 and C21. Oil degrading microorganisms are unique in possessing the ability to take in hydrocarbons and convert them to fatty acids, similar to those in butter, which can then be metabolised by conventional ß-oxidation (Fig. 3.1). Aromatic hydrocarbons are degraded first by excising any side chains and converting them to fatty acids, and then breaking the benzene ring to give a diterminal acid or acid aldehyde (see Hopper chapter 1 this volume). The gasolines and similar low distillate fuels are less susceptible to microbial attack due to their inherent toxicity resulting from disruption of the cell membrane and the high distillate fuels are less susceptible due to their large molecular structure and very low solubility in water.

Microbial spoilage became apparent with the increased use of middle distillate fuels for heating, diesel engines and gas turbines in the 1950's, and was widely recognised by the the early 1960s. Hostetler and Powers (1963) described the symptoms as "a black or brown sludge which caused excess water and particulate matter to become suspended in the fuel leading to filter plugging, choked injector nozzles and sometimes line plugging". It is not clear whether these slimes were fungal or bacterial in origin but they were undoubtedly microbial and the authors recorded high bacterial counts of 10^7-10^8 cells ml^{-1} in both the fuel and water in the bottoms of infected tanks.

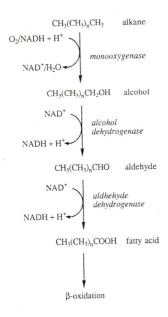

CH$_3$(CH$_3$)$_n$CH$_3$ alkane

O$_2$/NADH + H$^+$

NAD$^+$/H$_2$O

monooxygenase

CH$_3$(CH$_3$)$_n$CH$_2$OH   alcohol

NAD$^+$

NADH + H$^+$

alcohol dehydrogenase

CH$_3$(CH$_3$)$_n$CHO   aldehyde

NAD$^+$

NADH + H$^+$

aldhehyde dehydrogenase

CH$_3$(CH$_3$)$_n$COOH   fatty acid

β-oxidation

Fig. 3.1. Bacterial degradation of aliphatic hydrocarbons.

Origins of Microbial Spoilage

Microbial deterioration takes place primarily at the oil-water interface and so spoilage only occurs when water is present either in the form of a water bottom or as water droplets on tank walls, filters or in coalescers. The consequences of microbial spoilage are shown in Table 3.1. Clean and dry fuel is immune to microbial attack and for it to become susceptible it must be contaminated water, essential nutrients such as nitrogen, phosphorus sulphur and other trace elements. Additionally, an inoculum of fuel degrading microorganisms is required.

Table 3.1. The consequences of microbial spoilage

1	A moisture haze in the fuel
2	A dense layer of emulsified oil droplets in place of the sharp oil-water interface
3	An interface slime composed of either filaments of the fungus *Hormoconis resinae*, or an insoluble polymeric material secreted by oil-degrading bacteria, or a mixture of the two
4	The migration of fragments of fungal filaments and sheets of bacterial polymer from the oil-water interface up into the fuel
5	A high water content in the fuel
6	An increase in viscosity particularly at low temperatures due to the presence of the bacterial polymer in the fuel
7	Filter, valve, coalescer and fuel pump blockages
8	A blackening of the water bottoms by precipitates of iron sulphide due to the activity of sulphate reducing bacteria
9	Sulphide souring of the fuel

These factors enter the fuel by a variety of routes described in Table 3.2. Initially the filamentous fungus *Hormoconis resinae* (formerly known as *Cladosporium resinae*) was the prime deteriogen of middle distillate fuels. *H. resinae* produced a black filamentous

Table 3.2. Routes for entry of components to fuel spoilage

Water enters the fuel as:	Essential mineral nutrients enter the fuel as:	Microorganisms enter the fuel as:
Water vapour in humid air.	Dust particles entering fuel tanks through vents.	Airborne contamination.
Rain water draining through the fuel in a floating roof tank.	Insects and other small animals which enter the tank and become entrapped in the fuel so that their corpses sink down to the water bottom where they decay to release nutrients which enhance microbial growth.	In contaminated fuel returned to the tank.
Soil or drainage water entering as leaks or seepage through small fractures.	The fuel itself may contain added ingredients such as flow improvers and corrosion inhibitors which also dissolve in the water further enhancing its ability to support microbial growth.	In water which enters the tank.
Harbour water used to ballast marine tankers.	Water which gets into the tank often carries inorganic salts in solution and may be further enriched by organic pollution.	
Water used for product separation in pipeline shipments.		

slime at the oil-water interface, and a black glutinous film on the walls of infected tanks which often led to metal corrosion. In conditions of violent agitation, as may occur in aircraft or ships, this slime could be taken up into the fuel where it entered the fuel lines and caused pump malfunction and fuel line blockage. Cases have been reported of jet aircraft experiencing flame out or engine failure as a result of fuel blockage and at least one warship had to return to port on only one engine. Water containing mineral salts such as sodium chloride is highly corrosive to jet engines and so coalescers are installed in the fuel system to remove any water droplets. Coalescers contain cellulose fibres which are perpetually coated with water and thus the coalescers themselves are highly susceptible to microbial attack and blockage by microbial slime. The fuel systems of jet aircraft were also particularly vulnerable to microbial corrosion following infestation of their fuel tanks and instances were reported of fuel dripping from wing tanks which had been perforated by corrosion (Miller *et al.* 1964; Rogers and Kaplan 1965; Edmonds and Cooney 1967). Diesel powered ships, gas turbine warships and battle tanks were also affected and spoilage has even been found in road vehicle diesel fuel. Sulphate-reducing bacteria were often associated with *H. resinae* in cases of tank corrosion and perhaps due to differences in the climate or the composition of the fuel some navies experienced more problems from the the activity of sulphate reducing bacteria than from *H. resinae*. In aviation the problem was largely restricted to military and private aircraft which spend much of their time on the ground. Civilian airliners spend most of their time at high altitudes where the temperature is so low that the water bottoms are permanently frozen and rarely succumb to microbial spoilage. However, severe infection has been found in civilian airliners operating in tropical regions. This spoilage in aircraft fuel systems has been controlled primarily by improved fuel handling, particularly the repeated removal of water, but also by the addition of the antifreeze, ethylene glycol monomethyl ether (EGME), which is also fungistatic, the use of the biocide, Biobor JF and more recently by the use of a mixture of isothiazolones marketed as Kathon FP. These problems have not been restricted to fuel as fuel system hydraulic oils are also susceptible to microbial attack and fungal slimes have even been been found in the hydraulics of space launch systems.

Microbial spoilage has now reappeared with increasing frequency and severity in diesel fuels and gas oils. There has also been a significant shift in the organisms responsible from the fungus *H. resinae*, to bacteria, principally, *Pseudomonas spp.* and *Alcaligenes spp.*, yeasts and sulphate reducing bacteria. The increased frequency of bacterial spoilage of fuels may be due to several factors including those described below.

The Progressive Evolution of Fuel Tank Deteriogens

Middle distillate fuels are a relatively recent product which has only been used extensively for the last forty years. It is customarily stored in large tanks and in the bottom of these tanks a small volume of water accumulates by condensation from the fuel and other sources. A tank containing a large volume of an insoluble substrate held over a small volume of water presents the microflora with a new environment and a certain time is required for colonisation and the necessary physiological and biochemical adaptations before this new environment can be fully exploited. Forty years cannot be considered a long time even for microbial evolution and thus as time passes we find an increasing diversity of spoilage organisms and spoilage mechanisms.

Changes in Refinery Practice (Albinson 1987)

A middle distillate fuel is defined as those hydrocarbons present in crude oil with a 50% boiling point between 371°F and 700°F (Williams and Meyers 1987). The specific composition of middle distillate fuels is determined by the crude oil from which it is distilled. Whereas forty years ago most crude oil came from the Middle East, it now comes from a number of different oil fields in Russia, the North Sea, Nigeria, Venezuela as well as the Middle East. The demand for middle distillate fuel is now so great that it can only be satisfied by processes such as catalytic cracking which breaks up the larger high boiling molecules to give shorter molecules with a middle distillate boiling point. Fuels produced in this way contain more aromatics and so are more soluble in water. They may have a specific gravity close to 1.0 and so more readily emulsify in water. In contrast the true or natural middle distillate fuel has a specific gravity of 0.8. Finally at the refinery different products are blended to make up the desired fuel. Thus the chemical composition of middle distillate fuels today is quite different from that which was produced forty years ago.

The Increased use of Fuel Additives (Snelgrove 1987)

Fuels now formulated by the addition of a range of additives, such as flow improvers, detergents and corrosion inhibitors which by partitioning carry nitrogen, phosphates and other nutrients into the water bottom.

Extended Storage

Increased economies in fuel use has led to longer storage times thereby giving the microflora longer time to adapt and develop vigorous fuel deteriogens. The most extreme case of this must be the strategic reserves held by NATO and similar military organisations. Here millions of tonnes of oil are held in large underground tanks and caverns for many years. These often have large water bottoms due to the ingress of soil water and one such cavern was even said to have an underground stream running through it. Such conditions are ideal breeding grounds for spoilage organisms.

Fuel Deteriogens

Many microorganisms can metabolise hydrocarbons in the laboratory (Singer and Finnerty 1984) and some of these regularly occur as fuel deteriogens. Hettige and Sheridan (1984) isolated 25 different fungi from diesel fuel. However, many fungal spores can remain viable in fuel for a limited time and unless such isolates have been cultured under fuel as the sole carbon source they cannot be classed as fuel deteriogens. The common deteriogens of fuel are *H. resinae, Penicillium spp., Candida spp., Rhodotorula sp., Pseudomonas spp.* and *Alcaligenes spp.* Whilst *H. resinae* is the dominant fuel deteriogen amongst the filamentous fungi, it may be replaced by other species in certain environments. Hill and Thomas (1975) found *Aspergillus fumigatus* to be the prime deteriogen in the fuel tanks of supersonic aircraft which are subject to above ambient temperatures; Hettige and Sheridan (1989a) reported that *Penicillium corylophilum* replaced *H. resinae* in fuel tanks containing sea water and we have found *Phialophora sp.* in a hydraulic oil from a tropical environment. Ten to fifteen years ago the prime spoilage agent in most tanks was *H. resinae* but during the past ten years the organism has been largely replaced by oil degrading and membrane producing bacteria in diesel fuel, gas oils and similar fuels which contain the products of refinery enhancement by catalytic cracking. However, *H. resinae* is still the prime deteriogen in jet fuel which tends to be the genuine middle distillate product.

Heavy microbial growth in the water bottom leads to anaerobiosis, the proliferation of sulphate-reducing bacteria, resulting in sulphide souring of the fuel and corrosion of the tank walls. Neihof and May (1983) found that sulphate-reducing bacteria were present in 17% of the tanks of ships with water compensated fuel systems. A list of common fuel deteriogens is given in Table 3.3.

Physiology of Hydrocarbon Uptake

The ætiology of fuel spoilage can be attributed to the physiology of fuel deteriogens and the unique nature of the fuel tank environment whereby microorganisms are presented with an abundant carbon and energy source with virtually no water, or water containing very little carbon. Many hydrocarbon degraders require close contact with their substrate and adhere to the oil-water interface by means of lipophylic mannan fatty acid complexes in the cell wall (Rosenberg and Rosenberg 1985) whilst others remain dispersed throughout the water bottom. However, before fuel deteriogens can exploit the fuel tank environment they must bring the oil into what is effectively an aqueous solution since it is only in this form that the oil can pass through the cell wall and

Table 3.3. Common microbial
deteriogens of middle distillate fuels

Aspergillus spp.
Hormoconis resinae
Candida tropicalis
Trichoderma viride
Yarrowia (Candida) lipolytica
Candida guilliermondii
Candida rugosa
Cephalosporium sp.
Fusarium sp.
Rhodotorula sp.
Phialophora sp.
Penicillium spp.
Paecillomyces spp.
Alcaligenes spp.
Acinetobacter cerificans
Micrococcus sp.
Pseudomonas spp.
Pseudomonas aeruginosa
Pseudomonas oleovorans
Desulfovibrio desulfuricans

plasma membrane. This process involves the action of both biosurfactants and oil solubilising agents.

It cannot be doubted that biosurfactants play an important role in the biodegradation of hydrocarbons by dispersing the oil as an emulsion thereby increasing the area of the oil-water interface and so maximising the activity of the solublising agent. Oberbremer *et al.* 1990 reported that the rate of hydrocarbon utilisation could be doubled by the addition of sophorose lipids as biosurfactants. A wide range of microbial biosurfactants have been identified with a variety of chemical and physical properties (Zajec and Mahomedy 1984; Gutnick and Minas 1987). They are either anionic, cationic, polyionic or zwitterion surfactants. However, biosurfactants are non-specific and their production is not restricted to oil degrading organisms. One biosurfactant, "Emulsan", is only released when the organism producing it enters the stationary phase (Pines *et al.* 1983). During the growth phase it is present as a lipopolysaccharide attached to the cell wall, where it is probably involved in either oil uptake or attaching the bacterium to the oil-water interface. Thus it would seem that the hydrophilic end of the molecule is only formed when the polymer detaches from the cell wall. It is widely accepted that the surface of the cell walls of hydrocarbon utilising organisms are coated with polysaccharide fatty acid complexes which binds with alkanes and are responsible for the adhesion of the cells to the oil-water interface (Kappeli and Fiechter 1977).

It has been claimed that oil deteriogens take up oil directly, either as emulsified droplets or pseudosolublised in the form of a micro-emulsion, without the oil entering into a truly aqueous solution. (Miura *et al.* 1977). However, there is strong evidence that hydrocarbons can only enter the cell via the aqueous phase in a solublised state (Reddy *et al.* 1982) and the uptake of oil by direct contact of the plasma membrane with hydrocarbon droplets does not occur. The mechanisms of hydrocarbon uptake is discussed in an excellent review by Ratledge (1988) who also proposed a model for hydrocarbon uptake. In this model a surfactant carries the oil, presumably as microdroplets to the surface of the cell wall where the oil is released into an amphipathic receptor/channel which conveys to hydrocarbon molecule to the plasma membrane. The hydrocarbon then passes through the membrane and accumulates as droplets in the cytoplasm. However, this model does not differentiate between

62   Biodegradation: Natural and Synthetic Materials

solubilising agents and surfactants. Solublising agents produced by filamentous fungi, yeasts, and bacteria have been shown to take up individual hydrocarbon molecules into the aqueous phase and carry them to the cell. They also have molecular specificity taking up some molecules but not others (Reddy *et al.* 1982 and 1983; Lindley and Heyderman 1986 and Thomas *et al.* 1986).

Further evidence to support the distinctive role of solubilising agents as compared with surfactants occurred fortuitously during experiments at Hatfield to control fungal growth in hydraulic fluid. When fungi such as *H. resinae* are grown on fuel oil a mat of hyphae forms at the oil-water interface and feeding hyphae grow up into the oil. These hyphae are always found to be sheathed in a film of water, the hyphosphere, which separates the wall of the hypha from the oil. In these experiments *H. resinae* was inoculated into a water bottom below oil containing a large and expectedly lethal concentrations of pentachlorophenol laurate (PCPL). PCPL is totally insoluble in water but readily soluble in oil and it was hoped that this biocide would be carried with the oil into the fungal cells without any biocide entering the aqueous phase. The biocidal properties of PCPL are based on the fact that when fungi such as *H. resinae* are placed on an agar plate containing a 100 ppm dispersion of PCPL, esterase enzymes produced by the hyphae hydrolyse the laurate to release pentachlorophenol which then kills the fungus. However, when *H. resinae* was grown in fuel oil containing 3,000 ppm PCPL, it was unaffected by the presence of the biocide, grew vigorously up into the oil, and was indistinguishable from the untreated control. Since the fungus was taking up the oil and using it as a carbon and energy source, it necessarily follows that had the oil been taken up as emulsified microdroplets or in any form other than single, biocide free molecules from the aqueous phase, PCPL would also have entered the hyphae with fatal consequences. The water from the hyphosphere of *H. resinae* was also found to contain an agent which markedly increased the solubility of oil in the water (Smith 1991).

Fuel degrading organisms produce both surfactants and solubilising agents. These are unlikely to be one in the same as the solubilising agents are unstable and loose their activity after 24 h, unlike biosurfactants which can be long-lived. Thus the following model is suggested for oil uptake which is based on the combined action of biosurfactants and solubilising agents:

i   Biosurfactants produce an emulsified layer of oil at the oil-water interface and around feeding hyphae.
ii   The emulsified hydrocarbons offer a much larger surface to the solubilising agent.
iii The solubilising agent or carrier, combines with individual hydrocarbon molecules and takes them into the aqueous phase.
iv   Once in the aqueous phase the hydrocarbon molecules and their carrier pass through the cells wall and pass through the plasma membrane into the cell.

Thus while many organisms produce biosurfactants, it is the possession of solubilising agents that is the distinguishing feature of fuel deteriogens.

Since oil can only enter the cell in aqueous solution it follows that successful fuel deteriogens will be those which are able to increase the area of the oil-water interface. Thus a microscopic examination of the the interface slime produced by fuel deteriogens shows this to consist of a layer of emulsified oil and either fungal hyphae, yeast or bacterial cells. Oil degrading fungi such as *H. resinae* and *Phialophora spp.* exploit the filamentous habit by producing feeding hyphae which grow from the oil-water interface, up into the oil thereby further increasing the oil-water interface. These oil inhabiting hyphae may fragment and release spores into the fuel which then carries the infection in the fuel wherever it goes.

Bacteria and yeasts also invade fuel oil, by producing biosurfactants which cause water droplets containing the cells to enter the oil. This may cause the fuel immediately above the water bottom to acquire bacterial counts in excess of 10^6 viable units ml^{-1} and again enables the deteriogens to be carried in the fuel from tank to tank and ultimately into the user's fuel system. These droplets should not be confused with the moisture haze which sometimes occurs as a side effect of biosurfactant formation. In such cases the water occurs as micro-droplets which are less than 1 μm in diameter, and free of microorganisms. However, moisture hazes do not invariably accompany microbial infections in the water bottom and it is not unusual to find bright fuel over a heavily infected water bottom.

Production of Insoluble Amphipathic Membrane Polymers

Bacteria have compensated for the lack of the filamentous growth habit by developing an alternative method of water entrapment based on the formation of a membrane polymer which also carries water up into the oil. This material is probably derived from a bacterial biosurfactant. It would seem that the surfactant molecules first form a layer on the oil-water interface then polymerise to form a skin or membrane at the oil-water interface. The deteriogenic bacteria become attached to this polymer which then moves up into the oil taking the attached bacteria with it. The polymer is able to absorb water and act as a wick, drawing water up from the interface, thereby providing an environment which supports the growth of the attached bacteria (Smith 1988). In this way oil degrading bacteria, like the filamentous fungi, are able to move up into the oil phase and so increase the surface area available for hydrocarbon uptake. The polymer readily adheres to metal or other surfaces and so enables water droplets to become attached to the tank wall where they remain secure when the water bottom is drained off. The full structure of this polymer is not known, but preliminary analysis has shown that it is composed of several sugars including glucose, galactose and mannose. During the last three years this polymer has been found with increasing regularity in road vehicle diesel fuel, gas oil and jet fuel and, unless the bacteria producing this material are controlled, the problem will become severe.

Symptoms of Biodeterioration in Fuel Oil

Thus symptoms of microbial infection in a fuel storage tank may be summarised as follows:

i   The upper layers of fuel may be unaffected, especially if the fuel has been standing for some time, as both water droplets and fungal fragments tend to settle to the lower regions of the tank.

ii In the middle and lower regions of the tank the fuel develops a moisture haze which may or may not contain bacteria and yeasts. Hyphal fragments of *H. resinae* and flakes of membrane polymer may also be present.

iii The oil-water interface is replaced by a layer of emulsified oil droplets and microbial slime consisting of fungal filaments and/or bacterial membrane polymer.

iv Below this the water bottom may be turbid and if microbial activity has been such
     that conditions are anaerobic, the odour of hydrogen sulphide will be detectable and
     black deposits of iron sulphide will be present due to the activity of sulphate
     reducing bacteria. In some cases this is so severe that the water bottom is uniformly
     black in colour.

Since microbial growth is concentrated at the oil-water interface, it follows that the
degree of microbial infection in a fuel tank can only be determined by examining
samples taken from this region. Thus the best indicator of fuel tank contamination is
the condition of the oil-water interface. In an infected tank this ceases to be a sharp,
clean boundary and is replaced by either a layer of emulsified droplets, a pellicle
composed of bacteria, yeasts or fungal hyphae, a thick grey, brown or black slime layer
containing fungal hyphae or sheets of bacterial polymer. The water bottom may be
either densely turbid or relatively clear and there may be a thick sediment. When
sulphate reducing bacteria are present the sediment, water bottom and the interface layer
may become blackened by the formation of iron sulphide.

Diagnosis of Microbial Spoilage

It is important to remember that a fuel tank is a two phase system and these two phases
may have had quite unrelated histories. Fuel is moved from tank to tank while the water
bottoms largely remain in the tank where they formed. Thus the condition of the fuel
may usually be taken to represent its storage history, while the water bottom represents
the condition of that particular tank. However, a badly infected fuel will infect a clean
water bottom and *vice versa*.
    The diagnostic features whereby the condition of a tank and fuel which it contains
may be assessed are as follows:

Visual inspection

Much valuable information can be obtained by simple visual observation supported by
microscopic examination. Thus the fuel should be examined for moisture haze or
turbidity; the oil-water interface for a slime or emulsification and the water bottom for
turbidity, suspended solids and blackening by iron sulphide due to the presence of
sulphate reducing bacteria. Often the presence of sulphate reducing bacteria can be
diagnosed by the odour of hydrogen sulphide when the sample bottle is opened.

Microscopic examination

If a slime layer is present at the oil-water interface this should be examined under the
microscope for emulsification, bacterial polymer, bacterial cells, yeast cells and fungal
hyphae.
    When examining samples taken from aircraft fuel tanks part of the sample should be
filtered and the filter examined under the microscope for fungal fragments. In such cases
fungal contamination and spoilage within the aircraft's fuel system can be diagnosed
from the frequency and appearance of the fungal fragments recovered on the filter.

Cultural examination

Procedures for monitoring the microbiological content of light distillate fuels have been described by Herbert *et al.* (1987) and Smith (1987). In these tests both the fuel and the water bottom is sampled. The water bottom is examined by conventional cultural techniques. The fuel is filtered, the filter washed with a non-toxic detergent, rinsed with distilled water or Ringer solution, placed on an agar plate and examined for microbial growth after due incubation. If the fuel is heavily contaminated it will be necessary to resuspend the organisms on the filter by sonication in a mild detergent solution and then perform viable counts on the resulting suspension.

A number of rapid or on site methods are commercially available for monitoring the microbiological condition of fuel tanks (Stockdale and Watkinson 1989). The microflora of the fuel can be estimated by placing a sample of the fuel over a nutrient solution containing a dye and the number of organisms estimated by the time taken for the dye to change colour. Alternatively, the fuel may be shaken with a detergent solution and then a dip slide used to estimate the number of organisms present. However, these tests do not differentiate between oil spoilage organisms and other bacteria. The tests for water bottoms range from dip-slides for general contamination, specific cultural tests for sulphate reducing bacteria, to rapid methods such as estimating the amount of bacterial ATP present in the sample and specific tests for quantifying SRB's based on measurements of hydrogenase activity.

At Hatfield Polytechnic we have developed a spoilage potential test for fuels in which five 5 ml aliquots of the fuel are placed over 1 ml of Bushnell and Haas solution and incubated for 14 days at 25°C. The incidence of microbial growth and slime at the oil-water interface is then recorded on a scale from 1 to 10. This reflects the abundance and vigour of the deteriogens present in the fuel and hence the microbiological hazard the fuel presents to a users fuel system. Whilst this test will assess the spoilage potential attributable to either fungi or bacteria, the spoilage potential due bacteria can be assessed in seven days by placing 20 ml of the fuel over 2 ml of bacterial Bushnell and Haas water bottom medium in a 250 ml flask and shaking at 25°C.

Control of Microbial Spoilage

The two major strategies to control microbial spoilage are good housekeeping and the use of biocides. Good housekeeping is based upon minimising the size of the water bottom in storage tanks by regular draining and preventing the ingress of water. This has been delightfully illustrated in the video 'Microbial Problems in Fuel - Diagnosis and Control' produced by the Institute of Petroleum, London.

Whilst biocides tend to be added to the fuel it is in the water bottom that they must act for it is here that the deteriogens abound. There are two types of fuel biocide, the fuel based biocide and the water bottom biocide.

Fuel Based Biocides

These are biocides which are added to and dissolve in the fuel but also partition into the water bottom to establish a lethal concentration. However, since the oil-water ratio in a fuel tank is usually around 1000:1 a lethal dose partitions into the water bottom but the bulk of the biocide is retained in the oil. Thus the oil retains its biocide protection as it is transferred from tank to tank. Shennan (1988) listed eighteen biocides which are commercially available as fuel preservatives. Of these, five were based on isothiazolones and two on a benzisothiazolone. Most were recommended to be applied at rates between 100 and 200 ppm of the formulated product (the concentration of active ingredient was often significantly less than this). Andrykovitch and Neihof (1987) compared the efficacy of five fuel biocides, a benzimidazole fungicide, an organoboron, a pyridinethione and two isothiazolones against *H. resinae* and found a methylchloro/methylisothiazolone mixture to be the most efficacious. Smith and Crook (1983 and 1986) reported on the efficacy of Benomyl as a fuel fungicide. Hettige and Sheridan (1989a and b) examined six biocides against three fungal deteriogens of diesel fuel and demonstrated the efficacy of Proxel AS (benzisothiazolone), Benomyl, and Imazalil in field trials. However, fungicidal activity alone is no longer an acceptable criterion on which to assess the efficacy of a fuel biocide. Activity against yeasts, bacteria and sulphate reducing bacteria is equally important.

An effective fuel biocide should not only protect the fuel in the storage tank, it should also maintain that protection throughout its time in the users tanks and fuel system. To achieve this, the biocide must be applied at such a concentration that, having dissolved in the oil, it is then able to partition into the water bottom of the storage tank and into any water in the users' fuel system in sufficient amounts to establish a biocidal concentration. Thus when testing fuel biocides the critical test is to place the treated fuel over at least two successive water bottoms.

Water Bottom Disinfectants

Fuel biocides should not be confused with water bottom disinfectants; the latter are either oil dispersible products which partition completely into the water bottoms or water soluble products which are added directly to the water bottom. Whilst these will disinfect the storage tank water bottom and protect the fuel for as long as it is in the tank they give no protection down stream and thus protect neither the users' tanks nor their fuel systems.

Biocide Pollution

Both fuel biocides and water bottom disinfectants present the manager of the tank farm with a disposal problem for when the tanks are drained the water bottom will contain the biocide at its end-use concentration. The water bottoms drained from tanks are customarily discharged either into the local sewage system or directly into the sea or a nearby river. Clearly a relatively large volume of water containing a biocide at end use concentration presents an unacceptable pollution hazard. The discharge of such water into rivers, the sea or the sewage system will not be viewed with enthusiasm by the regulatory authorities. Thus tank drainings from biocide treated fuel tanks may have to be either treated to neutralise the biocide or else taken away by a contractor for safe disposal.

Conclusion

Thus to conclude, middle distillate fuels are susceptible to spoilage by a range of filamentous fungi, yeasts and bacteria but this will only occur when water is present. Spoilage can be controlled by good housekeeping and the elimination of water when ever possible and by the application of biocides which maintain a hostile environment in the water bottom.

References

Aamand J, Jorgenson C, Arvin E, Jenson BK (1989) Microbial adaptation to degradation of hydrocarbons in polluted and unpolluted groundwater. Journal of Contamination and Hydrology 4:229-312

Albinson B (1987) Crude oils and refinery practices. In: Microbiology of Fuels, R. N. Smith (ed) Institute of Petroleum, London pp 9-19

Andrykovitch G, Neihof RA (1987) Fuel soluble biocides for the control of *Cladosporium resinae* in hydrocarbon fuels. Journal of Industrial Microbiology 2:35-40

Bossert I, Bartha R (1984) The fate of petroleum products in the soil ecosystem. In: Petroleum Microbiology R. M. Atlas (ed) Macmillan Publishing Company, London

Edmonds P, Cooney JJ (1967) Identification of microorganisms isolated from jet fuel systems. Applied Microbiology 15:411-416

Gradet A, Short WL (1980) Managing hazardous wastes under RCRA. Part II Chemical Engineering 87 (15):60-68

Gutnick DL, Minas W (1987) Perspectives on microbial surfactants. Biochemical Society Transactions 15:22S-35S

Herbert BN, Hill EC, Oates PD, Powell D, Shennan Jl, Whittle R (1987) A method for testing light distillate fuels. In: Industrial Microbiological Testing, Hopton J, Hill EC (ed) Blackwell Scientific Publications, London pp 215-219

Hettige G, Sheridan JE (1984) Mycoflora of stored diesel fuel in New Zealand. International Biodeterioration 20:225-227

Hettige G, Sheridan JE (1989a) Interactions of fungi contaminating diesel fuel. International Biodeterioration 25:299-309

Hettige G, Sheridan JE (1989b) Effects of biocides on microbial growth in middle distillate fuel. International Biodeterioration 25:175-190

Hill EC, Thomas AR (1975) Microbiological aspects of supersonic aircraft fuel. In: Proceedings Third International Biodeterioration Symposium, Sharpley JM, Kaplan AM (eds) Applied Science Publishers, London pp 157-174

Hostetler HF, Powers EJ (1963) Bugs, Surfactants and Woes. American Petroleum Institute Div of Refinery. Philadelphia Pa

Kappeli O, Fiechter A (1977) Component from the cell surface of the hydrocarbon utilising yeast *Candida tropicalis* with possible relations to hydrocarbon transport. Journal of Bacteriology 131:917-21

Lapinskas J (1989) Bacterial degradation of hydrocarbon contamination in soil and ground water. Chemistry and Industry (London) 23:784-789

Lindley ND, Heyderman MT (1986) The uptake of n-alkanes from mixtures during growth of the hydrocarbon-utilising fungus *Cladosporium resinae*. Applied Microbiology and Biotechnology 23 (5):384-388

Miller RN, Herron WC, Kringens AG, Cameron JL, Terry BM (1964) Microorganisms cause corrosion in aircraft fuel tanks. Materials Protection 3:682-685

Miura Y, Okazaki M, Hamada S, Murakawa S, Yugen R (1977) Assimilation of liquid hydrocarbons by microorganisms. I. Mechanism of hydrocarbon uptake. Biotechnology Bioengineering 19:701-714

Neihof R, May M (1983) Microbial and particulate contamination in fuel tanks of naval ships. International Biodeterioration Bulletin 19 (2):59-68

Okpokwasili GC, Somerville C, Sullivan, Grimes DJ, Colwell RR (1986) Plasmid mediated degradation of hydrocarbons in estuarine bacteria. Oil and Chemical Pollution 3 pp 117-129

Oberbremer A, Mueller-Hurtig R, Wagner F (1990) The effect of microbial surfactants on hydrocarbon degradation in a soil population in a stirred reactor. Applied Microbial Biotechnology 34 pp 485-489

Pines O, Bayer EA, Gutnick DL (1983) Localisation of emulsan-like polymers associated with the cell surface of *Acinetobacter calcoacetricus*. Journal of Bacteriology 154 pp 893-905

Ratledge C (1978) Degradation of aliphatic hydrocarbons. Developments in Biodegradation of Hydrocarbons-1 Wilkinson RJ (ed) Applied Science pp 1-46

Ratledge C (1988) Products of hydrocarbon-microorganisms interaction. In: Biodeterioration 7 Houghton DR, Smith RN, Eggins HOW (eds) Elsevier Applied Science, London pp 219-236

Reddy PG, Sing HD, Roy PK, Barhuah JN (1982) Predominant role of hydrocarbon solubilisation in the the microbial uptake of hydrocarbons. Biotechnology and Bioengineering XXIV (6):1241-1270

Reddy PG, Sing HD, Pathak MG, Bhagat SD, Baruah JN (1983) Isolation and functional characterisation of hydrocarbon emulsifying and solubilising factors produced by a *Pseudomonas* species. Biotechnology and Bioengineering XXV (2):387-401

Rogers MR, Kaplan AM (1965) A survey of the microbiological contamination of a military fuel distribution system. Developments in Industrial Microbiology 6:80-94

Rosenberg M, Rosenberg E (1985) Bacterial adherence at the hydrocarbon-water interface. Oil and Petrochemical Pollution 2 (3):155-162

Shennan JL (1988) Control of spoilage of fuels in storage. In: Biodeterioration 7, Houghton DR, Smith R N, Eggins HOW (eds) Elsevier Applied Science, London pp 248-255

Singer ME, Finnerty WR (1984) Microbial metabolism of straight chain and branched alkanes. In: Petroleum Microbiology Atlas R.M (ed) Collier Macmillan Publishers London pp 1-59

Smith RN (1987) Fuel testing. In: Microbiology of Fuels Smith RN (ed) Institute of Petroleum, London pp 49-54

Smith RN (1988) Bacterial extra-cellular polymers: A major cause of spoilage of middle distillate fuels. In Proc. 7th International Biodeterioration Symposium. Houghton DR, Smith RN, Eggins HOW (eds) Elsevier Applied Press, London 256-262

Smith RN (1991) Developments in fuel microbiology. In Proc. 8th International Biodeterioration Symposium (In press)

Smith RN, Crook B (1983) The growth and mortality of *Cladosporium resinae* in biocide treated fuel oil. In: Biodeterioration 5. J Wiley and Sons Ltd, London pp 486-493

Smith RN, Crook B (1986) Long term end use tests for fuel biocides. In: Biodeterioration 6. Barry S, Houghton DR (ed) p118-123 CAB International

Snelgrove DG (1987) The chemistry of fuels and additives. In: Microbiology of Fuels Smith RN (ed) Institute of Petroleum, London pp 21-34

Song H, Pedersen TA, Bartha R (1986) Hydrocarbon mineralisation in soil: relative bacterial and fungal contribution. Soil Biology and Biochemistry 18 (1):109-111

Song HG, Bartha R (1990) Effects of jet fuel spills on the microbial community of soil. Applied and Environmental Microbiology 56 (3) 645-651

Song HG, Wang X, Bartha R (1990) Bioremediation potential of terrestrial fuel spills. Applied and Environmental Microbiology 56:(3) 652-656

Stockdale H, Watkinson RJ (1989) Review of rapid Techniques for the estimation of organisms in petroleum products. In: Rapid Methods for Diagnosis of Microbial Problems in the Petroleum Industry Wilkinson RJ (ed) Institute of Petroleum, London pp 1-20

Thomas MJ, Yordy JR, Amador JA, Alexander M (1986) Rates of dissolution and biodegradation of water insoluble organic compounds. Applied and Environmental Microbiology 52 (2):290-296

Wang X, Bartha R (1990) Effects of bioremediation on residues, activity and toxicity in soil. Soil Biology and Biochemistry 22:(4) 501-503

Williams HR, Meyers CJ (1987) Manual of Oil Analysis. Matthew Brener, London pp 558

Zajec EJ, Mahomedy AY (1984) Biosurfactants: intermediates of amphipathic molecules in microbes. In: Petroleum Microbiology Atlas RM (ed) Collier Macmillan Publishers London: 221-229

Chapter 4

Biodegradation of Nitriles and Cyanide

J. M. Wyatt and S. J. Palmer

Introduction

The microbial degradation of numerous compounds has been studied and the biochemical pathways and mechanisms of enzyme action have been elucidated particularly with respect to pure cultures of bacteria. This research has been extremely valuable but to date industrial application of the knowledge has been somewhat limited. However, public awareness of the environment and governmental pressure in the form of the recent "Green Bill" has stimulated industry into taking measures to reduce the discharge of compounds likely to cause environmental problems. Biodegradation can play a significant role as, when it is achievable, it is by far the most economic method of treatment for removal of pollutants from a waste effluent .

What is biodegradation? Basically it is the removal of waste products and potential pollutants by biological means, and is generally considered to be the microbial conversion of an organic compound to its mineral entities, carbon dioxide and water or biomass. Biodegradation is of course not new; it happens around us all the time, being part of the cycle of Nature that forms the basis of life on our planet. Microbes play the major role in this cycle.

The growth of the chemical industry this century has generated a wide variety of man made (anthropogenic) compounds. Such compounds can cause problems of disposal and if they enter the environment can have a detrimental effect. Chemical production is usually associated with the formation of large amounts of undesired by-products and wastes resulting from the entropy of chemical reactions.

Chemicals used in industry today are either biogenic (naturally occurring) or xenobiotic (novel chemical structures not found in nature). All biogenic compounds are biodegradable and interestingly so are many xenobiotics. However, there are many others that are not readily degradable and which may also be toxic. Chemical Abstracts lists approximately six million organic chemicals of which approximately five million are xenobiotic. The majority are produced only on a laboratory scale but there are over

100 000 actively traded in over 50 tonnes per annum and this is increasing by about 2000 new compounds each year.

These numbers contrast drastically with the ecotoxicological data that is available, which is on only about 3000-4000 compounds in total. Therefore the dangers arising from exposure of the environment to chemicals and their decomposition products, and the effects and hazards they may cause are unknown for the majority of commercially traded substances.

Hazardous wastes pose major disposal problems for all industrialised nations and a need exists for effective and permanent solutions. Millions of tons of wastes are generated each year that require some degree of detoxification before they can be safely released into the environment. Microbial degradation of such wastes is rapidly being adopted as the most convenient and cost effective method for removing potential pollutants.

Compounds and new approaches are now being utilised that will enable biodegradation disposal methods to be used for applications that were previously considered not possible.

Cyanide

Cyanide is produced on a large sale by the chemical industry and is used in the production of a range of basic chemicals. These include monomers such as methylmethacrylate and adiponitrile which are used for the manufacture of plastics and synthetic fibres. Inorganic cyanide (hydrogen cyanide) has a wide range of uses, particularly when complexed with metals in such industries as electroplating, mining, steel production and paint manufacture.

Cyanide, because of its toxicity, is a strictly regulated compound and industries that utilise it need to ensure that all discharges from their processing do not contain significant levels. A variety of treatment processes have been developed to remove cyanide from effluent streams some of which are biologically based.

Cyanogenesis

Cyanide is a potent inhibitor of the cytochrome oxidase enzymes of respiration and therefore exceedingly toxic to living cells. Despite this toxicity cyanide is synthesised by a wide range of organisms including plants, fungi, bacteria and a few insects (Knowles 1976).

Plant cyanogenesis is via the production of stable compounds (cyanogens) that, on hydrolysis, will liberate hydrogen cyanide. Numerous plants are cyanogenic, including such agriculturally important species as cassava, flax, sorghum and alfalfa. The majority of plant cyanogens are glucosidic derivatives of cyanohydrins (α-hydroxynitriles) although certain plants form cyanolipids. The cyanogenic glucosides are formed from several amino acids, for example linamarin from valine, amygdalin from phenylalanine and dhurrin from tyrosine. The probable pathway of formation of cyanogenic glucosides is shown in Figure 4.1. and involves the conversion of the amino acid to the aldoxime, then to the nitrile which is subsequently hydroxylated and glycosylated (Cyanide compounds in Biology 1988).

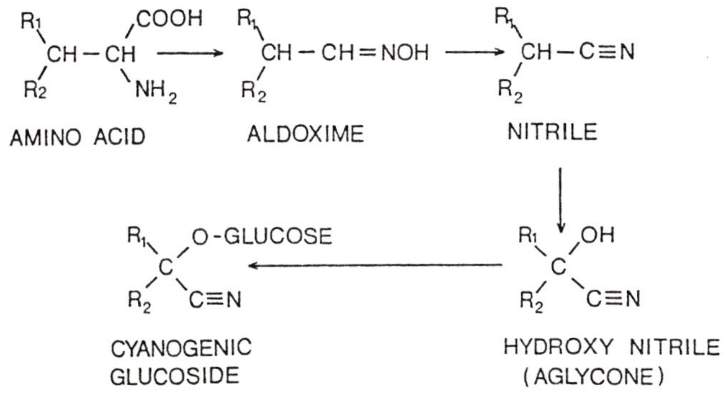

Fig. 4.1. Typical biosynthetic pathway for cyanogenic glucoside formation.

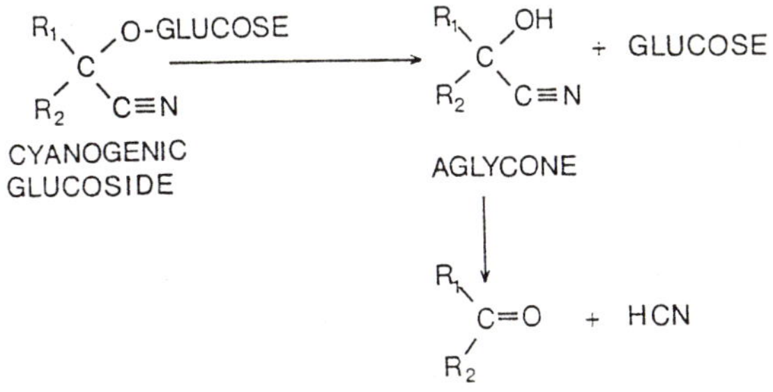

Fig. 4.2. The release of cyanide from the cyanogenic glucoside.

The release of hydrogen cyanide from the cyanogenic glucoside occurs in two steps - the glucose moiety is removed by a glucosidase and then a nitrilase cleaves the cyanide from the agylcone (Fig. 4.2). If the plant is damaged or attacked by a fungal pathogen, cyanide is released by the breakdown of the cyanogenic glucoside as a defence mechanism.

Cyanide, being a normal fungal metabolite, is produced widely by fungi but the method differs from plant cyanogenesis and is not the result of degradation of cyanogenic glucosides. There are many hundreds of fungal species that are cyanogenic. Cyanide production has been demonstrated to occur during active growth on a range of media for certain fungi but significantly higher levels were observed during growth on complex media. The production of cyanide in the fungi has been shown to be very similar to cyanide biosynthesis in non-photosynthetic bacteria.

Cyanide production has been studied extensively in the snow mould Basidiomycete, in the bacteria *Chromobacterium violaceum* and several *Pseudomonas* species (Harris *et al.* 1987). When both fungi or the cyanogenic bacteria are cultured on media that support rapid growth, the microbial production of cyanide exhibits the typical characteristics of secondary metabolism. Cyanide is produced towards the end of growth as the microbe enters the stationary phase and has been demonstrated to be produced from a defined precursor. The metabolic precursor is glycine and a second primary metabolite methionine acts as a stimulator of cyanide formation. The level of cyanide production is also affected by the iron and phosphate content of the medium. Glycine has been shown to be converted to cyanide without breaking the carbon-nitrogen bond. The bacterial enzyme system that catalyses the conversion has been demonstrated to be associated with the cytoplasmic membrane but has proved difficult to work with as it is highly sensitive to oxygen. The metabolic route for the conversion of glycine to cyanide has not been fully elucidated, with several possible pathways proposed. For example one postulated pathway is analogous to the formation of cyanogenic glucosides suggesting the route of cyanide formation is via N-hydroxyglycine and formaldoxime. The function of cyanogenesis in bacteria and fungi is unclear, like the majority of secondary metabolic processes.

Some interesting work on *Escherichia coli* demonstrated that when growing exponentially this non-cyanogenic bacterium has a greater requirement for C1 units than for glycine. However, only stoichiometric amounts of glycine and C1 units are provided from serine by serine hydroxymethyltransferase. A glycine cleavage enzyme converts the excess glycine to C1 units. In the cyanogenic bacterium *Chr. violaceum* this glycine cleavage enzyme is only present in very low amounts. As high intracellular levels of glycine can be toxic to microbial cells it is possible that cyanide production is a mechanism to remove excess glycine.

Microbial Degradation of Cyanide

Many microorganisms that can produce cyanide (cyanogenic microbes) have also been reported to assimilate cyanide. A wide variety of products are formed including alanine, glutamic acid, α-aminobutyric acid, ß-cyanoalanine and γ-cyano-α-aminobutyric acid. It has also been observed that many non-cyanogenic microorganisms can also degrade cyanide. A number of different enzymic routes for cyanide detoxification have been identified.

ß-Cyanoalanine Synthase [EC 4.4.1.9, L-cysteine hydrogen sulphide-lyase (adding HCN)]

This enzyme can be found in a variety of cyanogenic as well as many non cyanogenic microorganisms.

HCN + cysteine (or o-acetylserine) → ß-cyanoalanine + H_2S (or acetate)

It has been shown to enable a microorganism, a strain of *Enterobacter*, to exhibit a tolerance to cyanide and grow in its presence. The enzyme has been studied in detail in the cyanogenic microorganism *Chr. violaceum* (Macadam and Knowles 1984). This microorganism produces cyanide as a secondary metabolite which is then rapidly lost from the growth medium. β-cyanoalanine is formed from cyanide and L-cysteine or o-acetyl-L-serine by the enzyme β-cyanoalanine synthase. The enzyme has two subunits, a molecular weight of 70 000 and contains pyridoxal phosphate.

Rhodanese [EC 2.8.1.1, thiosulphate: cyanide sulphur transferase]

The enzyme rhodanase catalyses the formation of thiocyanate and sulphite from thiosulphate and cyanide.

$$S_2O_3^{2-} + CN^- \rightarrow SO_3^{2-} + SCN^-$$

This enzyme will also catalyse many other reactions involving the transformation of sulphur-containing molecules. Its primary role is probably in sulphur metabolism.

Nitrogenase [EC 1.18.6.1, reduced ferredoxin:dinitrogen oxidoreductase (ATP - hydrolysing)]

The enzyme nitrogenase reduces atmospheric nitrogen in a number of bacteria. This "fixation" of atmospheric nitrogen is an important step in the nitrogen cycle. The enzyme can catalyse the reduction of several other substrates in addition to dinitrogen, one of which is cyanide. The catalytic process of this enzyme is ATP dependant. Cyanide may be reduced by this process to methane and ammonia, methylamine and possibly also to formaldehyde and ammonia via hydrolysis of a two electron intermediate.

$$HCN \rightarrow CH_2NH \rightarrow CH_3NH_2 \rightarrow CH_4 + NH_3$$

$$HCHO + NH_3$$

Nitrogenase reduction of cyanide has been observed in photosynthetic bacteria.

Cyanide Hydratase [EC 4.2.1.66 formamide hydrolyase]

The number of plant species capable of producing cyanogenic glucosides and other cyanogenic compounds is thought to be about 2000. The physiological significance of cyanogenic compound production is not understood. The compounds may well have a simple protective role, the cyanogens hydrolysing to release cyanide during infection or structural damage of the plant. This release of cyanide deters predation and any successful pathogen on these plants must either be resistant to or have a means of degrading cyanide.

Many fungal pathogens of cyanogenic plants have been found to possess the enzyme cyanide hydratase that detoxifies cyanide by converting it to non-toxic formamide.

$$HCN + H_2O \rightarrow HCONH_2$$

Cyanide hydratase activity has only been detected in fungi and is inducible by low levels of cyanide. Several fungal detoxification mechanisms have been investigated in detail for potential application in the remediation of solutions of waste cyanide. The fungus *Gloeocercospora sorghi* has been studied in detail (Nazly *et al.* 1983). The organism was induced to form cyanide hydratase and then immobilised using a polyelectrolyte flocculating agent. A stoichiometric conversion of cyanide to formamide was observed and the immobilised fungus, in a cartridge system, was shown to continuously degrade a cyanide containing solution (70 mM) for up to three months.

Cyanide Oxygenase

A strain of the bacterium *Pseudomonas fluorescens* has been isolated that can utilise cyanide as a source of nitrogen for growth (Harris and Knowles 1983a). The microorganism can convert cyanide to carbon dioxide and ammonia under aerobic conditions. The ammonia is subsequently assimilated for growth.

The enzyme system is inducible by low concentrations of cyanide and has a requirement, in cell free extracts, for NADH or NADPH for activity. This system consumed one molecule of oxygen for each molecule of cyanide degraded and is thought to consist of at least two enzymes (Harris and Knowles 1983b). The stoichiometry of the overall reaction is:

$$HCN + O_2 + NAD(P)H + 2H^+ \rightarrow CO_2 + NH_4^+ + NAD(P)^+$$

The preliminary evidence suggested the presence of the enzyme cyanide oxygenase which could either be a dioxygenase as above or a monooxygenase involving the formation of an intermediate. If a monooxygenase the intermediate would be cyanate:

$$HCN + O_2 + NAD(P)H + H^+ \rightarrow HOCN + NAD(P)^+ + H_2O$$

The cyanate formed could then be degraded by cyanase [EC 3.5.5.3 cyanate aminohydrolase] to carbon dioxide and ammonia:

$$HOCN + H_2O \rightarrow CO_2 + NH_3$$

Cell free extracts of *Ps. fluorescens* from cultures grown on both ammonium and cyanide can degrade cyanate.

Biological Treatment of Cyanide Wastewater

Wastewaters containing cyanide are produced by a wide range of industries for which cyanide is an indispensable reagent. Production of some optical brighteners and dyes by the chemical industry requires cyanide and it is also used extensively in the metal finishing and mining industries.

A number of physical and chemical treatment processes have been used to remove cyanide from industrial effluents. These include use of chemical oxidising reagents such as ozone, peroxide, hypochlorite and alkaline chlorination. Also physical and physical/chemical separation techniques such as evaporation, flotation following complexation, reverse osmosis, activated carbon and ion exchange. Other methods such as electrolysis and catalytic oxidation have been tried.

Biodegradation of cyanide is known to occur in nature and has been applied to biologically treat cyanide-bearing wastes in a number of situations, from experimental model systems in the laboratory through to pilot plant and full scale biotreatment systems. In terms of capital costs per volume treated, biotreatment is often less expensive than many of the alternatives (Green and Smith 1972) and with regard to operational costs biotreatment is usually the cheapest option.

The lower cost of biotreatment originates from the nature of the process. Catalysts lower the energy requirement for a particular chemical conversion and use of biomass or extracted enzymes achieves the degradation of cyanide without a high energy input. A viable biomass may be regarded as a self-regenerating catalyst, hence the cost of replacement of reagents would be negligible in comparison to chemical treatment.

Biological treatment systems for cyanide should be based on a process which destroys cyanide, converting it to more environmentally acceptable compounds. This is advantageous in comparison to treatment processes such as ion exchange, evaporation, activated carbon or reverse osmosis which simply remove cyanide from waste water and produce a concentrated cyanide waste. Cyanide complexation can also produce a potentially hazardous end product as stable complexes such as iron complexed cyanides, can photo-dissociate to release free cyanide.

Two major catabolic pathways form the basis of biological treatment systems for cyanide: oxidation to carbon dioxide and ammonia, and hydration to formamide. The biological treatment systems devised for cyanide degradation are of two distinct types - non-viable systems utilising enzyme preparations, or viable biomass systems which may be either aerobic or anaerobic.

Enzymic Biotreatment

Two enzymic cyanide detoxification processes have been developed based on the hydration of cyanide. Imperial Chemical Industries (ICI) screened a number of microorganisms selecting *Fusarium lateritum* as a source of the enzyme cyanide hydratase. The enzyme system "Cyclear" was used by ICI immobilised in a fluidised bed reactor operated in a plug-flow configuration, to treat continuously flows from a few cubic metres per day to several hundred cubic metres per day. In addition, smaller and larger flows could be treated by two other reactor and system configurations.

The use of this cell free enzyme has the advantage of being able to treat very high concentrations of cyanide. Indeed it was recommended for use between 200 ppm and 10 000 ppm of cyanide (Clarke 1986). However, the enzyme had several disadvantages. The reaction was a single step leaving formamide as a by-product. Also the enzyme was inefficient at concentrations less than 200 ppm of free cyanide, was adversely affected by metal-toxicity and could not degrade metal-cyanide complexes.

Novo Industries have also developed a biotreatment system for cyanide based on the enzyme, cyanide hydratase, but their reagent catalysed the hydration sequence a stage further to produce formate, a compound with no recognised toxicity and itself easily biodegraded in conventional aerobic or anaerobic biotreatment systems:

$$\text{HCN} \xrightarrow[\text{Cyanide}\ \text{Hydratase}]{\quad H_2O \searrow \quad} \text{HCONH}_2 \xrightarrow{\ H_2O \searrow\ } \text{HCOOH} + \text{NH}_3$$

Cyanide · Formamide · Formate

However, apart from producing a very innocuous and easily biodegradable by-product, the enzyme system suffered all the other disadvantages experienced with the ICI system.

Viable Cell Biotreatment

The majority of biotreatment processes used for cyanide removal from waste water are based on viable cell bio-oxidation processes.

Aerobic Biotreatment Aerobic biotreatment of cyanide-containing wastes has been practised using various process configurations from activated sludge to immobilised cells in fixed film reactors. For over 50 years cyanide removal has been noted in differing sewage treatment plants (Zabbar and Helwick 1980). The first definitive study of the activated sludge treatment of cyanide, thiocyanate and cyanate in 1960 (Ludzak and Schaffer 1960) showed that, following a period of acclimation of two to three weeks, a cyanide concentration of up to 60 mg l^{-1} could be removed before any toxic effects were observed.

Activated sludge systems are heterogeneous populations of a wide range of microorganisms. The diversity within the population ensures that a range of compounds may be utilised by the sludge, and the composition of the population can alter when a feed containing a toxic compound is introduced. This is because some of the microorganisms will be capable of utilising the compound and some will not and may in fact be inhibited by it. Heterogeneous populations have the advantage of being more adaptable and stable, due to the diversity. For specific wastes which contain a compound of particular interest (or concern) an alternative biotreatment strategy is to employ a monoculture of a microorganism which exhibits both an affinity for the compound of interest as a carbon or nitrogen source, and a high rate of biotransformation of the compound.

The mechanism of cyanide removal in biological systems was not studied scientifically until 1975 (Raef et al. 1975) This study demonstrated that apart from biological metabolism of cyanide, abiotic mechanisms could function in the biological systems to remove cyanide. These include chemical reaction between the cyanide and certain carbon compounds, absorption onto cells or biological flocs and air-stripping of the cyanide from solution. All are significant factors in operating a biological treatment unit for cyanide-bearing wastes.

Many of the field application studies have involved activated sludge systems. Results from such trials could be ambiguous due to two important factors - cyanide absorption and cyanide removal. Activated sludge systems contain bacteria that produce extracellular polymers which may bear a net charge encouraging cells to flocculate. The bacterial cell surface also has charged areas and these are known to absorb or complex certain ions (Sterrit and Lester 1986). Suspended non-flocculant cells show negligible uptake of cyanide, but flocculating cells exhibited significant removal of cyanide at a very rapid rate, characteristic of an absorption process. Flocculation is an essential part of the activated sludge process as it allows settlement of biomass under gravity in solution. Cyanide thus may be removed from solution by absorption and the influent detoxified, but the form of cyanide is important because absorption processes with metals and biomass, for example, are reversible under certain conditions.

Cyanide in solution can react with certain carbon compounds such as glucose which is commonly used as a carbon source in microbiological studies. Glucose was observed to react with cyanide in aqueous solution to give a product that was biodegradable. The reaction was pH-dependent and pseudo-first order, but slow reaction of cyanide occurred at neutral pH. The importance of this factor relates to the nature of the wastewater treated and the biotreatment strategy pursued. A waste stream containing cyanide with no reducing sugar or aldose content would be less likely to remove cyanide by this non-biological means. This would be important if the bacterial population, be it heterogeneous or not, was not capable of degrading cyanide itself. Obviously it is important to establish the mechanism of cyanide removal by any microbial population employed. Another aspect of the chemical removal of cyanide is that if the compound produced itself is not metabolised, then a cyanide related compound with possible toxic effects is being produced. Therefore it is preferable that destructive removal of cyanide, such as biological oxidation, is occurring in the biotreatment process to give non-toxic products.

Definitive proof of cyanide biodegradation was found by using radiolabelled cyanide ([14]CN) (Raef *et al.* 1975) Radiolabelled carbon dioxide was recovered, demonstrating that biological oxidation of cyanide had occurred. The proportion of cyanide metabolised increased as the biomass concentration increased, as would be expected if metabolism of cyanide were occurring. A biomass suspended solids concentration of approximately 2 g l^{-1} resulted in most of the cyanide present being metabolised under aerobic conditions.

The most successful field application of aerobic cyanide biotreatment in metals containing wastewater to date is provided by the full scale biotreatment facility at Homestake Mining Company's operation in the US. Cyanide is essential to Homestake in the operation of their gold mine at Lead, South Dakota. However, use of cyanide presented a difficult waste disposal problem. Homestake exhaustively tested a number of physical and chemical cyanide treatment processes as well as biotreatment in order to derive the most cost-effective and efficient means of treating their mine and tailings wastewaters. These are discharged at a maximum rate of 2.5×10^7 ld^{-1}.

Following pilot plant studies with chemical, physical and biological systems for cyanide removal, Homestake chose to develop a biotreatment system because the physical and chemical treatment systems investigated were less effective due to a combination of inadequate treatment performance, residual toxicological effects associated with the effluents and prohibitive capital and operating costs (Mudder and Whitlock 1984a). The physical and chemical processes investigated included ion exchange, ozonation, acidification and volatilisation, Prussian blue oxidation and precipitation, copper catalysed hydrogen peroxide oxidation, carbon absorption and alkaline chlorination.

During development of a biological treatment process Homestake tested a number of biotreatment systems which included a suspended growth (activated sludge) and attached growth (fixed film) processes. The company attempted activated sludge treatment and found it efficient but too prone to toxic shock due to influent variations in metals. Typically, suspended biomass systems are prone to toxic shock. The activated sludge system eventually failed after operation for 60 days.

To produce a system more resistant to toxic shock Homestake began testing fixed film (attached growth) systems in a number of reactor formats. Trickling filters, aerobic biological filters, tower reactors and rotating biological contactors (RBC's) gave the best performance averaging more than 90% removal of total cyanide for the RBC's and over 85% for the tower reactor. Free cyanide removal was over 97% for the RBC's and over 95% for the tower reactor (Mudder and Whitlock 1984b).

The RBC's consisted of two reactors in series - a 0.5 m diameter disc and 2 m diameter RBC downstream. For this system initial hydraulic loading was 25.47 ld^{-1}m^{-2} (of packing surface area). For the tower the loading rate was 4.89 lmonth^{-1}m^{-2} which is an operational rate 960 times greater than that in the RBC system. The tower dimensions were a height of 6.1 m and a diameter of 0.61 m. The tower reactor resembles a packed bed plug flow reactor. Such systems often have a greater surface area for attached growth support than an RBC unit, depending on the packing.

These systems operated without a supplementary carbon source and the bacterial isolate used in this system was deliberately selected as one that could use cyanide as the sole carbon source. Although neither of the two successful reactor systems were operated aseptically to ensure a monoculture, the plant influent itself acts as a selective biological growth medium so that only cyanide-utilising microbial strains could colonise the bioreactors. The only additive was phosphate, made up to give the influent a phosphate level of 5 mg l^{-1}. The other advantage to this approach is that any abiotic chemical removal of cyanide from the system by reducing sugars or equivalent compounds can be ruled out. The reactors operated over a six month trial period which included seasonal variation and winter. Operated at influent temperatures as low as 11°C, these reactors showed no significant loss of cyanide removing activity.

Although aeration in the RBC's may have air-stripped some free cyanide, the wastewater contained thiocyanate and complexed cyanide, which were both removed. Additionally, a tower reactor containing packing may be regarded as a sealed unit and would minimise any cyanide stripping. The performance of the tower reactor, as has been stated, was also very efficient at free cyanide removal.

The costs for Homestake in the operation of a biological system were more competitive than any of the other available technologies. The company decided to operate a biological treatment system using RBC's with a capacity to treat $2.5 \times 10^7 \text{ld}^{-1}$ of cyanide-bearing wastewater with free cyanide concentrations of up to 20mg l^{-1} in the influent. The plant construction began in 1983 and is now in operation with 48 RBC units providing the biotreatment capacity.

Further evidence for metabolism of the influent cyanide is the ammonia produced in the biotreatment system (a metabolic oxidation product of cyanide). Homestake also built in plant capacity to biologically remove the ammonia produced.

Anaerobic Biotreatment Anaerobic biotreatment of cyanide-containing wastewaters has been attempted since the early 1960's. One of the first studies into anaerobic biodegradation of cyanide resulted in the development of a two stage anaerobic digestion system for cyanide removal (Howe 1965). The system consisted of a primary reactor operating under mesophilic conditions (i.e. heated to 38°C) to achieve a high rate of digestion. A secondary reactor was placed downstream of the primary and was unheated, as the major part of the influent cyanide was expected to be degraded in the primary reactor. The treatment system was acclimatised to cyanide concentrations in the influent of up to 100 mg l^{-1} and achieved between 60% and 70% removal of influent cyanide.

Only limited application of anaerobic biotreatment has occurred and this is possibly attributable to the perceived sensitivity of the methanogenic sequence of anaerobic biodegradation to toxic shock. However, several studies have shown that methanogenic populations in digesters do adapt to the presence of toxic compounds and methane production is regained (Fedorak and Hrudey 1989).

In anaerobic digesters and other anaerobic systems several different populations of anaerobes interact to give sequential degradation of complex compounds to ultimately produce carbon dioxide and methane. In a full scale operation the methane produced is usually used as a fuel and burnt to heat the digester which is often maintained at about 35°C. Predominant populations in anaerobic systems include fermentative, acetogenic and methanogenic populations:

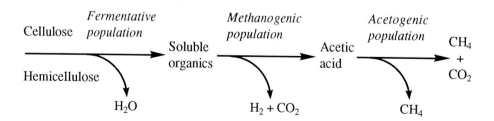

Several studies have been carried out to confirm that anaerobic digesters can adapt to cyanide toxicity and successfully degrade cyanide. The effect on the methanogenic activity of adding cyanide to a phenol degrading anaerobic reactor has been investigated (Howe 1965). A disturbance of methanogenic activity was followed by the gradual resumption of methane production and was observed after initial addition of cyanide, indicating that the system acclimatised to the chemical. The addition of ^{14}CN to the system was monitored over 20 days and over 96% of the radiolabelled carbon remained in the liquid phase with only trace amounts of radiolabelled methane and carbon dioxide were detected in the reactor headspace. Cyanide in this system was therefore not being degraded to carbon dioxide and methane. Instead, the removal observed was due to transformation of the cyanide to an unidentified product.

This transformation was perhaps indirectly due to biological activity, as acetic acid and subsequently formic acid are produced during anaerobic digestion. These and other compounds produced by anaerobic microbial activity might be the reactants that formed a new compound with the influent cyanide.

In summary anaerobic digesters are known to be sensitive to cyanide toxicity. However, they are also to be able to adapt, by mechanisms as yet not fully elucidated, to remove low levels of cyanide from influents. Anaerobic digestion systems are complex but do possess a number of advantages compared to the activated sludge process. Advantages of anaerobic digestion versus activated sludge are:

1   a high degree of waste stabilisation at high organic loading rates;
2   a low production of excess sludge;
3   the excess sludge produced settles well;
4   low nutrient requirements;
5   lower energy costs;
6   the methane produced can be used to heat the process and often excess methane can be produced as fuel for other processes;
7   the anaerobic sludge can survive for up to 12 months without influent addition or appreciable loss of activity (Lettinga et al. 1979).

Disadvantages include the lack of experience at present in full-scale application of anaerobic digestion to industrial wastewater treatment, the prolonged start-up period (8 weeks - 12 weeks) and, as has been shown on several occasions, the sensitivity of the methanogenic population of the digester to cyanide toxicity, unless carefully acclimated. Although cyanide toxicity to cytochrome oxidases (essential in bio-oxidation processes) is well known, cyanide is extremely reactive and can interact with a range of enzymes. Hence anaerobic systems are also affected by cyanide toxicity.

In addition to strictly aerobic or anaerobic treatment systems, recent work with industrial effluents has been successful in using anaerobic and aerobic systems in series, the anaerobic systems being used for pretreatment (Richards and Shieh 1988). Where bio-oxidation of cyanide occurs, one of the products is ammonia, which itself can be toxic. Ammonia oxidation to nitrate can be performed aerobically but if any problems exist with nitrate discharge, nitrate itself can be removed by having an anoxic area in a biotreatment system. In an anoxic region nitrate is utilised as an oxidising agent and dinitrogen is produced. This biotreatment strategy has been applied to treat a phenolic waste containing up to 60 mgl^{-1} of free cyanide (Richards and Shieh 1989).

Application of Biotreatment Technologies

From the examples of cyanide wastewater treatment processes discussed it can be seen that a variety of technological approaches have been attempted to try and achieve a successful biotreatment process.

Very high concentrates of free cyanide (HCN) can be treated using cell-free enzymes, as viable microbial populations could not operate at these inhibitory concentrations. The application of these systems however has been limited due to the major disadvantages described. Thus for wastewaters with a high free cyanide concentration and no toxic metal content cell-free enzyme systems can be employed but should be linked downstream to a biotreatment system for removal of residual cyanide and by-products of the process.

Anaerobic biotreatment systems avoid air-stripping of free cyanide but some ambiguity exists as to their capabilities with regard to the destructive degradation of cyanide. Although anaerobic systems may be more robust than aerobic systems in certain circumstances, such as activated sludges, aerobic fixed-films have perhaps been demonstrated to be the most practical, as aerobic processes in general provide a more rapid rate of removal. However, recent applications of anaerobic biotreatment for cyanide-bearing wastes have tended to utilise a dual system approach, typically employing an aerobic system downstream of an anaerobic primary reactor.

Most cyanide-bearing wastes contain quite low levels of cyanide compared to the levels treatable by the ICI "Cyclear" process. Many cyanide-bearing wastewaters that arise from the metal industries contain complexed cyanides and also levels of metals that may be inhibitory. These liquid wastes may be successfully treated by the use of aerobic viable biomass which has the added advantage of being, in effect, a self-regenerating catalyst if bio-oxidation of cyanide occurs. However, with regard to general robustness and resistance to shock loading (by cyanide or metals) it is advantageous to utilise a fixed film bioreactor.

Homestake and others (Mudder and Whitlock 1984a,b) have observed fixed-film systems to be more resistant to toxic shock. This factor is particularly important for a system used to biotreat an aqueous waste containing cyanide and levels of metals that might be inhibitory. Other advantages exist in using a fixed microbial culture:

1   Higher culture densities can be obtained than in suspended cell systems (activated sludge).
2   Flow rates in the reactor can exceed the washout dilution rate because the biomass is fixed - in a passive settlement system too high a flow prevents biomass settlement. In addition, under toxic shock biomass washes out of an activated sludge system (bulking) but is retained when fixed.
3   Attachment is accepted as enhancing microbial growth rates - the intrinsic catalytic ability of the biomass may be enhanced.
4   Fixed film systems generate far less excess biomass than suspended cell systems such as activated sludge. This is particularly important here because any sludge produced required disposal and in this case might be metal contaminated, increasing sludge treatment expense.

Biological polymers and cells can accumulate metals, by active as well as passive means. Accumulation of metal can cause disposal problems with any excess sludge generated but this can be circumvented by periodically gently acid-washing the fixed film in the bioreactor, preferably with citric acid (Palmer 1988).

A fixed-film bioreactor can hence be operated successfully in a cyanide- and metal-bearing wastewater using metal-tolerant strains (such as that isolated by Homestake) and metal accumulation within the reactor can be cheaply and easily dealt with if required.

The successful application of any technology, including biological treatment, should always initially involve characterisation of the liquid waste because certain constituents of the waste, apart from the target compounds, may be of significance. The composition of the waste can influence the biomass and choice of reactor configuration. The use of model treatment processes in the laboratory can lead to pilot-scale application of the developed process. These development stages are significant if a successful transfer of a biotreatment technology to the field is to be achieved.

Nitriles

Organic cyanide compounds, nitriles, are found in the environment due to natural synthesis and also as the result of man. Certain natural nitriles were mentioned earlier, the cyanogenic glucosides produced by plants and ß-cyanoalanine produced by *Chr. violaceum* and other organisms. Plants produce other types of nitrile compounds such as cyanolipids, ricine and phenylacetonitrile. Many nitrile compounds are also manufactured by man on a large scale to be used as base chemicals for polymer manufacture and a variety of other chemical syntheses. Acrylonitrile and polymers derived from it are used widely in the manufacture of plastics and adiponitrile is used in the production of nylon.

Microbial Metabolism of Nitriles

Microorganisms oxidatively catabolise nitriles to the corresponding acid. A variety of microorganisms are capable of converting nitriles to amides and/or acids (Wyatt and Linton 1988). The nitrile-degrading enzymes are of two groups. The first group, nitrile hydratase enzymes, convert the nitrile to the corresponding amide and includes enzymes with the ability to hydrolyse a wide variety of structurally diverse nitriles. This activity has been described in a number of organisms including yeasts, fungi, green plants and a wide range of bacteria. The second group, nitrilase enzymes, convert the nitrile, which in this case is normally aromatic or heterocyclic, directly to the acid with no intermediate formation of the amide. The enzymes in this category are more specific for a narrow structural range of nitriles and these are predominantly either aromatic or heterocyclic.

The mechanism of microbial nitrile metabolism has been determined in a number of different bacterial species. Aliphatic nitriles are catabolised in two stages, via conversion to the corresponding amide and then to the acid plus ammonia, by a nitrile hydratase and amidase respectively (Fig. 4.3a). Benzonitrile and related aromatic and heterocyclic nitriles are converted directly to the corresponding acids and ammonia with little release of the amide as an intermediate (Fig. 4.3b). The aromatic nitrilase has been purified and it was demonstrated that no separate amidase was required for formation of the acid product.

The reaction sequence of nitrile to amide and then to acid catalysed by a nitrile hydratase and an amidase was first proposed by a Japanese research group in 1969

(a)   Aliphiatic Nitrile Metabolism

$$H_2O \qquad\qquad\qquad H_2O$$

RCN $\longrightarrow$ RCONH$_2$ $\longrightarrow$ RCOOM + NH$_3$
nitrile   amidase
hydratase

Nitrile   Amide   Acid   Ammonia

C-Source and/or N-Source

(b)   Aromatic/Heterocyclic Nitrile Metabolism

$$2H_2O$$

RCN $\xrightarrow{\hspace{2cm}}$ RCOOH + NH$_3$
nitriase

Nitrile   Acid   Ammonia

$$H_2O$$

RCONH$_2$ $\xrightarrow{\hspace{2cm}}$ RCOOH + NH$_3$
amidase

Amide   Acid   Ammonia

Fig. 4.3. Nitrile metabolism.

(Mimura *et al*. 1969). The researchers observed that ammonia and an amide accumulated in the culture supernatant when *Corynebacterium nitrilophilus* nov.sp.c-42 was grown on acetonitrile. In 1971 an organism was isolated from soil that was capable of growing on 4% acetonitrile and many other aliphatic nitriles (Fukuda *et al*. 1971). Cell suspensions of this organism were used to biotransform DL-α-aminopropionitrile to DL-alanine. When describing the degradative versatility of the *Corynebacterium* species it was noted that the organism was capable of growth on nitriles (Grant 1973) and assumed that the aliphatic nitriles were degraded via the amide to the acid as had initially been proposed by Mimura *et al*. 1969. Firmin and Gray (1976) demonstrated that the pathway of acetonitrile degradation was almost certainly hydrolytic in a *Pseudomonas* species. In the same year *Nocardia rhodochous* LL100-21 was isolated in a study of the utilisation of low molecular weight nitriles by Di Geronimo and Antoine. This organism could utilise acetonitrile as a sole carbon and nitrogen source for growth but could only utilise acrylonitrile and acrylamide as a nitrogen source, the acrylic acid formed not being further metabolised. The ability of this organism to degrade various nitriles and amides and the inducibility of the degradative systems has been elucidated in some detail (Collins and Knowles 1983; Linton and Knowles 1986). The aliphatic and aromatic/heterocyclic nitrile degrading enzyme systems can both be induced in this organism depending on the growth substrate (Table 4.4).

In 1976 a group of French workers isolated a total of eighteen organisms that were capable of growth on acetonitrile (Arnaud *et al*. 1976; Arnaud *et al*. 1977). One particular organism from these was selected for further study. Acetonitrile was catabolised in two stages in this organism, via conversion to the corresponding amide and then to the acid plus ammonia. These stages were catalysed by a nitrile hydratase and an amidase, respectively, as had been observed in all the other studies on aliphatic nitriles. The nitrile hydratase of this organism, *Brevibacterium* R312, was partially purified and the enzyme activity was found in the 180 000 g fraction of a centrifuged crude cell homogenate prepared by ultrasonic disruption of the bacteria. Activity was precipitated between 40% and 55% saturation with ammonium sulphate, was lost by dialysis and divalent cations were not required. The Michaelis constant (Km) of the enzyme of acetonitrile catabolism was high at 2.5×10^{-2} M. The enzyme is therefore a general nitrile hydratase and being highly non-specific, capable of hydrolysing a wide variety of nitriles.

Table 4.4. The induction of nitrile hydratase/amidase or nitrilase activity in *Nocardia rhodochrous*

	Growth Substrates						
	Aliphatic Nitrile	Aliphatic Amide	Aliphatic Acid	Aromatic Nitrile	Aromatic Amide	Aromatic Acid	Aliphatic Diacid
Aliphatic Nitrile	+	+	-	-	-	-	-
Aliphatic Amide	+	+	-	-	-	-	-
Aliphatic Acid	+	+	+	-	-	-	-
Aromatic Nitrile	-	-	-	+	-	-	-
Aromatic Amide	-	-	-	-	+	-	-
Aromatic Acid	-	-	-	+	+	+	-
Aliphatic Diacid	-	-	-	-	-	-	+

The microorganism was grown in the absence of acetonitrile yet retained activity suggesting the enzyme was constitutive, but this is debatable as no activity of the enzyme could be found when the organism was in the stationary phase of growth. The concomitant amidase was found to be inducible. The nitrile hydratase and amidase activities of this organism are thought to be cytosolic, suggesting acetonitrile and acetamide readily enter and leave the bacterium, probably by simple diffusion.

The broad substrate specificity of the nitrile hydratase and amidase from *Brevibacterium* was discussed by Jallageas *et al.* (1980). The organism was able to hydrolyse nearly all water soluble nitriles to the corresponding acids, providing the growth conditions were carefully chosen. A mutant of this organism was derived which could convert nitriles to the corresponding amides such as acrylamide or acetamide but was unable to further utilise these.

The French workers continued to study this *Brevibacterium* strain (Bui *et al.* 1982) and have investigated the Km of the nitrile hydratase with different substrates, concluding that the longer the side-chain of the nitrile substrate the lower the Km value. A mutant strain of the organism was prepared which had lost the nitrile hydratase activity suggesting it is due to a single enzyme for which the structural gene was lost.

Acrylonitrile in excess has been found to inhibit the nitrile hydratase of the Brevibacterium, but only above 0.2M. Acrylamide and propionamide, the nitrile hydratase bioconversion products, were demonstrated to be competitive inhibitors of the activity for acrylonitrile.

The economics of using a bioconversion to produce acrylamide using this organism were felt to be against such a process due to the inhibition of the enzyme by the end-product. The activity of Brevibacterium R312 has however been utilised to produce amides from the corresponding nitriles. A mutant strain of the organism which was unable to utilise any amides except L-α-aminoamides was immobilised in a polyacrylamide gel (Bui *et al.* 1984). A half-life of eight days was obtained in this immobilised whole cell reactor for the production of propionamide and isobuytramide.

The nitrile hydratase enzyme from the same organism has been partially purified and immobilised on an ion-exchange resin (DEAE-cellulose). Total conversion of propionitrile to propionamide was obtained for 15 days using a 1% (v/v) solution of propionitrile, however high substrate concentrations inhibited the bioconversion.

In 1979 the first of a series of papers on the microbial degradation of nitrile compounds was published by a group of Japanese workers. They initially reported the isolation of a microorganism capable of utilising acrylonitrile as sole source of carbon and nitrogen (Yamada *et al.* 1979). During the growth of this *Arthrobacter* species on acrylonitrile, acrylic acid was identified as a metabolite that was subsequently degraded. The subsequent three papers of the series described the utilisation of various aliphatic nitriles. These included the degradation of glutaronitrile by a *Pseudomonas* species (Yamada *et al.* 1980) various dinitriles by *Fusarium merismoides* TG-1 (Asano *et al.* 1980) and triacrylonitrile by the same fungus (Asano *et al.* 1981). The proposed pathway of glutaronitrile metabolism was via hydrolysis of the nitrile group at the other end of the molecule. Another group (Kuwahara *et al.* 1980) studying succinonitrile however suggested simultaneous hydrolysis of the two terminal nitrile groups.

The *Arthrobacter species.* isolated previously for its ability to degrade acrylonitrile was further studied (Asano *et al.* 1982a,b). The organism was grown on acetonitrile and the two enzymes the nitrilase (nitrile hydratase) and the amidase were both purified. The nitrile hydratase was inducible and comprised of two types of subunits (molecular weight 24 000 and 27 000) the enzyme having a molecular weight of 420 000. The amidase was also inducible and the estimated molecular weight was 300 000 - 320 000, the enzyme being composed of eight identical subunits.

An enzymic method for the production of acrylamide was described by the same workers (Asano *et al.* 1982c). Nearly 200 nitrile-degrading organisms were screened for their ability to produce acrylamide from acrylonitrile. One organism was selected, *Pseudomonas chlororaphis*, which had a high nitrile hydratase activity towards acrylonitrile and extremely low amidase activity to acrylamide. Using whole cells, acrylonitrile was added sequentially such that the concentration did not exceed 0.4 M and under optimum conditions 400 g l^{-1} of acrylamide was produced in 7.5 h.

The use of nitrile utilising bacteria as biotransformation catalysts has been realised in the laboratory if not as yet in commercial processes. Jallageas *et al.* (1980) describe the production of DL-lactic acid, acrylamide, L-methionine as examples of possible processes.

The use of an immobilised bacterial isolate has been described that is capable of the stereospecific bioconversion of α-aminopropionitrile to L-alanine (Macadam and Knowles 1985) The alanine formed was 87% in the L-form, whereas Jallageas *et al.* (1980) found that L-aminonitriles had a 50% conversion, the remainder being accounted for by formation of the corresponding D-aminoamide.

The studies to date in a wide range of bacteria and fungi have all demonstrated that aliphatic nitrile degradation occurs via hydrolysis to the corresponding amide by a nitrile hydratase. There is then a subsequent conversion to the corresponding acid and ammonia via an amidase (Collins and Knowles 1983) A number of patents have been filed on the bioconversion of nitriles to the corresponding amides and to a more limited degree conversions to the corresponding acids. The production of (especially) acrylamide has been described by a number of patents. Other amides described include methacrylamide, nicotinamide and benzamide. Japanese researchers have concentrated on increasing the yield of the bioconversions to achieve a commercially viable process.

The biological production of acrylamide from acrylonitrile is currently being performed by the Nitto Chemical Company of Japan on an increasing scale (4000 tons per annum in 1987). This process is to date the only major example of the production of a bulk chemical by modern biotechnological means.

Biodegradation of Nitrile-containing Waste Effluents

The microbial degradation of nitrile compounds is another important aspect of the biotechnological potential of nitrile-utilising microbes.

Many nitrile compounds are chemically synthesised by man on a large scale. Few chemical reactions result in the total conversion of reactants to products, 10%-20% of the input to the reaction usually results in side products. Therefore an inevitable consequence of the manufacture of these chemicals is the production of considerable waste effluents that contain the nitrile plus a variety of related compounds. Most nitriles and related compounds are highly toxic to living organisms and consequently pose a considerable threat to the environment if their release is not controlled. Nitrile utilising microorganisms can play an important role biodegrading these compounds at the source of their production thereby eliminating the risk of contamination to the environment.

Acrylonitrile and adiponitrile are commonly used nitriles manufactured on a large scale world-wide. The waste effluents produced during the manufacture of these compounds contain a number of potentially hazardous compounds and all attempts at acclimation of biological systems to biodegrade them has previously been unsuccessful. The wastes are thus difficult to dispose of, being removed at present by unsatisfactory methods such as chlorination and disposal at sea, or, in the USA, by pumping into deep pressure wells below the water table.

Acrylonitrile is manufactured by a process known as ammoxidation in which propylene and ammonia are catalytically combined to form acrylonitrile. The resultant waste effluent from this process has proved resistant to biodegradation using conventional biological technology. Kato and Yamamura (1976) found that they were unable to adapt an ordinary activated sludge system by gradual acclimation to biodegrade even dilute concentrations of this waste effluent. However by adding to the activated sludge system a microorganism isolated for its capability to utilise low concentrations of certain nitriles, these workers found that they were able to adapt the system to biodegrade a very dilute concentration of the mixed nitrile waste. The volume of the wastes produced has however limited the practical use of a system such as this due to the excessive requirement for dilution water.

Recently a novel approach has been taken to obtain a specialised microbial culture that was capable of biodegrading the hazardous waste effluents produced during the manufacture of acrylonitrile. The objective of the work was to obtain a microbial biomass that could convert all the potentially toxic monomeric compounds to their mineral entities, carbon dioxide, ammonia, water and biomass (Knowles and Wyatt 1987).

The production of acrylonitrile by the ammoxidation process results in two effluent streams. Both streams have high chemical oxidation demand (COD) levels (20 000 - 40 000 ppm). An analysis of the streams revealed they were typical of many industrial effluents, with the majority of the waste carbon being contained in relatively few compounds. Each major constituent was examined individually to determine if microorganisms could be obtained, by classical enrichment procedures, that were capable of mineralising that component. Certain components were quite toxic and required biodegradation systems to be developed to achieve their mineralisation. These consisted of an initial biotransformation to give a compound that could subsequently be mineralised. When isolates had been obtained that were either capable of biodegrading or biotransforming each of the compounds, all the isolates were combined as the inocula for a continuous culture.

A single-pass, continuous culture was operated with no recycling of biomass and the initial substrate was a mixture of the most readily degradable compounds. The concentration of the more toxic components was gradually increased, allowing adaptation of the culture which could subsequently biodegrade all the components in this synthetic waste. The resultant stable, mixed culture was then used to biodegrade the actual wastes. Finally, an activated sludge system could be established using the adapted mixed culture combined with activated sludge from a municipal water treatment plant.

This technique enables the biological treatment of wastewater from a chemical plant that was previously considered to be too toxic for a biological process. Similar microbial culture development or as the process is now known "Custom Blend" development can be applied to numerous industrial wastes and provides an interesting alternative to chemical or physical disposal of wastes previously thought to be too toxic or recalcitrant for biological treatment (Wyatt 1988).

Conclusions

The microbial metabolism of cyanide and nitriles has been studied in some detail. The toxicity of these compounds is such that emissions from manufacturing plants must be controlled. To achieve this end may require modification of the production process or on site degradation.

Modern techniques of biological degradation of these compounds has been demonstrated to be a practical alternative to other treatment methods, particularly in overall degradation efficiency and process economics.

References

Arnaud A, Galzy P, Jallageas JC (1976) Rev Ferm Ind Alimentaire 31: 39-44

Arnaud A, Galzy P, Jallageas JC (1977) Acetonitrilase from a Brevibacterium strain Agric Biol Chem 41:2183-2191

Asano Y, Ando S, Tani Y, Yamada H (1980) Mirobial degradation of nitrile compounds. Part III. Degradation of dinitriles by *Fusarium merismoides* T4-1 Agric Biol Chem 44:2497-2498

Asano Y, Ando S, Tani Y, Yamada H, Ueno T (1981) Microbial degradation of nitrile compounds. Part IV. Fungal degradation of triacrylonitrile Agric Biol Chem 45:57-62

Asano Y, Fujishiro K, Tani Y, Yamada H (1982a) Microbial degradation of nitrile compounds. Part V. J-1. Purification and characterisation Agric Biol Chem 46:1165-1174

Asano Y, Tachibana M, Tani Y, Yamada H (1982b) Microbial degradation of nitrile compounds. Part VI. Purification and characterisation of amidase which participates in nitrile degradation Agric Biol Chem 46:1175-1181

Asano Y, Yasuda Y, Tani Y and Yamda H (1982c) Microbial degradation of nitrile compounds. Part VII. A new enzymic method of acrylamide production Agric Biol Chem 48:1183-1189

Bui K, Arnaud A, Galzy PF (1982) A new method to prepare amides by bioconversion of corresponding nitriles Enzyme Microb Technol 4:195-197

Bui K, Fradet H, Arnaud A, Galzy PF (1984) A nitrile hydratase with a wide substrate spectrum produced by a Brevibacterium sp. J Gen Microbiol 130: 89-93

Clarke PM (1986) Enzymatic treatment of cyanide bearing effluents. In: Immobilisation of Ions by Biosorption Eccles H, Hunt S (eds) Ellis Horwood (London) pp 245-256

Collins PA, Knowles CJ (1983) The utilisation of nitriles and amides by *Nocardia rhodochrous* J Gen Microbiol 129:711-718

DiGeronimo MJ, Antoine AD (1976) Metabolism of acetonitrile and propionitrile by *Nocardia rhodochrous* LL100-21 Appl Environ Microbiol 31:900-906

Evered D, Harnett S (1988) Cyanide compounds in Biology CIBA Foundation Symposium, John Wiley and Sons p 140

Firmin JL, Gray DO (1976) The Biochemical Pathway for the Breakdown of Methyl Cyanide (Acetonitrile) in Bacteria. Biochem J 158:223-229

Fukuda Y, Fukui M, Harada T, Izumi Y (1971) Formation of α-amino acids from α-aminonitrile by cell suspensions of a strain of Corynebacterium Hakko Kogaku Zasshi 49:1011-1016

Grant DJW (1973) Degradative versatility of *Corynebacterium pseudodiphtheriticum* NCIB 10803 which uses amides as carbon source Antonie Van Leewenhoek 39:273-279

Green J, Smith DH (1972) Processes for the detoxification of waste cyanides Metal Finishing Journal (Aug) pp 229-234

Harris RE, Bunch AW, Knowles CJ (1987) Microbial cyanide and nitrile metabolism Sci Prog Oxf 71:293-304

Harris RE, Knowles CJ (1983a) Isolation and growth of a Pseudomonas species that utilises cyanide as a source of nitrogen J Gen Microbiol 129:1005-1011

Harris RE, Knowles CJ (1983b) The conversion of cyanide to ammonia by extracts of a strain of *Pseudomonas fluorescens* that utilises cyanide as a source of nitrogen for growth FEMS Microbiol Lett 20:337-341

Howe RHL (1965) Biodestruction of cyanide wastes - advantages and disadvantages Air Water Pollution 9:463-478

Jallageas JC, Arnaud A, Galzy PF (1980) Bioconversions of nitriles and their applications Adv Biochem Eng 14:1-32

Kato AK, Yamamura K (1976) Treating waste water conatining nitriles and cynaides US Patent Number 3 940 332 (Feb 24th) US Patent Office

Knowles CJ (1976) Micro-organisms and cyanide Bact Revs 40:652-680

Knowles CJ, Wyatt JM (1987) The Potential for Biotransforming Toxic Wastes to Harmless By-Products. World Biotech Rep 1(5):61-66

Kuwahara M, Yanase H, Ishida Y, Kikuchi Y (1980) Metabolism of aliphatic nitriles in *Fusarium solani* J Ferment Technol 58:573-577

Lettinga G, van Velsen AFM, de Zeeuw WJ, Hobma SW (1979) The Application of Anaerobic Digestion to Industrial Pollution Treatment. In: Anaerobic Digestion Stafford D A, Wheatley BI, Hughes DE (eds) Appl Sci Pub Ltd pp 167-186

Linton EA, Knowles CJ (1986) Utilisation of aliphatic amides and nitriles by *Nocardia rhodochrous* LL100-21 J Gen Microbiol 132:1493-1501

Ludzak FJ, Schaffer RB (1960) Activated sludge treatment of cyanide, cyanate and thiocyanate Eng Bull Purdue University 106: 439-460

Macadam AM, Knowles CJ (1984) Purification and properties of a β-cyano-L-alanine synthase from the cyanide-producing bacterium, *Chromobacterium violaceum* Biochim Biophys Acta 786:123-132

Macadam AM, Knowles CJ (1985) The stereospecific bioconversion of α-aminopropionitrile to L-alanine by an immobilised bacterium isolated from soil Biotechnol Lett 7:865-870

Mimura A, Kawano T, Yamaga K (1969) Application of micro-organisms to the petrochemical industry. I. Assimilation of nitriles by micro-organisms Hakko Kogaku Zasshi 47:631-638

Mudder TI, Whitlock JL (1984a) Biological treatment of cyanidation waste waters Minerals and Metallurgical Processing 1:161-165

Mudder TI, Whitlock JL (1984b) Biological removal of free and complex cyanides and thiocyanates from water U.S. Patent Number 4 440 644 (Apr 3rd) US Patent Office

Nazly N, Knowles CJ, Beardsmore AJ, Naylor WT, Corcoran EG (1983) Detoxification of cyanide by immobilised fungi J Chem Tech Biotechnol 33B:119-126

Palmer SJ (1988) Cadmium Biosorption by Bacteria PhD Thesis, University of Bath UK

Raef SF, Characklis WG, Kessick MA, Ward CH (1975) Fate of cyanide and related compounds in industrial waste treatment Eng Bull Purdue University 145: 832-840

Richards DJ, Shieh WK (1988) Anoxic/oxic activated sludge treatment of cyanogens and ammonia in the presence of phenols. In: Biotechnology for Degradation of Toxic Chemicals in Hazardous Wastes Scholze RJ, (ed) Noyes Data Cor NJ, USA pp 573-582

Richards DJ, Shieh WK (1989) Anoxic-oxic activated-sludge treatment of cyanides and phenols Biotechnol Bioeng 33:32-38

Sterritt RM, Lester JN (1986) Heavy Metal Immobilisation by Bacterial Extracellular Polymers. In: Immobilisation of ions by biosorption Eccles H, Hunt S (eds) Ellis Horwood (London) pp 121-134

Wyatt JM (1988) Biotechnological treatment of industrial wastewater Microbiological Sciences 5:186-190

Wyatt JM, Linton EA (1988) The Industrial Potential of Microbial Nitrile Biochemistry. In: Cyanide Compounds in Biology CIBA Foundation Symposium 140:32-48

Yamada H, Asano Y, Hino T, Tani Y (1979) Microbial utilisation of acrylonitrile J Ferment Technol 57:8-14

Yamada H, Asano Y, Tani Y (1980) Microbial degradation of nitrile compounds. II. Microbial utilisation of glutaronitrile J Ferment Technol 58:495-500

Zabban W, Helwick R (1980) Cyanide waste treatment technology - the old, the new and the practical Plating and Surface Finishing 67:56-59

Chapter 5

The Fate of Chemicals in Soil

N. Mackay and W. B. Betts

The Effects of Soil Processes

Introduction

The introduction of organic chemicals to the environment can cause a variety of ecological problems. One of the most serious of these is the accumulation of chemical agents in an ecosystem. Routes for their introduction are diverse and include direct dumping, accidental spillage, run-off, leaching from containment sites or vessels, and intentional application (e.g. agriculture). The types of chemicals are equally varied and range from industrial and household solvents to crude and refined oils (Calabrese and Kostecki 1989) and pesticides (Biggar and Seiber 1987; Grover 1989).

Chemicals applied to soil can have a biological impact throughout the environment. This is due to the wide variety of natural activities which occur, forcing continuous movement of chemicals between soils, living organisms, water and air (Goring 1972) as illustrated in Figure 5.1.

Once present in the natural environment many soil-applied chemicals are quickly subjected to one of several transformative processes which will eventually remove them. However, problems can arise when chemicals are not transformed rapidly but instead are retained in the environment. These can pose threats to a wide range of organisms not solely due to the toxicity of the agents (present at relatively low environmental concentrations) but often as a result of their bioaccumulation (McEwen and Stephenson 1979). The most dramatic examples of this are the persistent organochlorine pesticides (e.g. the insecticide DDT in Fig. 5.2) which have caused major declines in wildlife populations (Dempster 1987).

The degree to which organic chemicals persist (and their potential to bioaccumulate) is entirely due to the interaction between the chemicals and the environment. It is therefore important to study the mechanisms underlying removal of chemicals and to determine the factors which affect the rate of such losses (van der Zweep 1960). This

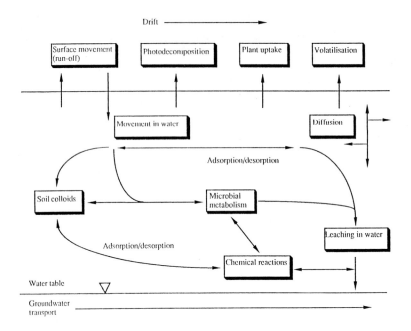

Fig. 5.1. Processes affecting chemicals in soil.

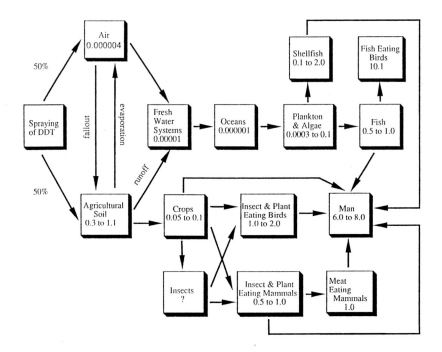

Fig. 5.2. The flow and bioaccumulation of DDT in the ecosphere. Quantities are quoted in ppm (After Miller 1975).

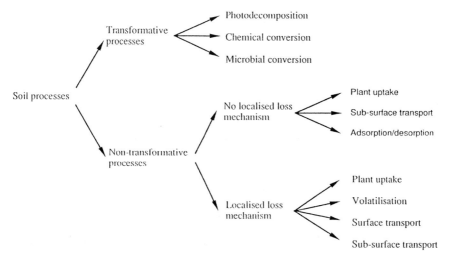

Fig. 5.3. Chemical fate categorisation.

requires the investigation of many interdependent processes occurring in a highly complex medium and affected by a multitude of factors (Wadleigh and Dyal 1970). Such research often requires sophisticated equipment, technical support, and a dedicated field site for study over a relatively long time scale. The associated expense of these undertakings can make it prohibitive (Seiber 1987). It is not surprising that the behaviour of most chemicals, once introduced to soil, remains poorly understood.

However, recognition of the importance of these studies has lead to codes requiring the estimation of persistence of certain soil-applied chemicals prior to registration in several countries around the world (van Voris 1985; Smith 1988; Anon 1990). As a result of this a variety of alternative methods have been considered which simplify the research design and reduce the financial burden, whilst still fulfilling the objectives of environmental protection legislation. These may prove to be invaluable research initiatives.

This chapter presents a brief discussion on the physical, chemical and biological processes within the soil environment and how these contribute to the transformation or persistence of chemicals. The discussion addresses how various models (or methods) deal with the study of these processes and how chemicals are affected by them.

Soil Processes

There are eight major processes affecting the fate of chemicals in soil, comprising adsorption/desorption, plant uptake, surface transport, sub-surface transport, volatilisation, microbial metabolism, chemical conversion and photodecomposition. They can be categorised as processes which completely remove chemicals from the environment, those which result in localised losses (i.e. removal of chemicals from the site of contamination or application) and those resulting in no localised losses (Fig. 5.3). The balance of fate processes is regulated by both the characteristics of the chemicals and by the conditions and properties of the soils involved. It is therefore essential to understand all of these interactions and their environmental significance.

Adsorption/Desorption

Adsorption/desorption limits the movement and distribution of chemicals within soil and therefore dictate the availability of any chemical for further processes. Adsorption is a reversible phenomenon characterised by the relative distribution of a chemical between the solid and liquid phase within soil (Hance 1989). Its quantification is of great importance, although the heterogeneous nature of soils and their adsorption surfaces often frustrates accurate assessment. Desorption, a rather different equilibrium process, is even more difficult to assess quantitatively, largely due to its slower rate (Hartley and Graham-Bryce 1980). Despite the difficulties in obtaining accurate data, existing descriptions of adsorptive soil-solute interactions have been invaluable in determining such factors as herbicide application rates.

Adsorption and desorption generally occur on surface active sites of clay minerals and organic matter which are both ubiquitous components of soil. Adsorption relies on the formation of several types of interactions with these sites depending upon the nature of the chemical and the soil. The interactions can include ion exchange, co-ordination with metals, hydrogen bonding, physical forces and entropy effects. Certain chemicals are subject to a greater sorptive effect due to the natural partitioning between polar and non-polar phases (Seiber 1987). This means that polar compounds will readily partition into the aqueous phase whereas non-polar compounds will partition most easily into an organic phase (such as humic matter). This phenomenon is most often described by the organic carbon partition coefficient.

The relative importance of adsorption and desorption depends upon the quantity of organic matter and clay minerals and therefore varies with the soil type. However, the quantity of organic matter in soil is generally used as the parameter to determine the extent of adsorption of chemicals. The UK Agricultural Development and Advisory Service (ADAS) and several herbicide manufacturers recommend dosage rate on the basis of soil organic matter content (Eagle 1983). Recent computer programs modeling the fate of chemicals within soil also employ organic matter content as a parameter related to adsorption and desorption (Mackay and Stiver 1990).

The environmental significance of the adsorption and desorption processes are summarised in Table 5.1. Soil possessing high organic and mineral matter contents will severely restrict the availability of most chemicals and this will retard losses by transport. However, substantial losses can still occur due to transformation as soil microbial activity is high in organic soils and the density of microorganisms in soil also tends to be higher near colloidal surfaces (Hance 1989). Adsorption then, does not always protect chemicals from degradation and indeed it can lead to enhanced degradation by surface catalysed hydrolysis (Armstrong and Konrad 1974). It does, however, protect chemicals from action from most other processes.

Table 5.1. Adsorption/desorption effects

	Environmental factors	Chemical factors
Factor causing increased adsorption	Higher: - organic matter content - mineral matter content	Higher: - organic carbon partition coefficient
	Lower: - moisture content - temperature	Lower: - solubility - vapour pressure

Plant Uptake

Hydrolytic enzymes which are responsible for the majority of chemical transformations in soil (Smith 1989) are found in plant systems, implying that plants may be capable of transforming soil-applied chemicals. If there are no enzymes present in the plant capable of using the chemical as substrate then uptake can either be considered as a localised loss or a no loss process depending upon whether the plant is harvested and subsequently removed from the ecosystem or re-introduced (e.g. by ploughing in). This often applies when considering the uptake of agricultural herbicides and insecticides in harvested crops.

The mass flow of water through the root system, brings water-borne solutes into contact with the plant (Hance 1989). As an approximation, the extent of uptake of a chemical is a function of its concentration in soil water and the surface area of exposed roots (Walker 1973). Compounds enter plants passively and are transported into the cell wall and xylem system because of their partitioning between soil water and the organic phase of the cell wall. This occurs to a greater extent with increasing lipophilic character of the chemical and simple partitioning ratios can be worked out for specific chemicals and plants. For example, the ratio of the concentration in roots and soil water of polar compounds will not fall below 0.8 due to the relatively high solubility of these chemicals (Briggs et al. 1982). Thus, the concentration will vary only slightly between external (soil) water and internal (cell) water.

Chemicals which are most susceptible to translocation once within the root system tend to be neither very polar nor very non-polar (Briggs et al. 1982). Very polar compounds, while being able to pass through cell walls and roots easily, will not concentrate within plants due to their high solubility and low lipophilicity. Conversely, very non-polar chemicals will only be present in soil water in very small concentrations limited by the solubility of the chemical in question. Naturally, this will limit the range of chemicals able to reach the root system of plants and those chemicals which do will be partitioned into cell wall material very quickly. Translocation of these chemicals will occur only very slowly, limited once again by their solubility and organic phase partitioning.

Apart from the specific conditions necessary for plant growth there are two common soil conditions which dictate uptake - high organic matter and high moisture content. As discussed earlier, a high organic matter content in soil will lead to increased chemical adsorption with only a limited chemical release into soil water and plants. Generally, a greater soil moisture content will lead to the existence of a larger interface between soil water and roots. This will increase partitioning into plants of soil water solutes, the extent of which is governed by the solubility of the chemical in question. These effects are summarised in Table 5.2.

Table 5.2. Plant uptake effects

	Environmental factors	Chemical factors
Factor causing increased plant uptake	Higher: - water uptake rate of plants - surface area of plant root system - lipid content of plants - moisture content of soils Lower: - organic matter content - mineral matter content	Plant uptake peaks with octanol-water partition co-efficient as 1.8

Plants are extremely important components affecting the soil ecosystem. Roots influence soil in many ways: carbon dioxide levels are raised by root respiration and both oxygen and mineral concentrations are reduced. There are also a variety of organic materials added to the soil by the root system and these "exudate" include glucose, fructose, pentoses, di-, tri- and oligo-saccharides and amino acids. This release of organic materials usually results in an increase of bacterial numbers (Campbell 1983). In addition, the ubiquitous mycorrhizal fungi associated with many types of root system further increase microbial populations (Cooper and Tinker 1978). Fungi, often dominating soil metabolism (Anderson and Domsch 1980) and root system microorganisms (by virtue of their numbers), also play an important role in the transformation of soil-applied chemicals.

Surface Transport

The dispersal of soil-applied chemicals by surface transport can cause environmental problems as demonstrated by the use of persistent organochlorine pesticides in the 1950's and 1960's. Aquatic systems fed by agricultural run-off were the habitat of a wide variety of organisms. The concentration of certain chemicals (mainly herbicides) transported in run-off was sufficient to kill aquatic vegetation and fish. In addition, surviving higher organisms that lived in these systems were found to have accumulated high concentrations of these chemicals. The attention given to this problem resulted in revisions to agricultural practices associated with agrochemicals. These changes were designed to minimise the damage caused by surface transport and one of the first to occur was in the types of chemicals which were marketed (Leonard 1989). There was a shift towards persistence testing before registration and marketing resulting in many persistent chemicals being withdrawn from sale in some countries. There were also changes in the use of agrochemicals such as more precise dosage calculations, restrictions in their use, and the introduction of drainage and erosion control procedures (Novotny and Chesters 1981).

There are four major mechanisms underlying surface transport of chemicals (Bailey et al. 1974):

1   Diffusion/turbulent transport from soil pores to run-off water.
2   Desorption from soil particles into the moving liquid boundary.
3   Dissolution of stationary chemical particulates into run-off water.
4   Scouring of chemical particulates followed by dissolution into run-off water.

Desorption from organic matter is ordinarily a relatively slow process, as discussed earlier. However, the impact of raindrops, in addition to dislodging and suspending soil particulates, produces instantaneous pressure gradients which greatly accelerates the desorption process (Ajuhla and Lehman 1983). A "mixing zone" concept has been used in which a certain depth of soil is assumed to have complete mixing of its soil-pore water and run-off water (Leonard 1989). Studies indicate a strong correlation between the pesticide concentration in the first centimetre of soil and in the run-off (Smith et al. 1978; Leonard et al. 1979).

The soil-related characteristics affecting chemical loss by surface transport can be summarised as organic matter content, moisture content, surface soil compaction, soil texture, topography and climate (Leonard 1989). Organic matter content will affect desorption and mobility, although its contribution to sub-surface desorption is minimised by the effect of rainfall. A lower initial moisture content prior to rainfall will decrease the extent to which chemicals in pore-water and adsorbed onto soil will be liable to desorption and diffusion. Compaction of surface soil will reduce infiltration, thereby increasing the extent of run-off and the concentration of chemicals in the run-off waters. Soil texture will also affect infiltration and run-off which is usually higher on finely textured soil.

Topography will naturally affect the drainage patterns of run-off and the extent to which soil will be subject to turbulent transport and scouring. Changes in the intensity, extent and timing of rainfall will also influence run-off. An excellent review has been written by Leonard (1989) discussing soil effects and processes with regards to surface transport in more detail.

Characteristics of the chemical which influence surface transport include solubility, formulation, application rate, placement, and susceptibility to sorption (Leonard 1989). The effects of these chemical characteristics are usually straightforward and warrant only brief comment. In a study of published data, Wauchope (1978) related the mode of pesticide transport to solubility. This showed that run-off was the chief means of transport and dissipation for surface-applied chemicals with solubilities less than 1 mgl^{-1}. The applied chemical's formulation, which can be either solid (pure or in a granular form) or liquid (pure or as an emulsified concentrate) will greatly influence its susceptibility to run-off. Heavy doses of chemicals are more vulnerable to run-off as these tend to remain on the soil surface in high concentrations for extended periods. Chemicals, either soluble or insoluble, which remain at the surface will eventually be washed away. Placement of a chemical can also affect its surface stability, for example, chemicals applied on a slope are more disposed to run-off than chemicals in plains.

The run-off process transports soil-applied chemicals beyond the soil environment into an aquatic one where they are encountered in the form of dissolved chemicals or particles (suspended or in sediments). Degradation then occurs in a completely different environment.

Conditions affecting surface transport are summarised in Table 5.3.

Table 5.3. Surface transport effects

	Environmental factors	Chemical factors
Factor causing increased surface transport	Higher: - moisture content - soil compaction - slopes (topography) - frequency of rainfall - intensity of rainfall - volume of rainfall - organic matter content - mineral matter content	Higher: - dosages of chemicals - organic carbon partition coefficient Lower: - solubility

Sub-surface Transport

This process takes place in an area of soil above the water table known as the vadose or unsaturated zone. Until recently, it was thought that the variety of processes occurring in the unsaturated zone would result in the efficient dissipation of any soil-applied chemical. This would ensure that the concentrations of any chemicals leaching into groundwater would be so small as to pose no adverse health effects (Rao *et al.* 1989). However, improved analytical techniques have led to the discovery of trace levels of certain organic contaminants in drinking water supplies. This coupled with a better

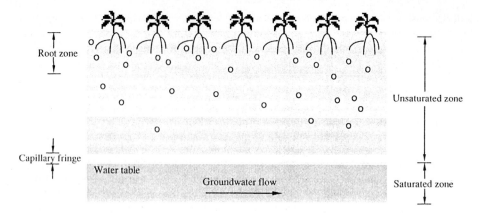

Fig. 5.4. Soil zones.

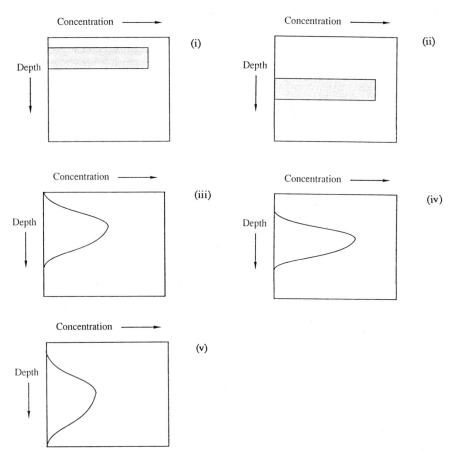

Fig. 5.5. (i) Initial incorporation scenario (ii) Mass flow only scenario (iii) Diffusion only scenario (iv) Combined mass flow scenario (v) Enhanced mass flow scenario.

understanding of possible chronic toxicological effects has led to changes in this view (Rao *et al.* 1989). Advances in groundwater monitoring techniques have allowed the discovery of at least 17 pesticides contaminating aquifers in the United States (Cohen *et al.* 1986). These findings have prompted the removal of some chemicals from usage.

Studies of water transport (or flux) in soil has been developed chiefly from the basic principles derived by the French scientist Darcy (1856) who stipulated that there are two basic types of soil water fluxes - those in saturated and unsaturated media. Flow in saturated media is considered to be in the liquid phase only and is generally known as groundwater flow. Separating the saturated zone and unsaturated zone above it are the water table and the capillary fringe (Fig. 5.4).

Flow in the unsaturated zone is diphasic due to the simultaneous flow of air with water (Meriaux 1982). The saturated and unsaturated transport laws are thus quite different and by far the more complicated of the two systems is flow in the unsaturated zone. Saturated, or groundwater flow, is not discussed further here as it is beyond the scope of this work. Further general readings on the topic can be found in an excellent text by Freeze and Cherry (1979).

When chemicals are applied to soil they can move downwards through the soil profile if dissolved in irrigation water or rainwater. This transport can be subdivided into two components which are distinct but occur simultaneously. Mass flow (also called convective or advective flow) is defined as the transport by a vehicle of water or air and diffusion (or molecular diffusion) which is the random movement of molecules tending to produce a uniform distribution of solute molecules within a solution or volume of air (Green and Khan 1987). The distinction is important, as mass flow can transport solutes over relatively large distances by the surrounding water, whereas with diffusion transport in soil is over a comparatively short distance.

The effect of the two transport components can be illustrated using a hypothetical scenario. Figure 5.5(i) shows the initial incorporation into soil of a chemical at 3 cm depth and at a concentration of 10 ppm. The individual and combined effects of the two processes can be considered as follows. Figure 5.5(ii) shows the result of mass flow only and the chemical has moved as a uniform pulse through the soil. In Figure 5.5(iii) diffusion was the sole process which resulted in a spreading above and below the "concentration peak" at the incorporation depth. In Figure 5.5(iv) both processes operated, culminating in a combination of pulsed transport and spreading known as hydrodynamic dispersion. The extent to which one process will dominate depends very much upon the structure of the soil. Rapid movement of water through extensive macropores or channels created by animals insects or plant roots can also lead to enhanced mass flow, in which case a different pulse pattern is developed (Fig. 5.5(v)). This enhanced flow is known as channelling, short-circuiting, by-passing, preferential flow or partial displacement (White 1985). Standard mathematical models describing convective-diffusional transport usually fail to describe this phenomenon, adding to the difficulty associated with predicting sub-surface transport.

In the long term chemicals may still be found close to the surface despite the actions of convective flow and diffusion. This is largely due to the rapid sorption of chemicals onto soil aggregates (mineral and organic matter) and subsequent diffusion into their micropores. Studies on black clay vertisols indicate that most water contained in soil aggregate micropores is not active in the flow process (Ritchie *et al.* 1972) and the greatest flow occurs, as expected, in the larger macropores around these aggregates. Thus, the quantity of the chemical which can move down through these macropores during a particular rainfall or irrigation event is quite small. Macropores drain quite quickly after saturation due to gravitational flow and so there is little opportunity for chemicals found in micropores and sorbed onto aggregates to equilibrate with macroporous water.

Leaching in a particular soil is dependent upon not only the adsorption and desorption processes but also the structure of the soil. This explains the initial rapid leaching of small quantities of chemicals applied to soil followed by the slower leaching of the chemical originally retained close to the surface. It is important to note that, as depth increases, the extent to which adsorption plays a key role in retardation of flow through soil diminishes, simply because the organic matter content of soils decreases rapidly below the rhizosphere (Green and Khan 1987). Sub-surface transport can be viewed as an adsorption- and desorption-dependent process in the long term and is therefore contingent upon the same soil and chemical characteristics. However, this dependance is often overshadowed by the effects of soil structure and climate, i.e. the ratio of macropores to micropores, the extent of "channelling" within soil and the degree of precipitation. These effects are summarised in Table 5.4.

Table 5.4. Sub-surface transport effects

	Environmental factors	Chemical factors
Factor causing increased sub-surface transport	Higher: - rainfall volumes - rainfall frequency - quantity of "channels" in soil - moisture content	Higher: - solubility
	Lower: - organic matter content - mineral matter content	Lower: - octanol-water partition coefficient

Volatilisation

Volatilisation can be the principal means of dissipation in the environment for some chemicals, resulting in losses far exceeding those caused by run-off. In addition, the distances through which chemicals can be distributed as a result of volatilisation are much greater than those due to any other mechanism. However, this "pollution potential" is offset by the enormous dilution capacity of the atmosphere (Taylor and Glotfelty 1988).

The capacity of a chemical to volatilise is related to its vapour pressure and the rate of movement away from the evaporation surface (Spencer 1987). The layer immediately above the evaporating surface is considered virtually immobile and vaporised chemicals must diffuse across it. Turbulence above this "boundary layer" acts to decrease its width and therefore increases the rate of volatilisation which becomes dependent upon the chemical vapour pressure and prevailing atmospheric conditions.

Soil adds another dimension to the volatilisation process. In order for volatilisation to occur from the soil surface a variety of processes must first occur within the soil in order for the chemical to be transported to the surface. Soil itself is a combination of solid, liquid and gaseous phases and the proportion of each is dependent upon the environmental characteristics of the soil and the climate. The tendency of a chemical to volatilise is dependent upon the phase in which it is found. It is logical to assume that chemicals found in one phase are subject to volatilisation to a greater extent than those located in another phase simply because of the difference in evaporation dynamics at different phase boundaries. Chemicals found in soil-air are subject to more

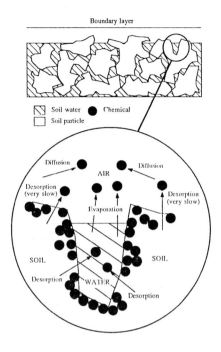

Fig. 5.6. Schematic of volatilisation from soil surfaces.

volatilisation than those found associated with organic matter, simply because of the different processes necessary to evaporate from a surface. This is illustrated in Figure 5.6.

The three major environmental parameters that affect volatilisation are temperature, soil moisture content and organic matter content. Temperature influences volatilisation through its effect on the vapour pressure and evaporation will increase between three and four times for every 10°C increase. Additionally, temperature can influence rates of diffusion within soil. Increased soil moisture content acts to increase volatilisation by reducing the number of surface active adsorption sites in soil, which in turn will decrease the rate of adsorption onto soil (Taylor and Glotfelty 1988). When dry soil is rewetted the rates of volatilisation will increase and this is related to two factors. First, the concomitant increase in vapour density in soils due to evaporation and second, the increased mobility of chemicals in soil water, either by diffusion or convective transport (Spencer 1987). Thus, chemicals with higher aqueous solubilities are more susceptible to volatilisation because of the large role soil-water plays in transport and desorption within soil. Soils with high organic matter contents are subject to lower volatility simply due to the extent of adsorption of chemicals onto what is ostensibly a solid organic phase.

The environmental and chemical effects on volatilisation are summarised in Table 5.5.

Table 5.5. Volatilisation effects

	Environmental factors	Chemical factors
Factor causing increased volatilisation	Higher: - moisture content - rainfall volumes - rainfall frequency - air turbulance	Higher: - vapour pressure - solubility - temperature
	Lower: - organic matter content - mineral matter content	Lower: - organic carbon partition coefficient

Transformative Processes

As we have seen, chemicals applied to the soil environment do not necessarily remain there. Instead, they can be removed by leaching into groundwater, volatilisation into the atmosphere, plant uptake and run-off into surface water courses. However, the chemical integrity of these agents in the environment is governed by three general transformative processes of which two are physico-chemical and one is biochemical.

Photodecomposition

Photodecomposition, or sunlight-induced transformation of soil chemicals can play an important role in their removal. Solar irradiation has been considered as an alternative to chemical and biochemical methods of decontaminating soil (Hoff *et al.* 1988). The successful abiotic degradation of a chemical (stable at normal temperature and pressure) necessitates a large energy input to initiate the reaction. Sunlight provides a readily available and abundant form of energy and is therefore a potential transformative agent.

Photochemical transformations in the atmosphere are well documented and it is known that some photodegradation products can have a greater toxicity and persistence than the starting substrates. However, in soil the availability of chemicals for transformation can vary and this complicates the situation (Hoff *et al.* 1988).

Since the majority of chemicals are applied to the soil surface it might be assumed that photolysis would play a major role in chemical transformation. But, the effectiveness of photolysis is limited by the structure of the chemical, the presence of reactants and sufficient irradiation energy. Additionally, the depth of the reactive photic zone in soils is a major limitation. The depth of this zone varies between soils and generally those having a low organic matter content are more transparent. Organic matter can also assist photolysis by being a rich source of photo-reactants. Photolysis (and volatilisation) can be augmented by an increased soil moisture content which enhances transport of the chemical to the surface.

The photodecomposition process begins with the absorption of solar irradiation which results in an excited molecule capable of undergoing transformations. Although many chemicals are capable of such transformations, relatively few are subjected to the appropriate level of irradiation energy required to drive the reactions. Shorter, and therefore more energetic, wavelengths of solar radiation are either absorbed (in part or in whole) by atmospheric ozone (wavelengths <295) or strongly attenuated as they pass through the atmosphere (ultraviolet radiation) (Miller and Herbert 1987). There is,

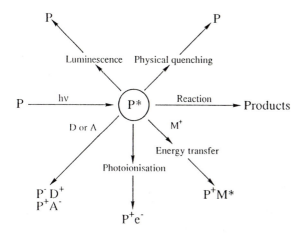

Fig. 5.7. Photo processes. (After Miller and Herbert 1987).

therefore, a significant variation to this process dependent on seasonal changes, climate and latitude.

As can be seen in Figure 5.7 transformation is only one of a variety of pathways that an excited state molecule can follow and it is often no more than a comparatively minor process. The relative importance of each pathway is related to the structural characteristics of the chemical and the environment in which it is found. The presence of a variety of environmental reactants such as nucleophiles and oxidising/reducing agents will determine the pathway employed. A discussion of the alternative pathways is beyond the scope of this chapter and readers are directed towards standard quantum mechanics textbooks.

Photolytic products rarely differ from those of chemical and biological transformations, although there may be differences in the relative yields from these. However, a variety of unique products can be generated during photodecomposition. For example the organophosphorus pesticide malathion undergoes photohydrolysis to r-nitrophenol, followed by photosubstitution reactions which depend upon the types of nucleophiles present (Nakagawa and Crosby 1974).

By far the most common reaction mechanism that takes place is photoxidation as an abundance of molecular ground-state $^3O_2$ promotes its reaction with free radicals. These can form oxidants and which can interact with soil chemicals generating a variety of products as a result of hydrogen atom extraction, nitrogen oxidation, side chain oxidation, hydroxyl radical addition to aromatics, and additions to double bonds (Miller and Herbert 1987). As another example, dehalogenation reactions can occur on chemicals such as PCB's and dioxins through photoreduction (Crosby and Wong 1977; Sunstrom and Ruzo 1978). Photoreduction of nitro groups to amines has also been observed for the pesticide parathion (Ruzo 1982). The overall environmental effects on photodecomposition are summarised in Table 5.6.

Table 5.6. Photodecomposition

	Environmental factors	Chemical factors
Factor causing increased photodecomposition	Higher: - solar irradiation - moisture content - soil reactant levels - photic zone depth	Dependent upon structure and bond types

Chemical Transformation

Since the 1960's there has been a shift from the development of persistent pesticides to degradable varieties. However, to ensure a degree of stability in the environment these non-persistent chemicals are often combined with other compounds such as anti-microbial agents and oils. Since the active chemical should be stable and effective in these complexes the manufacturer must be aware of the potential reactions between the pesticide and formulation chemicals, and familiar with any resulting products (Farmer and Aochi 1987).

Much of the research into chemical transformations in natural environments has focused on aqueous systems, recognising the major role played by water in the transformation process. As discussed earlier, water acts not only as a transportation medium but also as a reaction medium and a primary reactant itself (Farmer and Aochi 1987). Indeed, the most important chemical transformation process is that of hydrolysis in which a nucleophile (water) attacks the electrophilic branch or fragment of a chemical displacing the electrophile with a hydroxyl moiety. The rate of this bimolecular reaction is limited by the concentrations of both reactants. In most natural environments, however, the reaction is often first order or pseudo first order, as water is not rate limiting. In dry soils hydrolysis proceeds more slowly and degradation with organic and mineral matter surface catalysis is observed. A study by Armstrong and Konrad (1974) showed that hydrolysis of the herbicide atrazine occurred much more rapidly in the presence of soil. They were able to attribute catalytic activity to organic matter and identify the functional group responsible for the catalysis. In organic matter carboxylic acid moieties can serve as proton donors that act to withdraw electrons from ring nitrogens (Fig. 5.8). When attached to Cl^- carbon atoms become more electrophilic and this encourages nucleophilic attack by water, replacing Cl^- with OH^-. Thus, while acting to remove chemicals from solution by sorption, organic matter can also encourage the decomposition of some chemicals through surface catalysis.

In the field it is often difficult to determine the contribution of microbial and chemical mechanisms in the decomposition of chemicals, as the same environmental conditions can often lead to identical final products. The overall effects of chemical transformation in soil are summarised in Table 5.7.

Table 5.7. Chemical transformation

	Environmental factors	Chemical factors
Factor causing increased chemical transformation	Higher: - moisture content - organic matter content (by chemical catalysis) - mineral matter content (by surface catalysis)	Higher: - chemical electrophilicity

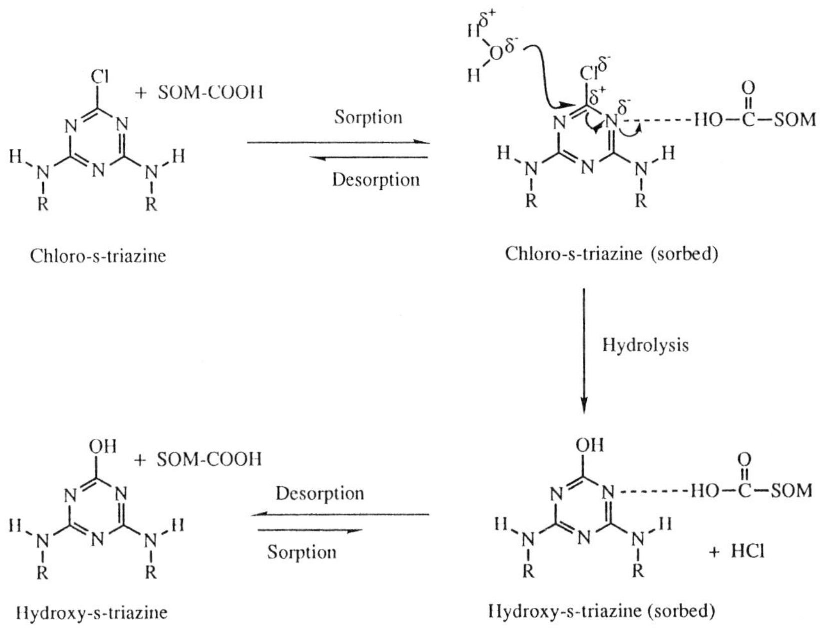

Fig. 5.8. Role of soil organic matter (SOM) in chemical transformations.

Microbial Transformations

It is now clear that the major (and sometimes only) mechanism of degradation for many pesticides in the natural environment is by microbial dissimilation (Sethunathan *et al.* 1982). The replacement of persistent pesticides with degradable varieties has often relied on the premise that microbial degradation is a most important transformation process in soil.

Interestingly, the biodegradability of certain pesticides has given rise to new problems related to stability over a required active lifetime. Recently some compounds used repeatedly in agriculture are becoming less effective as pest control agents simply because they are degraded too quickly (Racke and Coates 1988). This is due to enrichment of the microbial population at these locations with microorganisms which can either presently degrade the pesticide or which are capable of degradation after induction of the necessary enzymes.

The foundation work in this area was carried out on organochlorine herbicides such as 2,4-D, 2,4,5-T (Audus 1950; Loos 1975) which indicated that decomposition was stimulated by increases in temperature and moisture content as well as by increases in organic matter content in most soils. Classic soil perfusion experiments carried out by Audus (1950) demonstrated the microorganism-soil-chemical relationship. In these experiments chemicals were introduced into a soil perfusion apparatus and the course of chemical disappearance was studied as shown in Figure 5.9. Initially a small decrease in the concentration of the chemical is apparent as a result of soil sorption. This is followed by a lag phase during which the concentration remains relatively constant and at this stage there is very little multiplication of microorganisms. The length of this

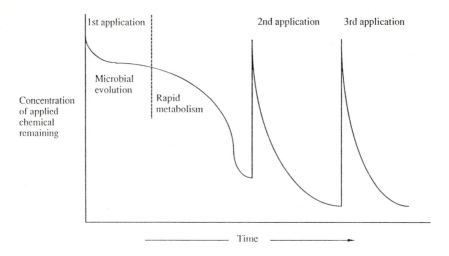

Fig. 5.9. Typical soil perfusion time course.

lag phase has been found to vary from chemical to chemical. There then ensues a period of rapid chemical disappearance which has been rationalised as a period of large biomass increase followed by metabolism of the added chemical. Subsequent applications of the chemical induce a more rapid disappearance without a lag phase.

The soil perfusion experiments demonstrate, albeit on a small scale, that some pesticides used currently in agriculture are becoming less effective with greater repetition of use. Soils exhibiting these characteristics have been called "problem soils" or "aggressive soils" and this phenomenon highlights the capacity of microorganisms to degrade a large number of structural families. This ability is the result of a range of enzymes that catalyse transformative reactions, including dehalogenases, oxygenases, and hydrolases. It is now known that enzymes capable of degrading a large number of different chemical structures are inducible in microorganisms. If the enormous diversity of microorganisms in soil is considered, then the potential for degradative activity is relatively high when compared with other sectors of the biosphere.

Microbial metabolism is environmentally dependent and the variability of degradation activity (affected by moisture content, organic matter content, pH, temperature, etc.) means that chemicals applied to soil one year may degrade faster or slower than in other years. There is usually greater biological activity in moist soils than in dry soils and thus more capacity for biodegradation to take place. In addition, water will compete with any resident chemicals sorbed onto organic or mineral matter and this will accelerate biodegradation simply on the basis of availability. It has been recognised in many tropical countries that in soils treated with pesticides accelerated biodegradation takes place under flooded conditions. This has been attributed to the concomitant increases in the number of aerobic and anaerobic bacterial populations.

Organic matter in soils has also been found to increase the rate of biodegradation and often corresponds to high native bacterial and fungal populations. This is particularly true with chlorinated pesticides such as DDT, Endrin, and Heptachlor (Castro and Yoshida 1974). Organic matter plays an important role in the adsorption and desorption processes. While organic matter may protect chemicals from the actions of some soil processes, it will not guard them from biodegradation or chemical degradation.

The effect of soil pH on biodegradation varies widely between chemical families. For example, most organophosphate pesticides have been found to undergo chemical hydrolysis in alkaline conditions with some members of that family demonstrating great instability in acidic soils (Sethunathan and MacRae 1969). Carbamate herbicides have also been found to be rapidly hydrolysed under alkali conditions (Seiber *et al.* 1978). However, there is little effect of pH on organochlorine pesticides. Many pH-related effects on degradation correspond to those variables affecting the activity of certain microorganisms or to the conditions under which certain enzymes are active.

Temperature also influences biodegradation because of its effect on microbial and enzyme activities. This phenomenon is well illustrated in the tropics where biodegradation proceeds faster than in temperate soils (Cho and Ponnamperuma 1971). The variation in temperature from season to season and with soil depth will therefore influence the rate of biodegradation.

Biodegradation is intimately associated with soil conditions that are affected by a whole host of interrelated physical, chemical and biological processes. Therefore questions related to biodegradation in soils can only be answered by taking into account the effects of these extremely complex factors. Such are the problems for researchers investigating the fate of chemicals in the environment as illustrated in Table 5.8.

Table 5.8. Microbial transformation

	Environmental factors
Factor causing increased microbial transformation	Higher: - degrading microorganism enrichment - moisture content - temperature (up to physiological limits) - pH (for certain chemicals) Lower: - pH (for certain chemicals)

Modeling of Soil Processes and Degradation of Chemicals

Introduction

Thirty to forty years ago soil-applied chemicals were subjected to only very brief laboratory investigations. Most of this research was related to determining rudimentary physico-chemical characteristics such as solubility, volatility, boiling point and melting point. The effectiveness of soil-applied chemicals was also tested either by application to field plots or by addition to more easily controlled greenhouse plots. An ignorance of the bioaccumulation phenomenon together with a recognition of the great ability of soil to dissipate chemicals led to environmental complacency amongst regulatory agencies, chemical manufacturers and consumers.

Further research into bioaccumulation and soil dispersion processes, eventually led to legislation demanding more intensive testing before release of chemicals to the market. This also stimulated the development of various models for predicting the fate of chemicals in soil. Generally, models were designed to provide a simple, rapid and inexpensive assessment of environmental fate whilst not compromising accuracy and reproducibility. However, there is no ideal model and each has specific advantages and disadvantages which limit the application. There are many varieties of models including small field plots, soil cores (e.g. lysimeters), simulation microcosms and computer simulations.

Field Methods

Initial methods to test the effectiveness of chemicals were commonly field based but following the enactment of environmental protection legislation these are now employed towards the very end of the testing regime. Once chemicals have passed the initial legislated tests in laboratories they can then (in theory) be deployed safely in the environment at predetermined dosages.

Field methods are, without a doubt, the best models for precisely determining the environmental fate of a chemical as they most closely mimic the target ecological characteristics. There are, however, several difficulties associated with these studies and perhaps the most obvious of these is the problem of cost. In order to undertake an investigation it is first necessary to locate and assess an appropriate field site. Most developed countries have undertaken systematic soil surveys providing researchers with information when choosing a field site if specific soil characteristics are required. It is then desirable to either purchase the site or seek the permission of the owner to proceed with the study. At this stage a large scale deployment of chemicals is possible, either by surface spraying or incorporation into the soil requiring specialised equipment and trained personnel. Most institutes interested in soil science or agriculture maintain and operate a number of field sites and without this type of support field studies can prove extremely expensive undertakings. In order to study the environmental effects of a chemical in a variety of different soils it may also be necessary to travel large distances adding further to the cost.

Other disadvantages of field studies are largely related to two limitations - a lack of flexibility in the system and inadequate control by the researcher. The different transformative processes operating in natural systems are very difficult to study independently in the field because of the system complexity. As the transformation products from different processes tend to be very similar it is difficult to assess the contribution of each. For example, the requirements for investigating the part played by chemical degradation during the dissimilation of a pesticide in a field system would include sterilisation of the soil to prevent biological degradation and surface screening from UV radiation to prevent photolysis. Both of these are impractical and generally this lack of flexibility in field studies reduces their appeal. They are, however, most often used to reveal the overall transformation process in soil (Nicholls et al. 1982; Walker 1989).

Despite these limitations processes such as adsorption, desorption, plant uptake, surface and sub-surface transport and volatilisation can all be studied as dynamic components in a field study to some extent (Nicholls et al. 1982; Smith and Milward 1985; Grover et al. 1988; Boesten et al. 1989; Walker et al. 1989). However, these investigations can be frustrated by the lack of control a researcher can exercise on such external interferences as the spray or drift from other chemicals in a nearby field, the effect of animal or human activities on the site, and the climatic conditions. Nonetheless, at a cost, field studies can provide the most accurate overall picture of the environmental fate of chemicals applied to soil. The advantages and disadvantages of field studies are summarised in Table 5.9.

Table 5.9. Advantages and advantages of field studies

Advantages	Disadvantages
- accuracy	- expense
	- requires specialised equipment
	- requires technical back-up
	- lack of flexibility
	- lack of control

Theoretical Methods

Theoretical methods (mathematical or computer models) are based on fundamental physical and chemical principles. In basic models these study the behaviour of the chemical under investigation as determined by its properties and activities in a described soil environment. Models of various complexities have been developed for a variety of different purposes (Jury *et al.* 1980; Jury *et al.* 1984a; Jury *et al.* 1984b; Boesten and van der Pas 1988; Nash 1989). General environmental models, which attempt to simulate the effects of combinations of these processes on chemicals applied to soil, have been formulated over the past 20 years and can very accurately simulate chemical-soil interactions. In view of the intricate systems modeled it is not surprising that they attain levels of extreme complexity.

Among the purposes of these general environmental models are predictions and monitoring of soil and groundwater contamination. The latter models include water transport (leaching) and feature algorithms which try to simulate the sub-surface flow patterns of chemicals and water caused by convective and diffusive motion. These are coupled to partitioning algorithms which attempt to simulate the distribution of the chemical between soil phases (air, water, organic carbon and mineral matter) (Mackay and Stiver 1990). The complexity of the sub-surface transport process is well acknowledged and for this reason these models tend to have the disadvantage of dealing with only "ideal" soil profiles in which soil at a certain depth is broken up into layers of assumed homogeneity. The number of these layers (which can be considered to be proportional to the number of iterations required in the model's algorithm) will dictate the level of complexity and therefore the relevance and accuracy of the model. Therefore these models are, by design, only as accurate as the theory which developed the algorithms, the soil data which is available and the information describing the chemicals. Despite this, models developed are today providing excellent simulations of the transport process (Carsel *et al.* 1984; Grenney *et al.* 1987; Jury *et al.* 1987; Barry and Sposito 1988; Padilla *et al.* 1988; Boesten *et al.* 1989; Loague *et al.* 1989; Sleep and Sykes 1989; Shaaban and ElPrince 1989; van Genuchten and Wagenet 1989; Wierenga and van Genuchten 1989). In addition, these models can be good tools for predicting potential environmental hazards beyond groundwater contamination. For example, if a model generates data describing a scenario in which volatilisation appears to predominate all other soil processes, then there is the possibility that the chemical will be subject to short or long range contaminant transport. Alternatively, if much of the chemical is shown bound to organic matter at the surface and virtually no volatilisation or sub-surface transport is indicated, there is the likelihood of a persistence problem which can be further modeled.

Models of persistence relate soil conditions (derived from soil and weather data) to chemical data over the long-term in an attempt to predict the dissipation of a chemical in a changing environment. Persistence is related to the availability of chemicals for degradation and most theoretical aspects of the soil dynamics involved in constructing these models build upon the partitioning algorithms from transport models. However, chemicals degrade in diverse ways under different conditions and therefore it has been difficult to set up general theories of environmentally dependent degradation. Most of the information on degradation is related to structural features or availability which is very difficult to quantify. Therefore the models require individual environment-dependent constants describing the susceptibility of each chemical to degradation under specific conditions. There are now several excellent examples of these models which have been developed and verified (Walker 1974; Walker 1978; Allen and Walker 1987; Jury *et al.* 1987; Monreal and McGill 1989). In addition, combinations of the transport and persistence models have been developed which give an even more complete, long-term forecast of the environmental fate of chemicals in soil (Jury *et al.* 1987; Lupi *et al.* 1988; Lupi 1989). However, they require a large body of data describing soil structure and conditions, the weather and the chemical under investigation. These models are subject to the pitfalls of each component and, as with all models, require sensitivity analysis and, ultimately, verification (Villeneuve *et al.* 1988).

Finally, because models attempt to simulate the real environment they are all inevitably compared to field studies. As distinct from field studies however, mathematical models represent complete flexibility and control (provided, of course, there is access to the data required). The simulations provided by these models are now so accurate and reliable that they are being insisted upon as a component of the registration process for agrochemicals in various countries around the world (Anon 1990)

Laboratory Methods

Early laboratory studies of soil-chemical dynamics formed the backbone from which theories of soil processes were derived. These theories were then later employed in the development of mathematical models. The investigations which produced these theories were undertaken with highly controlled microcosms for the study of specific processes. Using design modifications attempts were made to extend the uses of these microcosms to the study of the overall fate of chemicals in specified environments. The unification of these process-specific microcosms into a single, multi-purpose design has proved very challenging, as the system must be highly controllable and flexible while at the same time should generate an excellent imitation of a very complex environment. There are three basic types of model systems which could be described as laboratory methods. These are large scale lysimeters, small scale models (including columns, tanks, growth chambers and evaporation beds) and intermediate scale models such as soil core microcosms.

Lysimeters

A lysimeter is simply a column of soil of non-specific dimensions which can serve a wide variety of purposes and can be stored and maintained in different ways. These devices can be traced as far back as 1688 when De la Hire published a study on percolation of water through soil using a lysimeter (Kohnke 1968). Lysimeters, when used as models of chemical fate, are most often used as means of studying the potential of chemicals to contaminate groundwater (Kördel *et al.* 1988). They are generally large

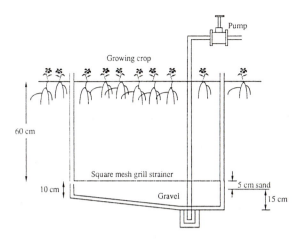

Fig. 5.10. Field lysimeter.

Table 5.10. Lysimeter characteristics

Core characteristics	-	Undisturbed soil cores (1.0 m - 1.30 m in depth ≤ 0.5 cm^2)
	-	Soil characteristics (Organic carbon ≤ 1.5%; clay < 10%; silt + clay < 30%)
Tests	-	Undertaken with radiolabelled chemical
	-	Infiltration water must be removed and analysed at least once per month
	-	Soil profile analysed in 10 cm strata for: - active ingredient - metabolites - non-extractable radioactivity
	-	Collection of climatic data, temperature profiles, precipitation distribution
Other treatment	-	In the event of low local precipitation, irrigation is required to bring in line with national precipitation average
	-	Timing of sowing, planting, plant density, fertiliser application etc should be consistent with agricultural practice

pipes stored upright in soil with specialised monitoring devices situated at the base (Fig. 5.10).

The soil which fills the lysimeter can be an intact core but more typically for large lysimeters a profile is constructed by careful addition of materials. For extremely large lysimeters, which can penetrate several metres and possess large surface areas, abstracting an intact core can prove very difficult. The lysimeter can imitate soil environments very well (if intact cores are deployed) since it is maintained in an almost identical manner to soil in a field. It also allows experimentation on intact or constructed cores of soil at a central site over long time periods (from months to years).

Since lysimeters are, by design, so similar to the real environment they possess many of the disadvantages of a field study, in particular the high cost. Despite requiring very little technical maintenance the outlay required to establish a lysimeter and the expense to remove it upon completion of the study can be prohibitive. The lysimeter is also rather inflexible, allowing only certain monitoring regimes. Time-course investigations can also be rather limited as removal of many samples will tend to disrupt the integrity of the system. However, upon completion of a study it is possible to obtain samples, thereby sacrificing the soil core to develop a very dependable "before and after" impression. Despite all the problems associated with lysimeters they are recognised legislative environmental protection tools used in pre-registration tests of many chemicals applied to soil. An example of proposed conditions for lysimeter testing of agrochemicals under German environmental protection legislation can be found in Table 5.10 (Anon 1990).

Small Scale Models

These are usually designed for studies over quite short time periods, incurring trivial costs and taking up relatively little space when compared to the lysimeter models. The development of systems which require little maintenance and which do not lead to distortion of the environment under examination (through dessication or gradual losses in microbial populations) has been very challenging. Successful devices include small scale columns (such as were used in the soil perfusion experiment described earlier) (Grenney *et al.* 1987; Wierenga and van Genuchten 1989) tanks (Albanis *et al.* 1988; Jayaraman *et al.* 1989) growth chambers (Schuphan *et al.* 1987) evaporation beds (Hodapp and Winterlin 1989) and controlled temperature chambers (Nash 1989).

The relatively small costs incurred in developing, establishing, maintaining and monitoring these systems is reflected in their simplicity and limited lifetimes. By virtue of their design they are not restricted by exposure to fixed conditions but can give the researcher almost complete and convenient control over the environment being examined. However, although very useful tools, these systems are generally not as reliable as lysimeters and thus cannot stand alone as general environmental models.

Soil Core Models

These models attempt to maximise flexibility, accuracy and control of the simulation in a system which is small in scale and cost, requires little maintenance and may be designed to run for several months. Existing models which approach these goals are essentially hybrids of all the systems discussed earlier. Three examples are discussed below in terms of design features, maintenance requirements, research potential and the advantages and disadvantages of systems. They are all essentially compromises on lysimeter systems (Gile *et al.* 1979; van Voris 1985) and are cores of soil surrounded by shells of plastic or steel which should be biologically inert (Fig. 5.11).

In microcosm 1 (Fig. 5.11(i)) (van Voris *et al.* 1985) the construction material is Driscopipe, a high molecular weight carbon black pipe used for underground pipelines that is impermeable, light weight, tough, rigid, highly resistant to acids, bases and biological degradation. These systems can duplicate and imitate all of the processes discussed earlier with the exception of surface transport. This latter factor must be studied utilising either field studies or custom built models such as that of Emmerich *et al.* (1989). The existing limitations are mostly related to scale, sampling and longevity

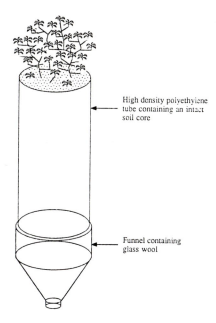

High density polyethylene
tube containing an intact
soil core

Funnel containing
glass wool

Fig. 5.11. (i) van Voris soil core microcosm.

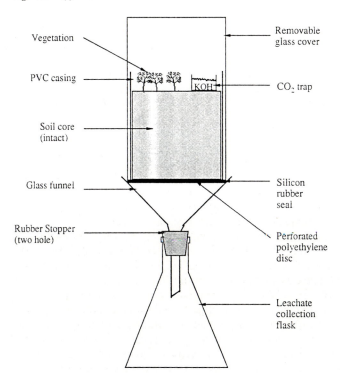

Vegetation

Removable
glass cover

PVC casing

CO_2 trap

Soil core
(intact)

Glass funnel

Silicon
rubber
seal

Rubber Stopper
(two hole)

Perforated
polyethylene
disc

Leachate
collection
flask

Fig. 5.11. (ii) Soil core microcosm.

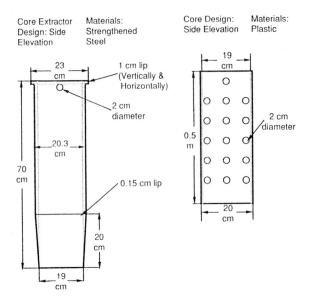

Fig. 5.11. (iii) Soil core and core extracter design.

but some of the shortcomings can be overcome by integration with computer simulations.

The failure to incorporate undisturbed soil in a microcosm is the single greatest flaw of microcosm design (van Voris *et al.* 1985). The soil systems described here are readily manipulated as a result of their size and are therefore easily extracted as an intact sample whilst also being easily stored and maintained. The relative ease of extraction when compared to lysimeters means that large numbers of the soil cores can be extracted for study. Cores can either be taken from a plot previously treated with the chemical of interest or soil samples may be taken for subsequent application in the laboratory. The temperature of the systems can be maintained with relative ease by placing them in a greenhouse, a controlled temperature cabinet or a room. The storage facility can be adapted to include such features as carefully composed artificial rainfall, boundary layer effects at the surface (by introduction of small volume air flow across the surface), photodecomposition (by illuminating with regulated UV light) and even plant uptake effects (by growing plants on the surface of the microcosm).

The systems can be monitored and sampled in a variety of ways. For example, sampling of microcosms 1 and 2 (Fig. 5.11(i) and (ii)).is achieved simply by sacrificing the core when a specimen is required. Sufficient cores can be extracted and set up such that a long term study can proceed with sufficient replication for the large number of samples required.

Microcosm 3 (Fig. 11(iii))is examined through ports drilled at specific depths. Soil samples can then be extracted as "mini-cores" which can be examined for any required chemical, physical or biological factors. The resulting holes can be repacked with soil from auxilliary cores treated and maintained in an identical way, and the ports resealed. The direct monitoring of temperature, pH, moisture content, conductivity and selective ions can be accomplished using integral electrodes (as in lysimeters). Systems such as these have tremendous potential as they can be adapted with little difficulty to study most of the processes discussed earlier. For example, by including a vapour trap on an exit port from the microcosm it may be possible to assess the extent of volatilisation. It is also possible to use these systems for purposes beyond the study of chemical fate. Microcosm 1 was originally developed for the determination of multi-species toxicity testing of fly ash. A variation on microcosm 1 has been developed as a method for studying the potential impact of genetically engineered microorganisms on nutrient dynamics in soil without release into an uncontrolled environment (Fredrickson et al. 1990).

The most obvious advantage of soil core microcosms and related systems is the financial benefit. van Voris et al. (1985) have undertaken an extensive cost-benefit analysis of the terrestrial microcosm developed for the United States Environmental Protection Agency at Battelle Pacific Northwest Laboratories. This was performed by comparison with alternative "small scale" tests and full scale field studies. Table 5.11 shows a comparison of the capabilities and characteristics of the three systems discussed to give an overall impression of their limitations and reliability. The comparative cost for a single-species bioassay is provided in Table 5.11. From this study it is clear that the system of van Voris is comparable in cost to the inexpensive "small scale" systems and considerably cheaper than a full-scale field study on a relatively small plot (1/10 acre).

Table 5.11. Comparison of experimental unit capabilities and characteristics

Characteristics of experimental unit	Experimental unit			
	Flower pot	York microcosm	van Voris microcosm	Field plot
Typical surface area	324-507 cm^2	283.5 cm^2	240.5 cm^2	10-100 m^2
Soil depth	20-25 cm^2	25-50 cm^2	60 cm^2	1-4 m
Reliable experimental period	3-6 months	6-12 months	24-48 months	decades
Reliable research cost factor [a]	3	4	5	9
Control of individual environmental factors	yes	yes	yes	no
Quality of prediction compared to field[b]	2	5	7	10
Soil temperature gradient deviation from field	major	minor	minor	none

[a] Relative cost for units and monitoring on a scale from 1 (least expensive) to 10 (most expensive)
[b] Reliability of obtained results on a scale from 1 (least reliable) to 10 (most reliable)

The effectiveness of the soil core microcosms is well documented (Gile et al. 1979; van Voris 1985; van Voris et al. 1985) demonstrating them as acceptable preliminary tools for the cost effective testing of the environmental fate of chemicals.

References

Anon (1990) Guide-lines for the testing of agrochemicals as part of the licensing procedure, Pt 4. Federal Biological Research Centre for Agriculture and Forestry, Department of Agrochemicals and Application Technology of the Federal Biological Research Centre, Braunscweig, FRG

Ajuhla LR, Lehman OR (1983) The extent and nature of rainfall-soil interaction in the release of soluble chemicals to run-off J Environ Qual 12:34-41

Albanis T, Pomonis P, Sdoukos A (1988) Describing movement of three pesticides in soil using CSTR in series model Water Air Soil Pollut 39:293-302

Allen RA, Walker A (1987) The influence of soil properties on the rates of degradation of metamitron, metazachlor, and metribuzin Pestic Sci 18:95-111

Anderson JP, Domsch HH (1980) Relationships between herbicide concentration and the rates of enzymatic degradation of 14-C Diallate and 14-C, Triallate Arch Environ Contam Toxicol 9(3):259-268

Armstrong DE, Konrad JG (1974) Nonbiological degradation of pesticides. In: Guenzi W (ed) Pesticides in soil and water. Soil Science Society of America, Madison, pp 123-31

Audus LJ (1950) Biological detoxification of 2,4-dichlorophenoxyacetic acid in soils: isolation of an effective organism Nature 166:365-67

Bailey GW, Swank RR Jnr, Nicholson HP (1974) Predicting pesticide run-off from agricultural land: A conceptual model J Environ Qual 3:95-102

Barry DA, Sposito G 1988) Application of the convection-dispersion model to solute transport in finite soil columns. Soil Sci Soc Am J 52:3-9

Biggar JW, Seiber JN (eds) (1987) Fate of pesticides in the environment. Agricultural Experiment Station, Division of Agriculture and Natural Resources, University of California, Publication 3320, Oakland Ca

Boesten JJTI, van der Pas LJT (1988) Modelling adsorption/desorption kinetics of pesticides in a soil suspension Soil Sci 146:221-231

Boesten JJTI, van der Pas LJT, Smelt JH (1989) Field test of a mathematical model for non-equilibrium transport of pesticides in soil. Pestic Sci 25:187-203

Briggs GG, Bromilow RH, Evans AA (1982) Relationships between lipophilicity and root uptake and translocation of non-ionised chemicals by barley Pestic Sci 13:495-501

Calabrese EJ, Kostecki PT (1989) Petroleum contaminated soils, vol 2 Lewis Publisher Inc, Chelsea MN, USA

Campbell R (1983) The structure and dynamics of microbial populations in soil. In: Wilkinson JF (ed) Microbial ecology, 2nd ed Blackwell Scientific Publications Ltd, Oxford

Carsel RF, Smith CH, Mulkey LA, Dean JD, Jowise PP (1984) User's manual for the pesticide root zone model, Release 1, United States Environmental Protection Agency. EPA-600/3-84-109

Castro TF, Yoshida T (1974) Effect of organic matter on the biodegradation of some organochlorine insecticides in submerged soils. Soil Sci Plant Nutr 20:363-370

Cho DY, Ponnamperuma FN (1971) Influence of soil temperature on the chemical kinetics of flooded soils and the growth of rice. Soil Sci 112: 184-190

Cohen SZ, Eiden C, Lorber MN (1986) Monitoring groundwater for pesticides in the U.S.A. In: Garner WY, Honeycutt RC, Nigg HN (eds) Evaluation of pesticides in groundwater. ACS Symposium No 315, American Chemical Society, Washington DC

Cooper KM, Tinker PB (1978) Translocation and transfer of nutrients in vesicular-arbuscular mycorrhizas, II. Uptake and translocation of phosphorus, zinc and sulfur New Phytol. 81:43-52

Crosby DG, Wong AS (1977) Environmental degradation of 2,3,7,8-tetrachlorodibenzo-p-dioxin Science 195:1337-38

Darcy H (1856) Les Fontaines Publiques de la Ville de Dijon, Dalmont, Paris

Dempster JP (1987) Effects of pesticides on wildlife and priorities in future studies. In: Brent KJ and Atkin RK (eds) Rational pesticide use. Cambridge University Press, Cambridge, pp 17-27

Eagle DJ (1983) Matching herbicide dose to soil type In: Pesticide reviews, MAFF Reference book 347. HMSO London

Emmerich WE, Woolhiser DA, Shirley ED (1989) Comparison of lumped and distributed models for chemical transport by surface runoff J Environ Qual 18:120-126

Farmer WJ, Aochi Y (1987) Chemical conversion of pesticides in the soil-water environment. In: Biggar JW and Seiber JN (eds) Proceedings of a technical seminar, Fate of pesticides in the environment. Agriculture Experiment Station, Division of Agriculture and Natural Resources, University of California, Publication 3320, pp 69-74

Frederickson JK, Bolton H, Bentjen SA, McFadden KM, Wi SW, van Voris P (1990) Evaluation of intact soil-core microcosms for determining potential impacts on nutrient dynamics by genetically engineered microorganisms Environ Toxicol Chem 9:551-558

Freeze and Cherry (1979) Groundwater. Prentice-Hall Inc, Englewood Cliffs, NJ USA

Gile JD, Collins JC, Gillet JW (1979) The soil core microcosm - A potential screening tool. United States Environmental Protection Agency Report. EPA-600/3-79-089

Goring CAI (1972) Agricultural chemicals in the environment: A quantitative viewpoint In: Goring CAI and Hamaker JW (eds) Organic chemicals in the soil environment, vol 2 Marcel Dekker Inc, NY USA pp 793-878

Green RE, Khan MA (1987) Pesticide movement in soil: Mass flow and molecular diffusion In: Biggar JW and Seiber JN (eds) Proceedings of a technical seminar, Fate of pesticides in the environment. Agricultural Research Station, Division of Agriculture and Natural Resources, University of California, Publication No 3320 pp 87-92

Grenney WJ, Caupp CL, Sims RC (1987) A mathematical model for the fate of hazardous substances in soil: model description and experimental results. Hazard. Waste Hazard. Mat 4:223-239

Grover R (1989) Environmental chemistry of herbicides, vol 1 CRC Press, Boca Raton, Fl, USA

Grover R, Smith AE, Shewchuk SR, Cessna AJ, Hunter JH (1988) Fate of trifluralin and triallate applied as a mixture to a wheat field J Environ. Qual 17:543-550

Hance RJ (1989) Adsorption and bioavailability In: Grover R (ed) Environmental chemistry of herbicides, vol 1 CRC Press, Boca Raton, Fla, pp 1 20

Hartley GS, Graham-Bryce IJ (1980) Physical principles of pesticide behaviour Vol 1 Academic Press, London

Hodapp DM, Winterlin W (1989) Pesticide Degradation in model soil evaporation beds Bull Environ Contam Toxicol. 43:36-44

Hoff RM, Dupont RR, Moore WM, McLean JE (1988) Evaluation of the use of solar radiation for the decontamination of soil residues. In: Proceedings of the 81st APCA Annual Meeting, Paper 88/6A.6 pp 45-88

Jayaraman J, Celino LP, Lee KH, Mohamad RB, Sun J, Tayaputch N, Zhang Z (1989) Fate of carbofuran in rice-fish model ecosystem - an international study. Water Air Soil Pollut 45:371-375

Jury WA, Grover R, Spencer WF, Farmer WJ (1980) Modelling vapour losses of soil-incorporated Triallate. Soil Sci Soc Am J 44:445-449

Jury WA, Farmer WA, Spencer WF (1984a) Behaviour Assessment Model for trace organics in soil: II. Chemical classification and parameter sensitivity. J Environ Qual 13:567-572

Jury WA, Farmer WF, Spencer WJ (1984b) Behviour assessment model for trace organics in soil: III. Application of screening model J Environ Qual 13:573-579

Jury WA, Focht DA, Farmer WJ (1987) Evaluation of pesticide groundwater pollution potential from standard indices of soil-chemical adsorption and biodegradation J Environ Qual 16:422-428

Kohnke H (1968) Soil physics, McGraw Hill Publishers Inc, London UK

Kördel W, Herrchen M, Klein M, Klein W (1988) Lysimeter experiments and simulation models to evaluate the potential of pesticides to leach into groundwater. Brighton crop protection conference - Pests and diseases 2:687-692

Leonard RA (1989) Herbicides in surface waters In: Grover R (ed) Environmental chemistry of herbicides, Vol 1 CRC Press, Boca Raton, Fl, USA pp 45-88

Leonard RA, Langdale GW, Fleming WG (1979) Herbicide runoff from upland Piedmont watersheds - data and implications for modeling pesticide transport. J Environ Qual 8:223-229

Loague KM, Green RE, Liu CC, Liang TC (1989) Simulation of organic chemical movement in Hawaii soils with PRZM: 1. Preliminary results for ethylene dibromide Pac Sci 43:67-95

Loos MA (1975) Herbicides - Chemistry, degradation and mode of action, Vol 1 Kearney PC, Kaufman DD (eds) Marcel Dekker, New York pp 1-128

Lupi C (1989) Modelling behaviour of pollutants in soil for risk assessment purposes, NATO challenges for a modern society 12:89-110

Lupi C, Bucchi AR, Piccioni A, Zapponi GA (1988) The environmental behaviour of chemicals in soil: atrazine as an example, Ecotoxicology and environmental safety 16:133-142

Mackay D, Stiver W (1990) Predictability of herbicide behaviour. In Grover R, Cessna AJ (eds) Environmental Chemistry of Herbicides, vol 2, CRC Press, Boca Raton, Fl, USA pp 281-297

McEwen FL, Stephenson GR (1979) The use and significance of pesticides in the environment. John Wiley and Sons Ltd, NY

Meriaux S (1982) Soil and water In: Bonneau M and Souchier B (eds) Constituents and properties of soils. Academic Press, London, pp 304-354

Miller GT (1975) Living in the environment, concepts, problems and alternatives. Wadsworth Publishers Ltd, Belmont, Calif. USA

Miller GC, Herbert VR (1987) Environmental photodecomposition of pesticides In: Biggar JW and Seiber JN (eds) Proceedings of a technical seminar, Fate of pesticides in the environment. Agricultural Experiment Station, Division of Agriculture and Natural Resources, University of California, Publication 3320, pp 75-86

Monreal CM, McGill WB (1989) Kinetic analysis of soil microbial components under perturbed and steady-state conditions in a gray luvisol. Soil Biol Biochem 21:681-688

Nakagawa M, Crosby DG (1974) Photonucleophilic reaction of nitrofen. J Agric Food Chem 22:930-33

Nash R (1989) Models for estimating pesticide dissipation in soil and vapour decline in air Chemosphere 18:2375-2381

Nicholls PH, Walker A, Baker RJ (1982) Measurement and simulation of the movement and degradation of atrazine and metribuzin in a fallow soil Pestic Sci 12:484-494

Novotny V, Chesters G (1981) Handbook of nonpoint pollution: sources and management. Environmental Engineering Ser, van Nostrand Rheinhold NY

Padilla F, LaFrance P, Robert C, Villeneuve J-P (1988) Modeling the transport and the fate of pesticides in the unsaturated zone considering temperature effects Eco Model. 44:73-88

Racke KD, Coates JR (1988) Enhanced degradation and the comparative fate of carbamate insecticides in soil. J Agric Food Chem 36:1067-1072

Rao PSC, Jessup RE, Davidson JM (1989) Mass flow and dispersion In: Grover, R. (ed) Environmental chemistry of herbicides, Vol 1 CRC Press, Boca Raton, Fla pp 21-44

Ritchie JT, Kissel DE, Burnett E (1972) Water movement in undisturbed swelling clay soil. Soil Sci Soc Am Proc 36:874-79

Ruzo LO (1982) Photochemical reactions of the synthetic pyrethroids. In: Hutson DH and Roberts TR (eds) Progress in pesticide chemistry. John Wiley and Sons Ltd pp 1-33

Schuphan I, Scharer E, Heise M, Ebing W (1987) Use of laboratory model ecosystems to evaluate quantitatively the behaviour of chemicals. In Pesticide Science Biotechnology, Proc Int Cong Pestic Chem 6th, pp 437-444

Seiber JN (1987) Solubility, partition coefficient and bioconcentration factor. In: Biggar JW and Seiber JN (eds) Fate of pesticides in the environment. Agricultural Experiment Station, Division of Agriculture and Natural Resources, University of California, Publication 3320, Oakland, Ca pp 53-59

Seiber JN, Cathan MP, Berril CR (1978) Loss of carbofuran from rice paddy water: Chemical and physical factors. J Environ Sci Health 13B: 131-140

Sethunathan N, MacRae IC (1969) Persistence and biodegradation of diazanon in submerged soils. J Agric Food Chem 17:221-225

Sethunathan N, Adhya TK, Raghu K (1982) Microbial degradation of pesticides in tropical soils In: Matsumura F and Krishna-Murti CR (eds) Biodegradation of pesticides. Plenum Press, New York NY pp 89-109

Shaaban Z, ElPrince AM (1989) A simulation model for the fate of pesticide residues in a field soil Plant and Soil 114:187-195

Sleep BE, Sykes JF (1989) Modelling the transport of volatile organics in variably saturated media. Water Resources Res 25:81-92

Smith AE (1988) Transformations in soil. In: Grover R (ed) Environmental chemistry of herbicides, Vol 1 CRC Press, Boca Raton, Fla pp 171-200

Smith AE, Milward LJ (1985) Loss of the herbicide Triallate from a clay soil containing aged a freshly applied residues Bull Contam Toxicol 35:723-728

Smith CN, Leonard RA, Langdale GW, Bailey GW (1978) Transport of agricultural chemicals from small upland Piedmont watersheds, US Environmental Protection Agency Rep EPA-600/3-78-056, US Government Printing Office, Washington DC

Spencer WF (1987) Volatilisation of pesticide residues In: Biggar JW and Seiber JN (eds) Proceedings of a technical seminar, Fate of pesticides in the environment. Agricultural Research Station, Division of Agriculture and Natural Resources, University of California, Publication No 3320 pp 61-68

Sunstrom G, Ruzo LO (1978) Photochemical transformation of pollutants in water. Pergamon Ser Environ Sci 1:205-22

Taylor AW, Glotfelty DE (1988) Evaporation from soil and crops In: Grover R (ed) Environmental chemistry of herbicides, vol 2 CRC Press, Boca Raton, Fla pp 89-130

van der Zweep J (1960) The persistence of some important herbicides in the soil. In: Woodford EK and Sagar GR (eds) Herbicides and the soil. Blackwell Scientific Publication, Oxford pp 79-86

van Genuchten MT, Wagenet RJ (1989) Two-site/Two-region models for pesticide transport and degradation: theoretical development and analytical solutions. Soil Sci Soc Am J 53:1303-1309

van Voris P (1985) Experimental terrestrial soil-core microcosm test protocol, United States Environmental Protection Agency Report EPA/600/3-85/047, USEPA, Corvallis Or

van Voris P, Tolle DA, Arthur MF, Chesson J (1985) Terrestrial microcosms: Applications, validation and cost-benefit analysis. In Cairns J (ed) Multispecies Toxicity Testing. Pergamon Press Ltd, NY, pp 117-142

Villeneuve J-P, LaFrance P, Banton O, Frechette P, Robert C (1988) A sensitivity analysis of adsorption and degradation parameters in the modelling of pesticide transport in soils. J Contam Hydrology 3:77-96

Wadleigh CH, Dyal RS (1970) In: Blesser RE (ed) Agronomy and health ASA Spec Publ No. 16 pp 9-19

Walker A (1973) Vertical distribution of herbicides in soil and their availability to plant: treatment of different proportions of the total root system. Weed Res 13:416-421

Walker A (1974) A simulation model for prediction of herbicide persistence. J Environ Qual 3:396-401

Walker A (1978) Simulation of the persistence of eight soil-applied herbicides. Weed Res 18:305-313

Walker A, Cotterill EG, Welch SJ (1989) Adsorption and degradation of chorsulfuron and metsulfuron-methyl in soils from different depths. Weed Res. 29:281-287

Wauchope RD (1978) The pesticide content of surface water draining from agricultural fields: A review. J Environ Qual 7:459-470

White RE (1985) The influence of macropores on the transport of dissolved and suspended matter through soil. Adv Soil Sci 3:95-120

Wierenga PJ, van Genuchten MT (1989) Solute transport through small and large unsaturated soil columns Groundwater 27:35-42

Chapter 6

The Effects of Sorption on the Bioavailability of Pesticides

G. K. Sims, M. Radosevich, X. T. He and S. J. Traina

Introduction

Despite extensive efforts to reduce the risks associated with agricultural chemicals, 39 pesticides have now been detected in groundwater from 34 states or provinces in the United States (Hallberg 1989). These discoveries have precipitated increased research emphasis on factors controlling transport of pesticides to groundwater. Perhaps much of the subsurface contamination resulted from localised direct contamination of individual wells, however the possibility remains that properly applied pesticides leached through soils in the absence of any predisposing factors such as uncapped wells, discontinuities in soil structure, etc.

Since clean-up of contaminants in groundwater may be extremely difficult and expensive, strategies for preventive action appear to be the best solution to groundwater contamination. There is great need, therefore, for more precise quantification of the susceptibility of pesticides to leach through soil (particularly subsoil) and to understand the factors affecting the persistence of pesticides *in situ*.

Dissipation of Pesticides in the Environment

A number of processes contribute to the ultimate fate of pesticides and other contaminants that find their way into the environment. These processes can be divided into two major groups which are summarised in Table 6.1. Of these processes, leaching, or more generally transport has received much attention recently. For more information on components of environmental fate, see Wolfe *et al.* (1990), Bollag and Liu (1990); Taylor and Spencer (1990) and Mackay and Betts, chapter 5 this volume. Pesticide transport in soils consists primarily of three physical processes: mass flow, dispersion, and sorption. These transport processes in turn are influenced by soil properties such as soil water content, bulk density, tortuosity, and dispersivity, as well as compound properties, including relative polarity or partition coefficient, and persistence or resistance to chemical or biological degradation. Of these factors, perhaps the most important influences on the fate of pesticides in soils are:

1) mobility of the compounds (described primarily by sorptivity), and
2) the compounds' relative resistance to decomposition (Jury *et al.* 1987).

Numerous reviews have recently addressed various aspects of transport of organic chemicals through soil (Alexander and Scow 1989; Bollag and Liu 1990; Bouchard *et al.* 1989; Carsel 1989; Harmon *et al.* 1989; Sawhney 1989; Weber and Miller 1989).

Table 6.1. A list of the major processes controlling the environmental fate of pesticides in soils

Transfer processes		Transformation processes	
1	Volatilisation	1	Microbial degradation
2	Leaching	2	Plant metabolism
3	Sorption/desorption	3	Chemical (abiotic) hydrolysis
4	Plant uptake	4	Photodegradation

Not all pesticides have pronounced tendency to be transported, as evidenced by absence of many pesticides in groundwater. Much attention has therefore been focused on contributions of compound properties (especially sorptivity and biodegradability) as they contribute to transport. Of particular interest has been the interaction of sorption and biodegradation processes, as it appears the interaction of the two processes rather than the processes alone actually determines persistence and mobility and thus ultimately controls transport. Herein, the effects of sorption on biodegradation of pesticides were the subject of review.

Sorption Mechanisms

Sorption mechanisms can be divided into the two broad categories, adsorption and partitioning. According to Chiou (1989), adsorption refers to the condensation of vapors or solutes by physical or chemical bonding forces, whereas partitioning denotes uptake in which the sorbed organic chemical permeates into the network of an organic medium by forces common to solution (e.g. van der Waals forces).

Adsorption can be further delineated from partitioning by the presence of competitive interactions when two or more adsorbing species are present. In reality, interactions between organic solutes and soil mineral and organo-mineral complexes are very complex. It is likely that a variety of mechanisms are responsible for the retention of any particular organic solute in a given system. As a result, the more general term sorption is used to describe retention with no distinction between the specific process of adsorption or partitioning. For sorption to occur, the net free energy change associated with the reaction must be negative:

$$dG = dH - TdS.$$

Given this relationship, sorption can be driven by changes in either enthalpy, entropy, or both (Hassett and Banwart 1989). The forces driving these mechanisms arise from bonding interactions between the sorbate and sorbent and interactions between the solute and solvent.

Enthalpy Driven Mechanisms

Ionic bonds may form between positively or negatively charged organic molecules and soil surfaces. Adsorption by this mechanism is more common for cationic pesticides due to the predominance of negatively charged sites on soil colloids. Paraquat and diquat, which contain permanent positive charges, are good examples of pesticides adsorbed by cation exchange (Koskinen and Harper 1990). Ionisable pesticides such as 2,4-D, picloram and s-triazines can also be ionically bound depending upon the pH of the medium (Hance 1988). Pyridine is also sorbed by an ionic mechanism.

A related process, ligand exchange, is an inner sphere complex that forms when a negatively charged organic functional group displaces a weaker ligand (usually an inorganic hydroxyl or water) at the surface of metal oxides and hydroxides. Partially chelated transition metals on clays and humic acids are also potential sites for binding of pesticides by ligand exchange. This mechanism has been proposed for the adsorption of triazines, substituted ureas, aminotriazole, and EPTC (Calvet, 1980).

Charge transfer is best described as a partial exchange of electrons when the pi orbitals and/or lone electron pairs of an electron-rich and an electron-deficient molecule overlap. This produces a resonance structure between donor and acceptor. The hydrogen bond is a special case of charge transfer occurring between electropositive H atoms and exposed electron pairs of electronegative atoms. Bonds of this type include -OH..O-, -OH..N-, -NH..O-, and -NH..N-. Essentially all pesticides contain substituents capable of forming hydrogen bonds.

Interactions between a charged ion and a neutral molecule with a permanent dipole moment are called ion (charge)- dipole interactions. Ions can also interact with neutral molecules with zero dipole moment. When a charge is brought near a molecule with zero dipole moment, the symmetrical electronic distribution can be distorted thus inducing a dipole moment. Some large organic molecules are easily polarised in this way, however, interactions of this type are purely speculative in the context of pesticide adsorption (Hance 1988). A transient dipole may also induce a dipole moment in a neighboring molecule causing a weak, short range electrostatic attraction (Koskinen and Harper 1990).

Entropy Driven Mechanisms (Partitioning)

The uptake of nonionic organic solutes by soil organic matter is made thermodynamically favourable by the gain in entropy produced when the organic solute is ejected from the aqueous phase (Traina and Onken 1991). The reaction is furthered by the attractive "solvation" forces between the solute and the organic matter matrix. Partitioning mechanisms have been extensively reviewed by Chiou (1989) and Hassett and Banwart (1989). The available data indicate that the degree to which nonionic organic pollutants are sorbed by partitioning in soils is strongly influenced by the amount of organic matter present and the water solubility of the compound (Gerstl and Yaron 1983; Loux et al. 1989a; Chiou 1989; Walker et al. 1989). Sorption is typically described by a distribution coefficient, K_d, which can be described as follows:

$$K_d = [X\text{-soil}]/[X] \tag{1}$$

where [X-soil] is the equilibrium concentration of the compound sorbed per unit quantity of soil and [X] is the equilibrium concentration of the organic solute remaining in solution. The distribution coefficient is commonly normalised to the total organic carbon content of the soil defining a new constant, K_{oc} as follows:

$$K_{oc} = K_d/f_{oc} \tag{2}$$

where f_{oc} is the mass fraction of organic carbon in the soil. The K_{oc} is usually obtained from a regression of K_d on f_{oc}.

The K_{oc} of a nonpolar organic compound can be estimated by its water solubility (S_w) versus its solubility in an organic solvent (Chiou 1989). This is readily apparent when one examines the relationship between K_{oc} and the octanol/water partition coefficient (K_{ow}), which is defined as the ratio of the concentration of the solute in the octanol and aqueous phases after partition equilibrium has been reached. Experimentally obtained data for a wide range of organic compounds and pesticides with different soils and sediments have demonstrated a linear relationship between log K_{oc} and K_{ow} (Hassett et al. 1983; Chiou et al. 1983). The general form of the equation is:

$$\log K_{oc} = a \log K_{ow} + b \tag{3}$$

where a and b are empirically determined constants. A typical regression equation (Hassett et al. 1983) follows:

$$\log K_{oc} = 0.909(\log K_{ow}) + 0.088 \tag{4}$$

It is possible to normalise the partition coefficient to the soil organic matter content to derive a new term, K_{om}. For organic matter containing 58% carbon, $K_{oc} = 1.72\ K_{om}$ (Chiou 1989). Again, a linear relationship can be developed with appropriate empirically determined constants (Chiou et al. 1983).

$$\log K_{om} = 0.904(\log K_{ow}) - 0.779 \tag{5}$$

While the partition coefficient (K_{oc} or K_{om}) is linearly related to the octanol/water coefficient (K_{ow}), it is inversely related to the solute water solubility (S_w) (Chiou 1989; Hassett and Banwart 1989). From a compilation of the available data, Hassett et al. (1983) obtained the following equation:

$$\log K_{oc} = -0.62(\log S_w\ \text{mg L}^{-1}) + 3.95\ (r^2 = 0.86) \tag{6}$$

A similar expression was developed for the relationship between log K_{om} and log S_w (Chiou et al. 1983).

$$\log K_{om} = -0.729 \log S_w + 0.001\ (r^2 = 0.996) \tag{7}$$

The relationships between K_{oc} and K_{ow}, and K_{oc} and S_w are illustrated in Figure 6.1.

It is important to note that partitioning applies primarily to nonionic organic molecules where sorption to inorganic soil surfaces is minimal. It is assumed that,

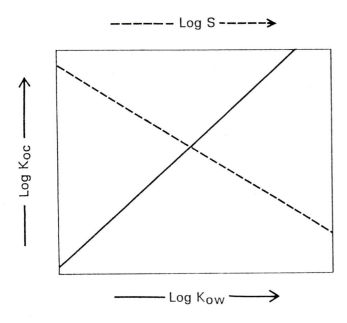

Fig. 6.1. Typical relationships between K_{oc} and K_{ow} and K_{oc} and S_w. Figure is modelled after Hasset and Banwart (1989). See that reference for a thorough review of the topic.

little sorption of nonionic organic solutes occurs on inorganic mineral surfaces due to the inability of these compounds to compete with water molecules for available adsorption sites (Chiou 1989).

Biological Degradation of Pesticides

Biological degradation is a major route for dissipation of most pesticides from the environment. Organisms responsible for pesticide biodegradation are largely bacteria and fungi. They may be involved actively, catalyzing extensive degradation of the pesticides, or passively, with one or more members of the community carrying out simple, gratuitous transformations. Degradation pathways may be either inducible or constitutively expressed. The collective effects of these transformations may result in conversion to either a stable or a readily metabolised product, and the products may be more or less toxic and more or less mobile than the parent compound. The time required for substantial biological degradation of pesticides is extremely variable, requiring days for some compounds such as the case of accelerated degradation of carbamothioates (Obrigawitch *et al.* 1983) to years for others, such as DDT. The relative susceptibility of a pesticide to biodegradation appears to be an intrinsic property of the compound, depending upon structural features, such as degree of halogenation. For more information on structure-biodegradability relationships, see Atlas and Bartha (1987) and Engesser and Fischer chapter 2 this volume. For examples of structure biodegradation experiments, see Alexander and Lustigman (1966), Sims and Sommers (1985; 1986).

Bioavailability of Sorbed/Bound Pesticides

Conventional wisdom suggests that most substances taken up from soil systems will come from the aqueous free pool rather than complexed or sorbed forms. As a general rule, sorption/complexation reduces availability of inorganic and organic species for uptake. For example, depending upon the exchange capacity, type of clay mineral, and distribution of cations, metals such as calcium held on exchange sites may be relatively unavailable to plants or microorganisms (Brady 1990). Similarly, uptake of pesticides by plants may depend on whether the compounds are sorbed to the soil matrix. Often, bioactivity of herbicides has been inversely correlated with sorption, which was in turn positively correlated with organic carbon content. Such was the case with alachlor, metolachlor (Peter and Weber 1985 a), imazaquin (Loux et al. 1989b; Basham et al. 1987), imazethapyr (Loux et al. 1989b), fluridone (Shea and Weber 1983), metribuzin (Peter and Weber 1985b), trifluralin, butralin (Peter and Weber 1985c), and a host of other pesticides. Such relationships are so common that herbicide application rates are often adjusted to soil organic carbon content.

Toxicity of substances introduced internally may also be affected by sorption. For example, uptake, toxicological effects, and induction of detoxification pathways (aryl hydrocarbon hydrolase) in guinea pigs were inversely related to organic matter content of TCDD-contaminated soils collected from Times Beach, MO, USA (Umbreit et al. 1986). Bioavailability of aromatic hydrocarbons, such a benzo[a]pyrene to benthic organisms was negatively related to sorption of the compounds to sediments (Varanasi et al. 1985). It is generally accepted therefore that substances in the sorbed phase are unavailable to higher organisms, unless released into the aqueous free pool.

There is growing evidence indicating that sorption of organic compounds by soil can also inhibit microbial degradation, implying that even microorganisms are unable to access sorbed materials (O'Loughlin et al. 1988; Mihelcic and Luthy 1988). Thus, the desorption kinetics of sorbed residues may ultimately control bioavailability and as a result, persistence of the compounds in nature. Much sorption and biodegradation data are available, unfortunately few authors have treated the two processes simultaneously. Furthermore, most of the data available were taken from correlations of soil properties with degradation rate, rather than direct measurement of sorption or desorption and degradation together. In order to satisfy the need for accurate modeling of the fate of organic contaminants in subsurface environments, we need a more complete understanding of the factors controlling bioavailability.

Perhaps the role of bioavailability in biodegradation has been demonstrated most clearly in modelling studies. Biodegradation of dinoseb was most adequately described by a model that accounted for dinoseb sorption (Stevens et al. 1990). Numbers of soil bacteria and nitrate-N (an inhibitor of dinoseb degradation) were also good predictors of biodegradation rates. Degradation of 2,4-D in soil was best described by a model that assumed the sorbed material was completely protected from biological degradation (Ogram et al. 1985). A two compartment model (describing a system containing a slowly accessible pool, such as a sorbed phase) provided the curve of best fit for mineralisation of low concentrations of phenol, aniline, and nitrotriacetic acid (Scow et al. 1986). Using an intra-aggregate radial diffusion model, Mihelcic and Luthy (1988) predicted that sorption would affect biodegradation rate by lowering the solution concentration of substrate available to the organism. The effect was thought to be more pronounced on very hydrophobic compounds since sorption/desorption equilibrium would probably be slower (Wu and Gschwend 1986).

Supplementing soil or water with substances capable of sorbing pesticides has been used frequently to assess the effects of sorption on degradation rate. Addition of activated carbon to soil containing ^{14}C-labelled maleic hydrazide increased the time required for degradation of the compound (Helweg 1975). Addition of charcoal to soil decreased degradation rates of either atrazine or chlorthiamid, but had little effect on linuron breakdown (Moyer *et al.* 1972). Also, added montmorillonite increased persistence of all three pesticides, even though sorption of linuron was unaffected by addition of the clay mineral. Treating soil with activated charcoal prevented degradation of DNOC whereas endothal degradation was unaffected (Helweg 1969). Adding filter ash eliminated degradation of monolinuron in soil (Suss *et al.* 1972) and persistence of both atrazine and DNOC was increased by the addition of straw ash to soil (Hurle 1978).

Much correlative data have been presented to support the hypothesis that increased sorption may reduce biodegradation rates. Degradation rates for several pesticides appeared to be related to the organic matter content, clay content, pH, or other factors determining the degree of sorption of pesticides to soil matrices. For example, degradation rates for chlorsulfuron and metsulfuron-methyl were negatively correlated with soil pH, whereas sorption was positively correlated with soil pH (Walker *et al.* 1989). In this case, microbial biomass was considered to be a major factor in degradation rates. Paraquat became unavailable when sorbed by soil colloids, and biodegradation rates were extremely slow (Fryer *et al.* 1975; Calderbank and Slade 1976). Sorption of imazaquin to clay and organic matter apparently increased the persistence of the pesticide in the field (Basham *et al.* 1987). Loss of clomazone was more rapid in a soil of lower sorptive capacity, however the availability of the compound to plants was also greater, leading to injury of subsequently planted sensitive crops (Loux *et al.* 1989b). Half lives of simazine, atrazine, propazine, and terbuthylazine increased with increased sorption in soil (Burkhard and Guth 1980).

Sorption effects on biodegradation have also been demonstrated in experiments with nutrient solutions, and occasionally with pure cultures of microorganisms. Weber and Coble (1968) noted that sorption of diquat to kaolinite did not affect degradation rates in nutrient solution, but in the presence of montmorillonite degradation was proportional to the aqueous concentration of the pesticide. Desorption kinetics may have explained discrepancies between the kaolinite and montmorillonite systems better than quantities sorbed. Similar results have been reported for compounds sorbed by partitioning reactions. Toluene sorbed to an organic soil was apparently rapidly desorbed, and was available to acclimated microorganisms, however the authors noted a residual pool which was slowly desorbed from the soil and was slowly degraded by the microorganisms (Robinson *et al.* 1990).

In our laboratory, a preliminary experiment was performed to determine the effect of adsorption on pyridine biodegradation by *Micrococcus luteus* (not previously published). *M. luteus* is capable of growth on pyridine as a sole source of carbon, nitrogen, and energy (Sims *et al.* 1986). The disappearance of pyridine with time was monitored by uv-visible spectrophotometry after the cells were introduced into flasks where pyridine was equilibrated with hectorite or hectorite coated with tetramethyl ammonium (TMA) ions (50% of the cation exchange capacity of the hectorite was saturated with TMA). The system pH was controlled at 5.3, 6.1, and 7.1, respectively. For comparison, pyridine degradation in growth medium was also monitored. As shown in Figure 6.2, the pyridine degradation at pH 7.1 was rapid (complete degradation in about a day) and the degradation rate was essentially the same with or without added clay. This was expected, because at this pH, less than 20% of the

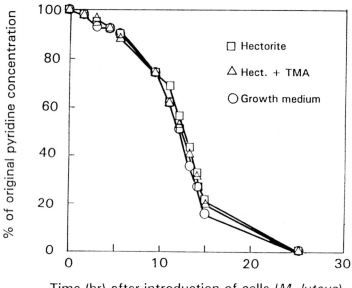

Fig. 6.2. Degradation of pyridine by *Micrococcus luteus* in medium at pH 7.1. The organism was grown in nutrient solution with pyridine as the sole carbon source. Pyridine degradation was measured by uv-visible spectroscopy.

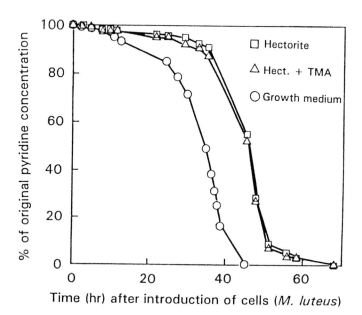

Fig. 6.3. Degradation of pyridine by *Micrococcus luteus* in medium at pH 6.1. The organism was grown in nutrient solution with pyridine as the sole carbon source. Pyridine degradation was measured by uv-visible spectroscopy.

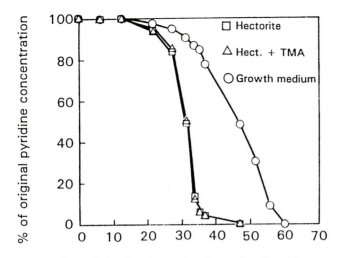

Fig. 6.4. Degradation of pyridine by *Micrococcus luteus* in medium at pH 5.3. The organism was grown in nutrient solution with pyridine as the sole carbon source. Pyridine degradation was measured by uv-visible spectroscopy.

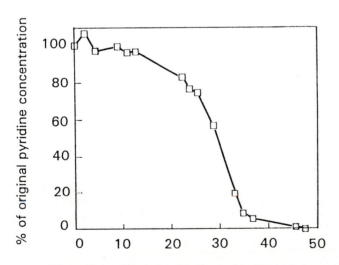

Fig. 6.5. Degradation of pyridine by *Micrococcus luteus* in medium at pH 7.1. Effect of adding a smectite-humic acid complex. The organism was grown in nutrient solution with pyridine as the sole carbon source. Pyridine degradation was measured by uv-visible spectroscopy.

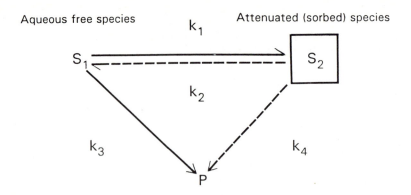

Fig. 6.6. Representation of a two compartment model described by Scow *et al*. (1986). The term S_2 (enclosed in box) represents a sorbed or inaccessible compartment. Note that k_2 and k_4 are rate constants for back reactions, both of which are thought to be either slow or unlikely. Assuming the direct uptake of material from S_2 by the organism does not occur (rate constant k_4 drops out), then the rate constant k_2 becomes the most critical value (the rate limiting step becomes desorption).

pyridine was adsorbed by the clay (based on sorption isotherms). At pH 6.1, pyridine degradation was considerably slower in the presence of clay as can be seen in Figure 6.3. At this pH, approximately 40% of the pyridine was adsorbed to the clay. However, at pH 5.3, when most of the pyridine (>50%) was sorbed, pyridine degradation was enhanced in the presence of clay (Fig. 6.4). Since *M. luteus* is sensitive to acidity, the clay may have protected the organism from the effects of low pH. Alternatively, more cells were adsorbed on the clay at low pH, placing the organism in close proximity to the sorbed substrate. In another experiment, degradation of pyridine was monitored in the presence of smectite-humic acid complexes containing about 3% organic carbon. The result is shown in Figure 6.5. At pH 7.1, pyridine degradation was completed within 50 h, which was twice as long as that observed previously in the growth medium either with or without added hectorite. But at lower pH (5.3 or 6.1), pyridine degradation was almost totally stopped (data not shown). Though these data suggest sorption effects on pyridine biodegradation, the possibility of toxic effects from the humic acid should not be overlooked. Similar effects were reported for biodegradation of naphthalene sorbed to TMA-hectorite (Kehrmeyer *et al.* 1990). The mechanism of retention in this case was by non-polar interactions, as naphthalene did not interact with unsubstituted (no TMA) clays. In these experiments, degradation rates as well as bacterial growth rates were significantly reduced as the TMA content of the clays was increased. Toxic effects of TMA on the organism were accounted for by examining growth on a non-sorbing substrate in the presence and absence of TMA-clay.

Sorption of Microorganisms to Soils

Stimulatory rather than inhibitory effects on biodegradation of added sorbants might be expected if microbes were sorbed to surfaces, and thus placed in close proximity to a sorbed compound (Ogram *et al.* 1985). Some experimental evidence suggests that immobilisation or sorption of microorganisms or enzymes may alter their activities.

For example, Hattori and Hattori (1987) demonstrated that the optimum pH for aerobic respiration was shifted upward in the presence of an exchange resin that immobilised cells of *M. luteus* or *Pseudomonas fluorescens*. The authors used both glucose and succinate (poor adsorbers) as substrates. Recall that in the previous section, we reported enhanced degradation of pyridine by sorbed cells at low pH. Growth rate and biotransformation of dehydroabietic acid, abietic acid, and isopimaric acid by *Mortierella isabellina* was retarded by the presence of a polyurethane support (Kutney et al. 1988). It was not possible to ascertain whether this effect was due to sorption of the substrate, diffusional constraints of nutrients through the foam or other limitations imposed by the foam. Conversely, Ogram et al. (1985) reported that sorbed and free cells degraded 2,4-D with almost equal efficiencies (based on results of modelling). Marshman and Marshall (1981) examined the effects of montmorillonite on the growth of mixed cultures of microorganisms. The authors found that the effects depended on the kinds of microorganisms, the substrates used, and the concentration of montmorillonite used. The authors proposed a mathematical description of the system in order to unravel the multiple effects of clay on the organisms.

The effects of sorption or attachment of cells on their ability to mediate biodegradation remain unclear, but may play an important role in the fate of organic compounds in nature. The most obvious effect of cell attachment on bioavailability is the resulting proximity of cells to the substrate of interest. Proximity to the sorption site can be a key factor in the ability of a particular cell to deplete the surface of sorbed material. This can be depicted by imagining the effects of moving a cell away from the source of a substrate, and examining the change in time required for diffusion of the material to the cell. Considering movement in only one dimension, if the molecule has a diffusion coefficient of 10^{-6} cm^2 s^{-1} and has only to move the length of the cell (10^{-4} cm) by diffusion from the surface, the time required will be:

$$dt = x^2/2D = 10^{-8} \text{ cm}^2/2 \times 10^{-6} \text{ cm}^2 \text{ s}^{-1} = 5 \text{ ms} \qquad (8)$$

However, if the distance is increased to 100 cell lengths (a reasonable distance in many soil pores), this time is increased to 50 seconds. Thus if both the cell and the substrate are sorbed to the same site, degradation rates should be enhanced, whereas fixing cells to a position distant from the substrate should retard degradation. A rather glamorous experiment would be required to prove this point. However, differences in the surface chemistry between microorganisms and their substrates might very well result in their sorption to different sites.

One factor that has been virtually ignored in bioavailability studies is the possibility of chemotactic movement of cells to the sorbant, which should become in such experiments a traceable point source of substrate. That many bacteria are chemotactic, and many fungi chemotropic is a well established fact. Chemotaxis of *Pseudomonas* to aromatic substrates has been clearly documented (Harwood et al. 1984). The role of chemotaxis in biodegradation in nature however remains completely unexplored.

Bound Residues

Pesticide dissipation/metabolism studies often uncover the presence of substantial quantities of unextractable pesticide carbon. It may be difficult to explain such "bound residues" by adsorption or partitioning reactions. Perhaps much of the material is sterically shielded from degradation by sorption or diffusion into inaccessible microsites

(Alexander 1965; Pignatello 1989). For example, EDB residues persisted in soil even though freshly added material was rapidly degraded (Steinberg *et al.* 1987). The authors noted that grinding the soil enhanced release of residual EDB into solution. EDB, which is highly volatile would be expected to diffuse into every available site given enough time.

In some cases, bound residues may best be described by some kind of coupling of the pesticide to humic materials. The pesticides may be either incorporated into humic materials during polymer formation, or may be bound to the surface of the existing humic materials Dec *et al.* (1990). Bollag (1983) reviewed literature on oxidative coupling of aromatic compounds to soil organic matter. In general, these reactions differ from sorptive reactions in the formation of covalent bonds that are much more stable than the weak interactions usually involved in sorption. In these cases, soil organic constituents (humic materials) must be decomposed in order to release the bound pesticide. The pesticide molecule may also be degraded during its release. Dec et al (1990) showed that 2,4-dichlorophenol was susceptible to slow microbial degradation when bound to humic acid or incorporated into synthetic humic materials. Hsu and Bartha (1974) immobilised radiolabelled 3,4-dichloroaniline by formation of a humic acid complex. This material was exposed to a soil community and pure cultures of two soil fungi. The radiolabel was released from the soil as carbon dioxide at a rate of 1% per week. *Penicillium frequentans* depolymerised the humic material releasing oligomers containing substantial amounts of radioactivity. *Aspergillus versicolor* mineralised the aniline rings, indicating the organism was able to completely degrade the bound pesticide.

The results of these studies demonstrated that even pesticides incorporated into humic acid structures can ultimately be degraded by soil microorganisms. Though oxidative coupling or other forms of incorporation of pesticides into humic material has been offered as explanation for the formation of bound residues, in most cases proof of the bonding mechanism was not available. Of the studies available, by far the best documented mechanisms of bound residue formation have been the coupling of anilines and phenols to humic materials. Pesticides generally are not screened for propensity to undergo oxidative coupling, and bound residues are usually examined by destructive techniques (dissolution of humic materials in base), thus little is known of the real role of oxidative coupling (or even diffusion into microsites) in the formation of bound residues.

A New Generation of Pesticides

Historically, pesticides have been applied to crops at rates approaching hundreds of grams to one or more kgha[-1]. Recently, more bioactive substances, such as the sulfonylureas can be extremely effective when applied to foliage at rates on the order of a few gha[-1]. Such low doses of pesticidal material may pose a minimal threat to the environment, particularly if the materials are rapidly degraded or inactivated in soil. Of course, few if any man made products are completely free of problems. For example, documenting dissipation of low dose pesticides, which may be bioactive at concentrations approaching sensitivity limits for instrumentation becomes a major challenge.

In the context of this review, one of the most interesting challenges will be facing a change of thinking that may be necessary to understand interaction of microorganisms with such trace quantities of pesticides. In other words, how or why do microorganisms degrade these materials? For example, metsulfuron is used foliarly at rates of about 3 gha^{-1}. Assuming all of the applied material eventually reached the soil and penetrated uniformly to a depth of 10 cm, there would be 3 mgm^{-3} of the pesticide in the soil. Assuming a molecular weight of 381 for the methylated form of the pesticide, the soil would contain 0.00787 mmoles of the pesticide/m^3 or 7.87 10^{-9} mmole cm^{-3}. Assuming a pore space of 50% with all pores completely water filled, all of the pesticide should be in half of the soil volume, thus the concentration in the pore space should be 15.74 10^{-9} mmole cm^{-3}. Assuming an average pore volume of 4.1 μm^3, each microorganism, or microcolony might *on the average* be confined to this pore volume (obviously colonies would require a larger pore than this). Therefore *on the average*, microbes may have access to 6.45 X 10^{-20} mmole pore^{-1}. Similarly, a pore with a volume of 1 μm^3 might contain 1.574 X 10^{-20} mmoles of the compound whereas a pore 1 mm^3 in volume would contain 1.574 X 10^{-17} mmoles. This represents a range of about one to 1000 molecules (Avagadros number= 6.022 X 10^{-20} molecules per mmole) available to microbes in pores between 1μm^3 and 1mm^3 in volume. Such low concentrations clearly would support little or no growth. It seems doubtful that such concentrations would supply sufficient pressure for an induction response to occur, especially if the pesticide itself served as the energy source for *de novo* protein synthesis. Neidhardt *et al.* (1990) proposed that approximately 2 X 10^4 μmol of high energy phosphate bonds might be required to synthesise the protein in a gram of bacterial cells. If for example an enzyme involved in biodegradation represented 0.01 % of the cells total complement of protein, approximately 2 μmol of high energy phosphate might be required for *de novo* synthesis of the protein in a gram of cells. Assuming a cell mass of 1.5 X 10^{-12} g per cell, about 2000 molecules of high energy phosphate would be required for an induction response to increase protein content by 0.01% in a single cell. Thus microbial *response* to low dose compounds appears unlikely (but perhaps not impossible if fueled with another energy source), suggesting that gratuitous transformations (such as cometabolism) would be the dominant or only route for biodegradation. Whether degradation of low dose pesticides proceeds by passive or active mechanisms, it is almost certain that if any sorption of these compounds occurs, the resulting soil solution will contain very little material indeed. Thus bioavailability may be an even more important component of the environmental fate picture with low dose pesticides.

Predicting Environmental Fate of Pesticides

Much recent attention has been focused on the use of models to predict the depth to which a contaminant, such as a pesticide, will leach through soils and sediments. Such fate models have been used to successfully predict the leaching through soils of H$_2$O and nonadsorbing solutes (e.g. NO$_3^-$), but these models have often inadequately described the fate of nonionic organic solutes (including pesticides) present at low aqueous concentrations (Simkins and Alexander 1984; Scow *et al.* 1986; Schmidt *et al.* 1985). Successful modelling requires development of biodegradation kinetic curves with good predictive capability. Appropriate curves might allow the user to predict concentration of residual pesticide at any point in time after application, assuming other losses are absent or accounted for. Understanding what factors affect degradation kinetics allows extrapolation over a wide range of environmental conditions and sites if key site specific measurements are made. In principle, the rate constants and shape of the degradation curves should be influenced by the chemistry of the compound, its concentration, the nature of the organisms involved, and a number of environmental parameters (Alexander and Scow 1989). A great deal of effort has gone into the preparation of kinetic curves for degradation of pesticides presently in use. Imperical data are generally fitted to some sort of decay curve, such as the power rate model (Hamaker 1972), the Monod model (Monod 1949), the logistic curve (Odum 1971), Michaelis Menten kinetics (Alexander and Scow 1989; Hance and McKone 1971; Hamaker et al. 1968; Soulas 1982), and multiple compartment models (Alexander and Scow 1989; Hamaker and Goring 1976).

In order for degradation kinetic curves to be suitable for field application, they must be calibrated over some realistic range of environmental conditions. Data taken from experiments with pure cultures generally yield different kinetics than those observed when soil is used (Focht and Shelton 1987). Often it has been suggested that substrates are not supplied as readily in soil as in aqueous solution, resulting in a slower kinetic response (Alexander and Scow 1989). This follows our previous discussion that biodegradation may be influenced by sorption processes. Moreover degradation kinetics may be a function of both desorption and associated diffusion kinetics.

Despite ample experimental evidence to suspect sorption/desorption as a controlling factor in biodegradation, existing fate models generally do not include terms to adjust biodegradation rates to bioavailability. In addition, many of the most important factors controlling mobility and persistence of pesticides, such as biomass or microbial activity, energy and electron acceptor supply, surface chemistry of soils and sediments, etc., change substantially as a function of depth through the profile. Accurate predictions of pesticide leaching may depend upon the ability to account for or dilute the effects of these changes as a function of depth, and from site to site. Some models do allow adjustment of biodegradation rates as a function of biomass present (Jury et al. 1987), however more often than not, the biodegradation parameter has been assigned a single non-adjustable half life, which was used to determine how long the compound would persist in the system, and therefore if it would be available for transport to the subsurface.

It has been demonstrated that conventional kinetic models (usually derived from the Monod equation) for biodegradation often do not fit experimental observations of soils containing low concentrations of organic pollutants (Scow et al. 1986). Frequently, a two compartment model more successfully describes mineralisation of traces of organic compounds in soils. Such a model represented in Figure 6.6 allows a substrate to be distributed into two separate compartments (S_1 and S_2), which could be construed as the aqueous free species, and some inaccessible species. In these models, the parent compound is converted to the product P, and the parameters k_1, k_2, k_3, and k_4 are first order rate constants. Scow et al. (1986) described this model with the following differential equations:

$$dS_1/dt = -(k_1 + k_3)S_1 + k_2S_2 \qquad (9)$$

$$dS_2/dt = k_1S_1 - (k_2 + k_4)S_2 \qquad (10)$$

which describe the change in the amount of substance in each compartment as a function of time. The rate at which the compound of interest is degraded or transferred to a certain compartment is considered to be proportional to the concentration or activity of substrate in that particular compartment. There is also a dependence upon the amount of substance in the other compartment. Therefore, this model supposes that degradation kinetics should be a function of not only the total concentration of substrate, but also its speciation within the system. Though not all biodegradation data fit this kind of model, it is noteworthy that data often do fit a two compartment or similar model much better than a first order or Monod model, the most common forms used in fate/transport programs. The apparent agreement of experimental data to the more complex model is likely due to a very real involvement of sorption reactions in the biodegradation of organic compounds in soils and sediments. As stated previously, several other modelling experiments have demonstrated a dependence of biodegradation on sorption or desorption kinetics (Mihelcic and Luthy 1988; Ogram *et al.* 1985; Stevens 1990). These observations strongly support a need for fate models to account for the effects of sorption/desorption on the kinetics of biodegradation.

Summary

Careful examination of the literature reveals numerous examples of reduced biodegradation rates when pesticides or other xenobiotic compounds were sorbed to natural or synthetic materials. These data clearly indicate that sorbed materials must be desorbed before they can be degraded by microorganisms. Several soil properties appear to be related to distribution of pesticides among soil compartments (pH, cation exchange capacity, dominant mineral species for ionic pesticides, organic matter content for most pesticides), and these properties often exhibit positive or negative correlation with degradation rate. Usually these data agree with a model that states that sorbed pesticides are less available to microbes, however, some authors have noted positive correlation between degradation and parameters correlated positively with sorption (commonly either organic matter content or pH). Though the relationship between sorption and bioavailablity is obvious, and has been supported by much circumstantial evidence, little direct proof of the nature of reported observations has been presented. Moreover, due to the complexity of sorptive and biodegradative processes, indirect measures of bioavailability are probably risky indicators of biodegradation rates. Direct measurement of desorption and biodegradation kinetics on the same system may be the most promising source of data for modelling bioavailability of pesticides in the environment. Regardless of what measures prove useful, it is clear that bioavailability should be addressed in some way when modelling the fate of pesticides and other xenobiotics in the environment.

References

Ainsworth CC, Zachara JM, Smith SC (1987) Failure of the linear partitioning model to describe sorption by soil profiles. Agron Abstracts, Amer Soc Agron p 165

Alexander M, Scow M (1989) Kinetics of biodegradation in soil. In: Sawhney DW, Brown K (eds) Reactions and movement of organic chemicals in soils. SSSA Special Publication number 22 pp 243-269

Alexander M, Lustigman (1966) Effect of chemical structure on microbial degradation of substituted benzenes. J Agr Food Chem 14:410-413

Alexander M (1965) Persistence and biological reactions of pesticides in soils. Soil Sci Soc Am Proc 29:1-7

Atlas RM, Bartha R (1987) Microbial ecology. Fundamentals and applications (2nd ed) Benjamin Cummings, Menlo Park CA

Basham G, Lavy TL, Oliver LR, Scott HD (1987). Imazaquin persistence and mobility in three Arkansas soils. Weed Science 35:576-582

Bollag JM, Liu SY (1990) Biological transformation processes of pesticides. In: Cheng HH, (ed) Pesticides in the soil environment: processes, impacts, and modeling. SSSA Book Series 2, SSSA Inc Madison WI pp 169-212

Bollag JM (1983) Cross-coupling of humus constituents and xenobiotic substances p 127-141. In: Christman RF and Gjessing ET (ed) Aquatic and terrestrial humic materials. Ann Arbor Science Publishers, Inc Ann Arbor Mich

Bouchard DC, Enfield CG, Piwoni MD (1989) Transport processes involving organic chemicals pp 349-372. In: Reactions and movement of organic chemicals in soils. SSSA Special Publication Number 22 Soil Science Society of America, Madison WI

Brady NC (1990) The nature and properties of soils, 10th ed MacMillan, New York

Burkhard N, Guth JA (1980) Chemical hydrolysis of 2-chloro-4,6-bis-(alkylamino)-1,3,5-triazine herbicides and their breakdown in soil under the influence of adsorption. Pestic Sci 12:45-52

Calderbank A, Slade P (1976) Diquat and paraquat. In: Herbicides-chemistry, degradation, and mode of action. Kearney PC, Kaufman DD (eds) pp 501-540. Dekker, New York

Calvet R (1980) Adsorption-desorption phenomena. In: Hance RJ (ed) Interactions between pesticides and the soil. Academic Press, London

Carsel RF (1989) Hydrologic processes affecting the movement of organic chemicals in soils. pp 439-446. In: Reactions and movement of organic chemicals in soils. SSSA Special Publication Number 22. Soil Science Society of America, Madison WI

Chiou CT, Porter PE, Schmedding DW (1983) Partition equilibria of nonionic organic compounds between soil organic matter and water. Environ Sci Technol 17:227-231

Chiou CT, Kile DE, Brinton TI, Malcolm RL, Leenheer JA (1987) A comparison of water solubility enhancements of organic solutes by aquatic humic materials and commercial humic acids. Environ Sci Technol 21:1231-1234

Chiou CT (1989) Theoretical considerations of the partition uptake of nonionic organic compounds by soil organic matter. In: Sawhney BL, Brown K (eds) Reactions and movement of organic chemicals in soils. SSSA Special Publication number 22 pp 1-29

Dec J, Shuttleworth KL, Bollag JM (1990) Microbial release of 2,4-dichlorophenol bound to humic acid or incorporated during humification. J Environ Qual 19:546-551

Focht DD, Shelton D (1987) Growth kinetics of *Pseudomonas alcaligenes* c.o. relative to inoculation and 3-cholorbenzoate metabolism in soil. Appl Environ Microbiol 53:1846-1849

Fryer J, Hance RJ, Ludwig JW (1975) Long-term persistence of paraquat in a sandy loam soil. Weed Res 15:189-194

Gauthier TD, Seitz WR, Grant CL (1987) Effects of structural and compositional variations of humic materials on pyrene K_{oc} values. Environ Sci Tecnol 21:243-248

Gerstl Z, Yaron B (1983) Behavior of bromacil and napropamide in soils: I. adsorption and degradation. Soil Sci Soc Am J 47:474-478

Hallberg GR (1989) Pesticide pollution of groundwater in the humid United States. Agric Eco Environ 26:299-367

Hamaker JW, Goring CAI (1976) Turnover of pesticide residues in the soil. p. 219-234. In: Kaufman DD (ed) Bound and conjugated pesticide residues. Am Chem Soc, Washington DC

Hamaker JW, Youngson CR, Goring CAI (1968) Rate of detoxification of 4-amino-3,5,6-trichloropicolinic acid in soil. Weed Res 8:46-57

Hamaker JW (1972) Decomposition: quantitative aspects. p 253-240. In: Goring CAI, Hamaker JW (eds) Organic chemicals in the soil environment. Marcel Dekker, New York

Hance RJ, McKone CE (1971) Effect of concentration on the decomposition rates in soil of atrazine, linuron, and picloram. Pestic Sci 2:31-34

Hance RJ (1988) Adsorption and bioavailability. In: Grover R (ed) Environmental chemistry of herbicides, vol I CRC Press, Inc Boca Raton Florida pp 1-19

Harmon TC, Ball WP, Roberts PV (1989). Nonequilibrium transport of organic contaminants in groundwater pp 405-438. In: Reactions and movement of organic chemicals in soils. SSSA Special Publication Number 22. Soil Science Society of America, Madison WI

Harwood CS, Rivelli M, Ornson LN (1984) Aromatic acids are chemoattractants for *Pseudomonas putida*. J Bacteriol 160:622-628

Hassett JJ, Banwart WL, Griffin RA (1983) Correlation of compound properties with sorption characteristics of nonpolar compounds by soils and sediments: concepts and illustrations. In: Francis CW and Auerbach SI (ed) Environments and solid wastes. Butterworths, Boston pp 161-178

Hassett JJ, Banwart WL (1989) The sorption of nonpolar organics by soils sediments. In: Sawhney BL, Brown K (eds) Reactions and movement of organic chemicals in soils. SSSA Special Publication number 22

Hattori R, Hattori T (1987) Interaction of microorganisms with a charged surface - a model experiment. Rep Inst Res Tohoku Univ 36:21-67

Helweg A (1969) Influence of charcoal-adsorbed herbicides on microorganisms. Weed Res 9:254-257

Helweg A (1975) Degradation of ^{14}C-maleic hydrazide in soil as influenced by adsorption on activated carbon. Weed Research 15:129-133

Hsu TS, Bartha R (1974) Biodegradation of chloroanailine-humus complexes in soil and in culture solution. Soil Science 118:213-220

Hurle K (1978) Einfluss des strohverbrennens auf aktivitat, sorption und abbau von herbisiden im boden. Med Fac Landbouww Rijksuniv Gent. 43:1097-1107

Jury WA, Focht DD, Farmer WJ (1987) Evaluation of pesticide groundwater pollution potential from standard indices of soil-chemical adsorption and biodegradation. J Environ Qual 16:422-428

Karickhoff SW, Brown DS, Scott TA (1979) Sorption of hydrophobic pollutants on natural sediments. Water Res 13:241

Kehrmeyer SR, Traina SJ, Peters NK, Sims GK (1990) Bioavailability of sorbed naphthalene to *Pseudomonas putida*. Am Soc Agron Ann Meeting San Antonio TX

Koskinen WC, Harper SS (1990) The retention process: mechanisms. In: Cheng HH (ed) Pesticides in the soil environment: processes, impacts and modeling. SSSA Book Series no. 2 SSSA, Inc, Madison WI pp 51-78

Kutney JP, Berset JD, Hewitt GM, Singh M (1988). Biotransformation of dehydroabietic, abietic, and isopimaric acids by *Mortierella isabellina* immobilised in polyurethane foam. Appl Environ Microbiol 54:1015-1022

Leonard RA (1990) Movement of pesticides into surface waters. pp 303-350. In: Pesticides in the Soil Environment. Soil Science Society of America, Madison WI

Loux MM, Liebl RA, Slife FW (1989a) Adsorption of clomazone on soils, sediments, and clays. Weed Sci 37:440-444

Loux MM, Liebl RA, Slife FW (1989b) Availability and persistence of imazaquin, imazethapyr, and clomazone in soil. Weed Science 37:259-267

Marshman NA, Marshall KC (1981). Some effects of montmorillonite on the growth of mixed microbial cultures. Soil Biol Biochem 13:135-141

Merkle MG, Bovey RW (1974) Movement of pesticides in surface water pp 99-106. In: Pesticides in soil and water. Soil Science Society of America, Madison WI

Mihelcic JR, Luthy RG (1988). The potential effects of sorption processes on the microbial degradation of hydrophobic organic compounds in soil-water suspensions. International Conference on Physiochemical and Biological Detoxification of Hazardous Wastes. May 3-5, Sands Hotel, Atlantic City New Jersey

Miller ME, Alexander M (1991). Kinetics of bacterial degradation of benzylamine in a montmorillonite suspension. Envrion Sci Technol 25:240-245

Mingelgrin U, Gerst Z (1983) Reevaluation of partitioning as a mechanism of nonionic chemicals adsorption in soils. J Environ Qual 12:1-11

Monod J (1949) The growth of bacterial cultures. Ann Rev Microbiol 3:371-394

Monreal CM, McGill WB (1989) Kinetic analysis of cystine cycling through the solution of a gray luvisol and an andept soil. Soil Biol Biochem 21:671-679

Moyer JR, Hance RJ, McKone CE (1972) The effects of adsorbants on the rate of degradation of herbicides incubated with soil. Soil Biol Biochem 4:307-311

Neidhardt FC, Ingraham JL, Schaechter M (1990) Physiology of the bacterial cell, a molecular approach. Sinauer, Sutherland Mass

O'Loughlin EJ, Sims GK, Traina SJ (1988) Effects of complexation and surface attenuation on biodegradation of aromatic xenobiotic compounds. Agron Abstr p 222

Obrigawitch T, Martin AR, Roeth FW (1983) Degradation of thiocarbamate herbicides in soils exhibiting rapid EPTC breakdown. Weed Science 31:187

Odum EP (1971) Fundamentals of ecology. Suanders WB, Philadelphia

Ogram A V, R E Jessup, Ou LT, Rao PSC 1985. Effects of sorption on biological degradation rates of 2,4-dichlorophenoxy acetic acid in soils. Appl Environ Microbiol 49:582-587

Onken BM, Traina SJ (1988) Cosorption of polycyclic aromatic hydrocarbons and nitrogen heterocyclic hydrocarbons by hydrated clay minerals. Agron Abstracts, Amer Soc Agron p 203

Peter CJ, Weber JB (1985a) Adsorption, mobility, and efficacy of alachlor and metolachlor as influenced by soil properties. Weed Science 33:874-881

Peter CJ, Weber JB (1985b) Adsorption, mobility, and efficacy of metribuzin as influenced by soil properties. Weed Science 33:868-873

Peter CJ, Weber JB (1985c) Adsorption and efficacy of trifluralin and butralin as influenced by soil properties. Weed Science 33:861-867

Pignatello JJ (1989) Sorption dynamics of organic compounds in soils and sediments. In: Reactions and movement of organic chemicals in soils. SSSA Special publication number 22. Soil Science Society of America, Madison WI USA pp45-80

Rao PSC, Davidson JM (1980) Estimation of pesticide retention and transformation parameters required in nonpoint source pollution models p 23-67. In: Overcash MR and Davidson JM(ed) Environmental impact of nonpoint source pollution. Ann Arbor Sci Publ Ann Arbor MI

Rao PSC, Jessup RE, Davidson JM (1988) Mass flow and dispersion. in Grover R. (ed.) Environmental chemistry of herbicides vol I CRC Press Inc Boca Raton, Florida pp 21-43

Robinson KG, Farmer WS, Novak JT (1990) Availability of sorbed toluene in soils for degradation by acclimated bacteria. Wat Res 24:345-350

Sawhney BL (1989) Movement of organic chemicals through landfills and hazardous waste disposal sites pp 447-474. In: Reactions and movement of organic chemicals in soils. SSSA Special Publication Number 22. Soil Science Society of America, Madison WI

Schmidt SK, Simkins S, Alexander M (1985) Models for the kinetics of biodegradation of organic compounds not supporting growth. Appl Environ Microbiol 50(2):323-331

Scow KM, Simkins S, Alexander M (1986) Kinetics of mineralisation of organic compounds at low concentrations in soil. Appl Environ Microbiol 51(5):1028-1035

Shea PJ, Weber JB (1983) Effect of pH on fluridone activity and persistence as determined by chlorophyll measurements. Weed Science 31:347-350

Simkins S, Alexander M (1984) Models for mineralisation kinetics with the variables of substrate concentration and population density. Appl Environ Microbiol 47(6):1299-1306

Sims GK, Sommers LE, Konopka A (1986) Degradation of pyridine by *Micrococcus luteus* isolated from soil. Appl Environ Microbiol 51:963

Sims GK, Sommers LE (1985) Degradation of pyridine derivatives in soil. J Environ Qual 14:580-584

Sims GK, Sommers LE (1986) Biodegradation of pyridine derivatives in soil suspensions. Environ Tox Chem 5:503-509

Soulas G (1982) Mathematical model for microbial degradation of pesticides in the soil. Soil Biol Biochem 14:107-115

Steinberg SM, Pignatello JJ, Sauhey BL (1987) Persistence of 1,2-dibromomethane in soils: entrapment in intraparticle micropores. Environ Sci Technol 21:1201-1208

Stevens TO, Crawford RL, Crawford DL (1990) Biodegradation of dinoseb (2-*sec*-butyl-4,6-dinitrophenol) in several Idaho soils with various dinoseb exposure histories. Appl Environ Microbiol 56:133-139

Suss A, Eben C, Siegmund H (1972) Verhalten von adsorbierten herbisiden im boden und deren verfugbarkeit fur die pflanve. Z Pfl Krankh Pflschutz, Sonderheft 6:65-74

Taylor AW, Spencer WF (1990) Volatilisation and vapor transport processes. In: Cheng HH (ed) Pesticides in the soil environment: processes, impact, and modeling. SSSA Book Series 2, SSSA, Inc, Madison WI pp 213-270

Traina SJ, Onken BM (1991) Cosorption of aromatic N-heterocycles and pyrene by smectites in aqueous solutions. Journal of Contaminant Hydrology 7: 237-259

Traina SJ, Spontak DA, Logan TJ (1989) Effects of cations on complexation of naphthalene by water soluble organic carbon. J Environ Qual 18:221-227

Umbreit TH, Hesse EJ, Gallo MA (1986) Bioavailability of dioxin in a soil from a 2,4,5-T manufacturing site. Science 232:497-499

Varanasi U, Reichert WL, Stein JE, Brown JE, Sanborn HR (1985) Bioavailability and biotransformation of aromatic hydrocarbons in benthic organisms exposed to sediment from an urban estuary. Environ Sci Technol 19:836-841

Wagenet RJ (1987) Processes influencing pesticide loss with water under conservation tillage. pp 189-204 In: Effects of conservation tillage on groundwater quality. Lewis Publishers, Chelsea, Michigan

Walker A, Cotterill, EG, and Welch, SJ (1989) Adsorption and degradation of chlorsulfuron and metsulfuron-methyl in soils from different depths. Water Res 29:281-287

Wauchope RD, Koskinen WC (1983) Adsorption-desorption of herbicides in soil: a thermodynamic perspective. Weed Sci 31:504-512

Wauchope RD, Savage KE, Koskinen WC (1983) Adsorption-desorption equillibria of herbicides in soils: naphthalene as a modelcompound for enthalpy-entropy effects. Weed Sci 31:744-751

Wauchope RD (1987) Effects of conservation tillage on pesticide loss with water. In: Effects of conservation tillage on groundwater quality. Lewis Publishers, Chelsea, Michigan pp 205-216

Weber JB, Coble HD (1968) Microbial decomposition of diquat adsorbed on montmorillonite and kaolinite clays. J Agric Food Chem 16:475-478

Weber JB, Miller CT (1989) Organic chemical movement over and through soil. *In* Reactions and movement of organic chemicals in soils. SSSA Special Publication Number 22. Soil Science Society of America, Madison WI pp 305-334

Wolfe NL, Mingelgrin U, Miller GC (1990) Abiotic transformations in water, sediments, and soil. In: Cheng HH (ed) Pesticides in the soil environment: processes, impacts, and modeling. SSSA Book Series 2. SSSA Inc, Madison WI pp 103-168

Wu S, Gschwend PM (1986) Sorption kinetics of hydrophobic organic compounds to natural sediments and soils. Environ Sci Technol 20:717-725

Chapter 7

Biosynthesis and Structure of Lignocellulose

W. B. Betts, R. K. Dart, A. S. Ball and S. L. Pedlar

Introduction

Lignocellulose is generally considered to be the most abundant organic chemical on earth and has attracted much attention over recent years, both as a direct energy resource and as a feedstock for production of fuel, chemicals and food. Lynch (1987) considers that approximately 50% of the world's biomass is in the form of lignocellulose (estimated at 3×10^{11} tonnes) and annual production is judged to be in the range $2\text{-}5 \times 10^9$ tonnes (Kirk and Fenn 1982). The majority of lignocellulose is found as wood and straw.

On a world-wide basis almost one billion tonnes of wood are used annually as fuel or feedstock for processes such as pulping (Kennedy 1988). Approximately $5\text{-}6 \times 10^6$ tonnes of the cereal straw produced each year in the UK is considered as waste and disposed of by burning (Doyle et al. 1988).

Lignocellulose is comprised of three major structural components, cellulose, hemicellulose and lignin, and is distributed widely throughout vascular plants where it forms the structural support system. Other extraneous, non-cell wall materials such as terpenes, resins and phenols are present in relatively minor proportions. The quantity of each component is variable and depends on several factors, including the species and age of the plant, and the part of the plant from which it was extracted (Fengel and Wegener 1983). In particular, the lignin content of softwoods is usually higher than in hardwoods, and the cellulose and hemicellulose content of hardwoods are higher than in softwoods. There is more uniformity in the composition of straw which generally contains less cellulose and lignin, but more hemicellulose, than wood (Fan et al. 1982). Approximate values for each component are shown in Table 7.1.

Table 7.1. Percentages of the different components of lignocellulose

	Lignin	Cellulose	Hemicellulose
Hardwoods	18-25	45-55	24-40
Softwoods	25-35	45-50	25-35
Grasses	10-30	25-40	25-50

Cell Wall Composition

Several layers of cell wall can be recognised, each containing varying amounts of the components. These include the middle lamella, the primary cell wall and three layers of secondary cell wall (Kerr and Goring 1975; Kirk 1983). The primary cell wall is variable in thickness (0.1-10.0 μm) and is composed almost exclusively of polysaccharides, although some glycoproteins and small quantities of phenolic compounds (including lignin) are present (Northcote 1972). It is a biphasic structure consisting mainly of rigid cellulosic microfibrils embedded in a matrix of non-cellulosic polysaccharides and glycoproteins (Table 7.2).

Table 7.2. Polymer composition of primary cell walls of higher plants

Polymer	% dry weight (approx) of unlignified primary cell wall	
	Grasses	Others
Cellulose	30	30
Pectin	5	35
Hemicellulose	64	30
Arabinoxylan	30	5
ß-Glucan	30	0
Xyloglucan	4	25
Glycoprotein	<1	5

The polymer composition of the primary walls of grasses differs markedly from that typical of other higher plants. In particular, the hemicellulose content is not only higher (approx 60% dry weight of the unlignified primary wall) but is also composed, in part, of different hemicelluloses such as β-glucan.

The hemicelluloses of secondary cell wall layers are built from a number of sugar residues, of which the most important are: D-xylose, D-mannose, D-glucose, D-galactose, L-arabinose and, to a lesser extent, L-rhamnose, L-glucose and various O-methylated neutral sugars. Like the primary layers, the secondary layers also contain polymers of D-glucuronic acid (and/or the derivative 4-O-methyl-D-glucuronic acid) and D-galacturonic acid. Many members of the *Phaeophyceae* contain alginic acids (poly-L-guluronic acid, poly-D-mannuronic acid and poly-D-glucuronic acid). A typical analysis of secondary cell walls in xylem might be: 40%-45% cellulose, 24%-30% lignin, 3%-4% hexuronic acid, 1% galactan. Additionally, mannan and xylan would be found to the extent of 4%, 18% and 10%, 7% in angiosperms and gymnosperms, respectively.

Lignin

Location and Functions of Lignin

The major fraction of lignin (Latin - *lignum*, meaning wood) is found in plant cell walls, although the highest concentration is present in middle lamellae, where it acts as a glue binding cells together. Other functions are shown in Table 7.3.

Table 7.3. Functions of lignin in plants
_____
1. Acts as a bonding agent between cells
2. Provides resistance to mechanical stress
3. Resists biochemical stresses (eg microbial attack)
4. Has antioxidant properties
5. Imparts flame retardant properties
6. Acts as a stabiliser against ultraviolet light
7. Assists in water-related functions (eg waterproofing, responses to
   humidity, water balance and water transport)
_____

Chemical Structure of Lignin

Lignin is an amorphous, phenylpropanoid polymer with a molecular weight reaching 10^5 daltons (Janshekar and Fiechter 1983; Kirk and Farrell 1987). It is not a single uniform structure but a collection of compounds with similar properties, whose molecular weights vary about a mean value. Unlike other polymers, such as starch or cellulose, which are linear with a regular repeating unit, lignin has a random three-dimensional structure with no typical repeating unit. In addition, the intermonomeric linkages are very stable, non-hydrolysable carbon-carbon bonds or relatively inert ether bonds.

Structure Determination

Many problems are encountered when attempting to determine and understand the complex structure of lignin which, due to its amorphous nature, cannot be studied by the X-ray method. The problems are compounded by the difficulty in preparing lignin samples using presently available physical and chemical methods, as secondary reactions cause changes in their structures (Hwang *et al.* 1990). Also, obtaining a sample uncontaminated with other lignocellulose components is almost impossible. Various preparation methods have been used, but lignin samples most suitable for both structure determination and biodegradation studies are probably those prepared on a small scale by ball-milling, with subsequent enzymatic treatment using cellulases and hemicellulases. However, even these may contain significant quantities of carbohydrate material.

A variety of chemical degradations aimed at elucidating the structure of lignin have appeared in the literature and have been reviewed by Crawford (1981). The major problem with these methods is that they produce a large number of low molecular weight degradation products, each present in a small quantity. The subsequent separation and identification of these compounds has been extremely difficult. However, on the basis of this type of work, useful composite structures for various native lignins have been prepared. Recent advances have suggested that it is possible to study directly the lignin bonding patterns in intact plant tissue (Lewis and Yamamoto 1990) and it is therefore likely that major refinements to the known structure will be made in the short term future.

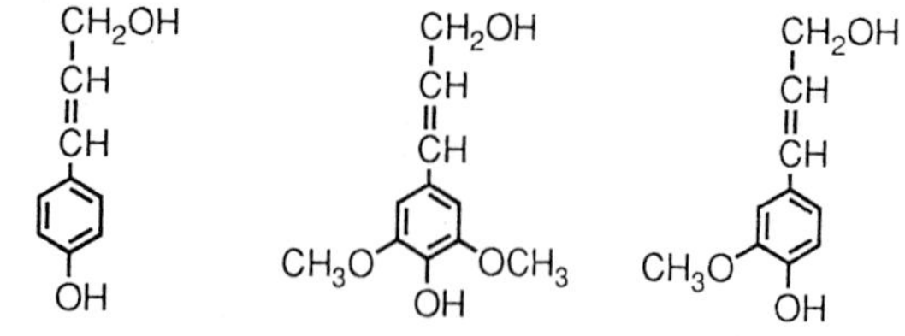

coniferyl alcohol (i) sinapyl alcohol (ii) *p*-coumaryl alcohol (iii)

Fig.7.1. Hydroxycinnamyl alcohol subunits of lignin.

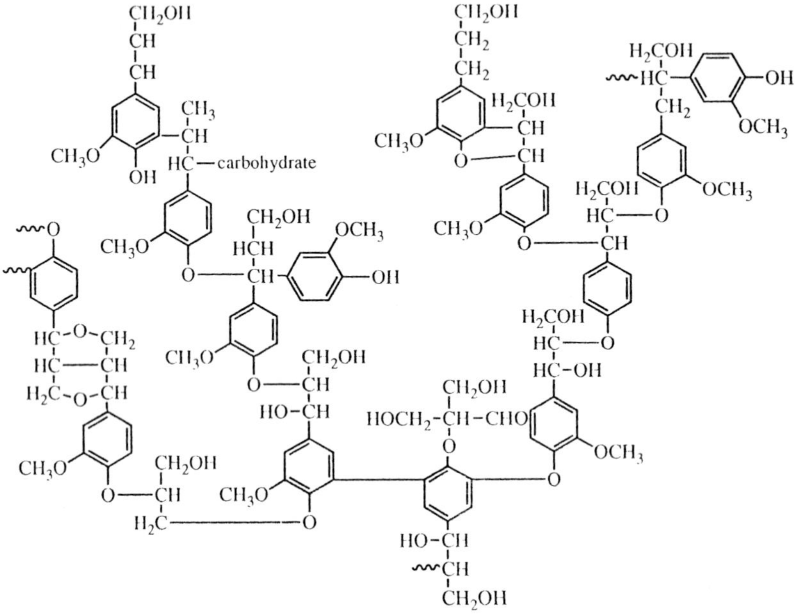

Fig. 7.2. Schematic structural formula of a softwood lignin (based on Sakakibara 1983).

Detailed Structure

Several different types of lignin can be distinguished, although all are based on the phenylpropane ($C_{6[ring]}$ - $C_{3[side\text{-}chain]}$) subunit structure of three *p*-hydroxycinnamyl alcohols (Fig. 7.1). An example is shown in Figure 7.2.

One variety is soft-wood (gymnosperm) lignin, composed of mainly coniferyl alcohol (Fig. 7.1i) with only small amounts of sinapyl alcohol (Fig. 7.1ii) and *p*-coumaryl alcohol (Fig. 7.1iii). The ratios of guaiacyl:*p*-hydroxyphenyl:syringyl units have been estimated at 94:5:1, however, Freudenberg (1968) reported somewhat higher quantities of syringyl units.

A second type is hardwood (angiosperm) lignin composed of approximately equal amounts of guaiacyl and syringyl units with only a small quantity of coumaryl units. The ratios have been estimated as coumaryl:coniferyl:sinapyl, 5:49:46 (Freudenberg 1968).

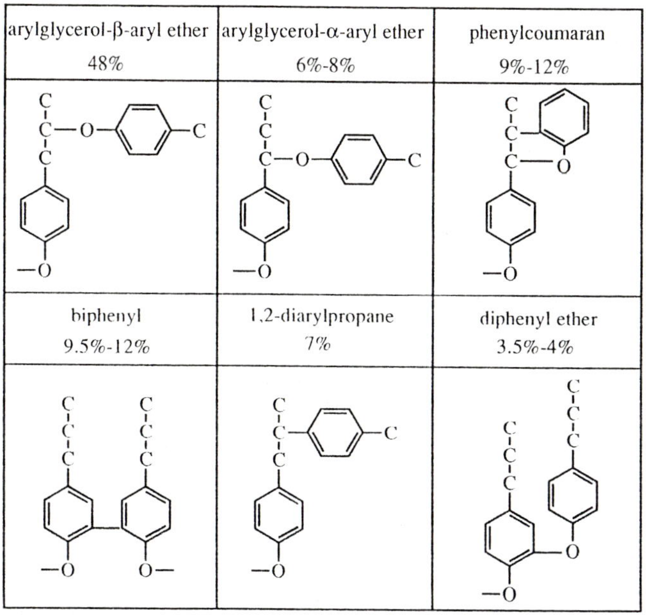

arylglycerol-β-aryl ether 48%	arylglycerol-α-aryl ether 6%-8%	phenylcoumaran 9%-12%
biphenyl 9.5%-12%	1,2-diarylpropane 7%	diphenyl ether 3.5%-4%

Fig. 7.3. Major bond types found in spruce lignin.

A third type is grass lignin, although there are arguments against a separate classification for this group (Adler 1977) which contains approximately equal amounts of coumaryl, coniferyl and sinapyl units. However, examination of the molecule shows that much of the coumaryl unit is present as *p*-coumaric acid esterified to the polymer (Nakamura and Higuchi 1976). A small quantity of coniferyl units may also be present as ferulic acid esters. Some researchers therefore regard grass lignins as modified hardwood lignins.

Intermonomeric Bonds

A wide range of different bond types are found in the lignin structure and the major ones are illustrated in Figure 7.3. Very few researchers have published figures for grass lignins, although it is known that these contain the additional ester bonds in which the acid moiety is supplied by *p*-coumaric and ferulic acids.

Other bonds formed include lignin-carbohydrate and lignin-protein structures. The association between lignin and carbohydrate is of three types:

i   hydrogen bonding;
ii   covalent bonding;
iii   physical encrustation.

Studies have suggested that there is one bond to carbohydrate per 36 phenylpropane units (Obst 1982) and that the lignin-saccharide linkage is an ether. The saccharide is of the hemicellulose type and arabinan has been implicated in aspen.

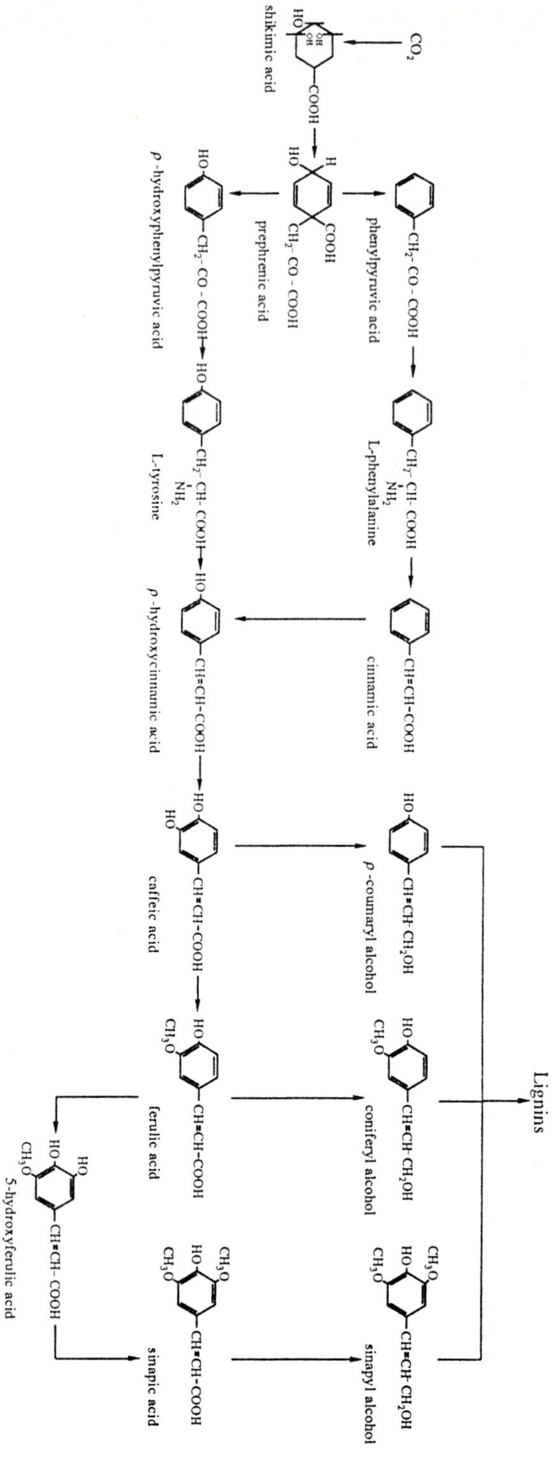

Fig. 7.4. Lignin biosynthesis in plants via the shikimic acid pathway.

Lignin also forms covalent bonds with proteins (Whitmore 1978) especially with the glycoproteins of the cell wall and evidence suggests that this may involve the amino-acid hydroxyproline.

Biosynthesis of Lignin

Shikimic Acid Pathway

The formation of hydroxycinnamyl alcohol derivatives of the type shown in Figure 7.1 takes place from the aromatic amino acid phenylalanine and to a lesser extent tyrosine, both of which are synthesised by the shikimic acid pathway (Higuchi 1985) (Fig. 7.4). In gymnosperms and most angiosperms, elimination of ammonia from phenylalanine by the enzyme phenylalanine:ammonia lyase (PAL) forms *trans*-cinnamic acid which is converted initially to *p*-hydroxycinnamic acid. This is further converted into substituted cinnamic acids by a series of hydroxylation and methylation reactions, the methyl group being provided by S-adenosyl methionine. Tyrosine is not incorporated into lignin in these species. In grasses however, the enzyme tyrosine:ammonia lyase (TAL) is found and this converts tyrosine into *p*-hydroxycinnamate which is then transformed into lignin. Both PAL and TAL are at low concentration in parts of the plant not undergoing lignification.

The absence of sinapyl alcohol from the angiosperms is due to several factors, including a deficiency of ferulate-5-hydroxylase, low activity of 5-hydroxyferulate methylase and a lack of reduction of sinapic acid.

The *p*-hydroxycinnamic acid derivatives are then reduced via their CoA derivatives to coniferyl alcohol, sinapyl alcohol and *p*-coumaryl alcohol which are termed monolignols (Freudenberg 1965). Their synthesis has been reviewed by Gross (1985). In grasses, the enzyme TAL is present and converts tyrosine directly to *p*-hydroxycinnamate.

Radical Mediated Coupling

Synthesis of lignins *in vivo* from these precursors is initiated by the enzymatic formation of phenoxy radicals, which can form a number of resonance structures each with a short half life (Fig. 7.5). Freudenberg (1965) showed that the phenoxy radicals could be generated enzymatically by laccase/O_2 or peroxidase/H_2O_2. The enzyme involved *in vivo* is a peroxidase, the evidence being reviewed by Higuchi (1985). The source of the H_2O_2 is a complex reaction involving superoxide radicals (Gross *et al.* 1977) formed by reduction of oxygen with NAD^+ (which is derived from the oxidation of NADH previously formed by malate dehydrogenase bound to the cell walls). This theory explains the formation of H_2O_2 at the lignification site, without the need to transport this highly toxic compound around the cell.

The highly reactive radicals can stabilise by coupling to another radical resulting in a quinone methide, which forms a dilignol by the addition of water. This coupling is chemical and random and yields a variety of dilignols, although certain types predominate. The rates of various dimerisations depend on the availability of each radical and on its half-life. It is possible to alter the percentage of each product formed by varying the quantity of the monomeric reactants (Sarkanen 1971). One major feature

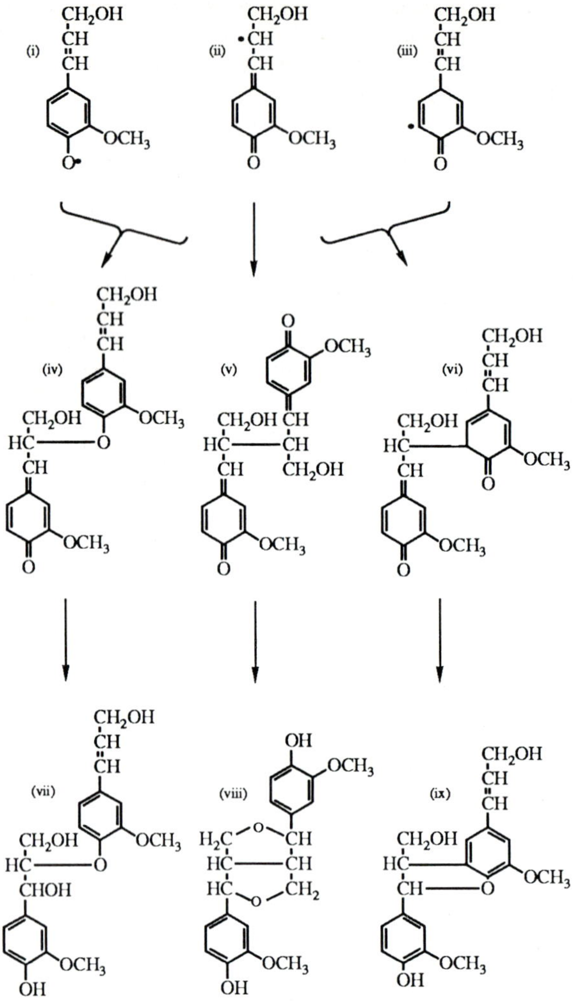

Fig. 7.5. Radical coupling of coniferyl alcohol during lignin biosynthesis.

of the products is that they are achiral due to the chemical, rather than enzymatic, nature of the polymerisation reaction. This has important implications for the enzymes breaking down lignin.

In vitro polymerisation of coniferyl alcohol using horseradish peroxidase and H_2O_2 produces a dehydrogenation polymer (DHP) with a molecular weight varying from 1 000–2 500 depending on the methodology used. DHP has very similar properties to soft-wood lignin. Interruption of this polymerisation reaction produces a mixture of di-, tri- and oligolignols, the main ones being the dilignols, guaiacylglycerol-ß-coniferyl ether (Fig. 7.5vii) and dehydrodiconiferyl alcohol (Fig. 7.5ix). Higher molecular weight DHPs (6 000) can be synthesised by using horseradish peroxidase confined to a dialysis bag (Tanahashi *et al.* 1981).

Further growth of the lignin molecule takes place by an endwise polymerisation. In this the favoured reaction is between a monomeric radical and the radical of a dilignol, rather than a reaction between two monomeric radicals. This type of addition results in the formation of a linear molecule. Coupling of the C_5 carbon of one ring to the C_5 of another gives a biphenyl structure and C_4(ring)-O-C_5(ring) coupling to give diaryl ethers is of importance as they can give rise to branches in the lignin molecule. Reactions of this type probably occur between oligomers rather than an oligomer and a monomer. When solutions of coniferyl alcohol are polymerised enzymatically in the presence of sugars, the sugar becomes bonded preferentially to the C_1(side-chain) of the quinone methide producing a carbohydrate-p-hydroxybenzyl ether of DHP. Higuchi's group showed that when glucuronic acid was used, an ester was formed, whereas with glucose the ring C_6 is involved in the formation of an ether bond (Tanaka et $al.$ 1976, 1979).

Evidence suggests that in plant cell walls, a considerable portion of the lignin is linked to the glucuronic acids of hemicelluloses by ester links and to other sugars by benzyl ethers. In addition to hemicelluloses, the lignin also may be linked to pectins. The biosynthesis of lignins has been recently reviewed by Higuchi (1990).

Cellulose

Occurrence and Structure

Cellulose makes up the basic structural material of the cell walls of higher plants and is found in some algae. In addition it is synthesised by some bacteria. Approximately 1.5×10^8 tonnes of cellulose, in the form of raw fibrous material, is consumed annually world-wide and 1.0×10^8 tonnes of this originates from wood pulp for uses in paper making (Kennedy 1988). Other uses include production of textiles, matrices and chemicals.

The structure of cellulose is complex and three major levels can be recognised (Table 7.4). Cellulose is a linear polymer composed of glucose molecules linked by ß(1:4)- glycosidic bonds; the basic repeating unit is cellobiose (Fig. 7.6). Glucose in cellulose alternates through 180° along the axis of the chain and therefore the terminal cellobiose can be in one of two stereochemically distinct units (Wood 1985). This implies there must be more than one enzyme capable of attacking end groups.

The cellulose molecule is water-insoluble, has a high tensile strength and is relatively recalcitrant to degradation compared to other glucose polymers such as starch. The degree of polymerisation in $situ$ can be high with figures in the order of 10 000-15 000 being reported, although numerous samples including commercial preparations may be considerably lower.

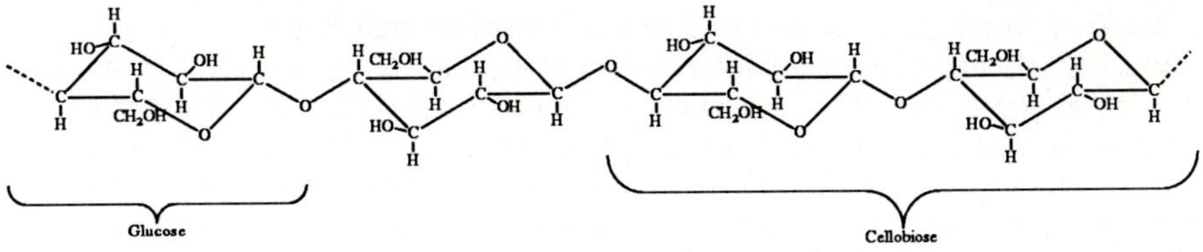

Fig. 7.6. Repeating units in cellulose.

Table 7.4. Levels of cellulose complexity

Structural level	Structural complexity	Properties
i	Chemical (Constituent molecules)	Steric properties and intramolecular interactions
ii	Physical (Macromolecules)	Aggregations and intermolecular interactions resulting in elementary fibres and crystal structure
iii	Morphological (Strands and cell structures)	Morphological arrangement of strands of fibres and composition of plant cell walls

Cellulose Fibrils

Cellulose molecules are arranged in bundles of 10-15 as subelementary protofibrils. These aggregate, in groups of approximately 40, as parallel protofibrils (40Å wide) which further associate to form larger microfibrils (250Å wide) which are very conspicuous in plant cell walls. The fibres of soft-woods are longer than other types. The chains of cellulose are held straight by O_6-O_2 and O_3-O_5 intrachain hydrogen bonding (Blackwell and Marchessault 1971; Blackwell et al. 1977). Flattened sheets are produced by the O_3-O_6 hydrogen bonding of adjacent chains and these are further associated by van der Waal's forces (Krassig 1985; Jeffries 1987).

Electron microscopy on hydrolysed and ultrasonically disintegrated cellulose fibres has been invaluable in elucidating the fibril nature of cellulose. However, new non-destructive analytical techniques such as 13^C solution NMR, electron spectroscopy, photoacoustic FTIR, secondary ion mass spectroscopy and fast atom bombardment MS have had a major impact on our understanding of the native cellulose ultrastructure (Stephenson 1987).

Crystalline and Amorphous Cellulose

Cellulose crystallises in polymorphic states and four different forms have been described (I, II, III and IV) (Atalla and van der Hart 1984). Only cellulose I is found occurring naturally and it is now generally accepted that this form consists of parallel chains i.e. the reducing groups are all at the same end of the crystal. Cellulose II is formed by solubilising I and allowing it to recrystallise. This is made up of anti-parallel chains (the polarity of the chains alternates), contains extensive hydrogen bonding and is extremely stable. The conversion of cellulose I to II is irreversible (Eriksson et al. 1990). Production of celluloses III and IV requires liquid ammonia and heat treatments. The degree of crystallinity is variable, depending upon the source of the cellulose, but in some samples of cotton it may be as high as 90%.

Throughout the crystalline cellulose are amorphous regions with reduced crystallinity and it is at these points that enzymatic hydrolysis commences. Resistance to hydrolysis, however, is only in part due to the crystalline state, a number of authors have shown that the susceptibility of cellulose to hydrolysis is related to the pore volume, increased enzyme accessibility to inner microfibrils and enzyme diffusion rates. It has been suggested that the amorphous regions result from the curvature of the cell membrane during cellulose synthesis (Jeffries 1987).

Biosynthesis of Cellulose

Cellulose has been found in bacteria as well as plants and *Acetobacter xylinum* has been used as a model organism by many groups researching cellulose biosynthesis. The biosynthesis of cellulose in bacteria has been reviewed by Ross *et al.* (1991). However, although some aspects of cellulose synthesis by bacteria is pertinent to cellulose synthesis in plants, not all are. For example, bis (3,5) cyclic diguanylic acid (Ross *et al.* 1987) is an activator of cellulose synthesis in *Acetobacter spp.* but appears to cause no stimulation in higher plants. It has been shown in bacteria that polymerisation and crystallisation of cellulose are tightly coupled, and that crystallisation is rate limiting. Addition of hemicellulose interferes with the synthesis of cellulose microfibrils and it is suggested that hemicellulose binding to the primary cell walls of higher plants may control cellulose polymerisation.

The precursor of cellulose is UDP-glucose but attempts to demonstrate cellulose synthesis by cell free extracts are thwarted by the synthesis of callose which is an unbranched polymer of glucose units linked by ß(1:3) glycosidic bonds. Synthesis of callose is part of the wound response of plants and it has been suggested that the preparation of cell free extracts damages the cell, stimulating the callose response and suppressing the synthesis of cellulose. Evidence suggests that there may only be one enzyme, a membrane-located glucosyl transferase, which synthesises both cellulose and callose. When the membrane is intact, with normal transmembrane electrical potentials and low levels of Ca^{2+}, cellulose is synthesised, but when the membrane is damaged, the electrical gradient is lost and Ca^{2+} levels fall with subsequent formation of callose.

Delmer (1987) reviewed cellulose synthesis in plants, considering the role of terminal complexes, globules and rosettes, and the control function of microtubules. Evidence suggests that UDP-glucose reacts to form cellobiose (or maltose) residues which are added to the reactive ends of glucan chains on globules at the site of membrane-bound rosettes, from where they are subsequently transported to the cell exterior. Microfibrils are generated in clusters and association of the chains occurs by non-enzymatic processes such as hydrogen bonding.

The approaches to investigate the complex components of cellulose biosynthesis have included autoradiographic techniques using radiolabelled sugars, coupled with electron microscopy to demonstrate synthetic reactions, ultrastructural details and locality. Cell fractionation techniques have been used to trace the movement of cellulose, precursors and intermediates, and biochemical methodologies using cell homogenates have been adopted to investigate sugar reaction mechanisms.

Hemicellulose

Hemicellulose is a general term applied to a group of chemically heterogeneous carbohydrates found in the cell walls of plants, in association with lignin, as an amorphous phase surrounding the cellulose strands. Most definitions are ambiguous and have included "any structural polysaccharide which is not cellulose" and "those plant cell wall polysaccharides soluble in alkali". The compounds were named hemicelluloses as they were considered to be related to cellulose and initially they were thought to be cellulose precursors; chemical analysis has shown this to be incorrect. They can easily be extracted with alkali and precipitated with acid, and are much less resistant to hydrolysis than cellulose.

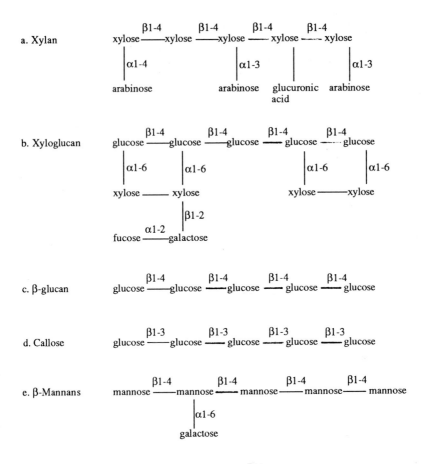

Fig. 7.7. Structures of hemicelluloses.

Hemicelluloses can be removed from lignocellulose by extraction with aqueous sodium hydroxide, and the amorphous polysaccharide mixture can be precipitated with acidic alcohol. The sugar residues present in these polysaccharides include D-xylose, L-arabinose, D-glucuronic acid, 4-O-methyl-D-glucuronic acid, D-galactose, L-galactose, D-mannose, L-rhamnose and L-fucose. Unlike cellulose which is a linear homopolymer with the same basic structure in all species, hemicelluloses are hetero-polysaccharides which may be highly branched, and which have widely differing structures from species to species. The branches may be mono-, di-, or short oligosaccharides. There may be a considerable degree of acetylation of the monomer. Hemicelluloses are considerably smaller than cellulose with a degree of polymerisation usually less than 200 and they are generally non-crystalline.

Classification of hemicelluloses is according to their chemical structure and three predominant types are found, distributed through various species: the xylans, glucans and mannans (Fig. 7.7). The xylans are the predominant type in angiosperms whilst mannans are found widely in gymnosperms.

Xylans

The quantity of xylans present in primary and secondary cell walls varies considerably (McNeil *et al*. 1984). They have a backbone of ß(1:4)-linked D-xylose residues which carry a single arabinose and/or D-glucoronic acid residue attached to the $_2$O or $_3$O position (Fig. 7.7a). The proportion of xylose residues carrying carbohydrate side-chains varies greatly between xylans. A high proportion of the xylose groups carry a 4-O-methyl ether group and some of the terminal arabinose residues carry phenol ether groups (Harris and Hartley 1980).

Glucans

Three different types of glucan hemicellulose have been identified and are classified as follows:

1   Xyloglucans are found in the primary cell walls of dicotyledons but they appear to be absent from most secondary cell walls. They are also found as a major component in seeds (Reid 1985). Xyloglucans have a backbone of ß(1:4)-linked glucose units which is identical to cellulose, but more than half the glucose residues have side chains attached at the $_6$O-position (McNeil *et al*. 1984) (Fig. 7.7b). The residue usually found is D-xylose linked by an α(1:6) glycosidic bond but ß(1:2)-linked D-galactose, α(1:2)-linked fucose and L-arabinose are also found.
2   ß-glucans are important constituents of the cell walls of grasses. They are made up of unbranched D-glucose residues most of which are ß(1:4)-linked but with approximately 30% being ß(1:3)-linked (Buliga *et al*. 1986) (Fig. 7.7c).
3   Callose is another polymer of D-glucose, which is ß(1:3)-linked and has been proposed as an intermediate in the synthesis of cellulose (Meier *et al*. 1981) (Fig. 7.7d).

Mannans

These occur mainly in secondary cell walls but may also be present in some primary cell walls. Those in secondary cell walls have a backbone of ß(1:4)- linked D-mannose groups interrupted by a number (approximately 30%) of ß-D-glucose residues (Fig. 7.7e). In gymnosperms, D-galactose residues are attached as side chains to the 6-position of some of the mannose groups (Aspinall 1980).

Synthesis

Hemicelluloses are not synthesised directly into the primary cell wall. Radiotracer experiments using [^{3}H] sugars, show that cell wall polysaccharides are synthesised in the Golgi body and are then carried by vesicles to the plasma membrane (Northcote and Pickett-Heaps 1966; Bowles and Northcote 1974; Camirand *et al*. 1987). The vesicles fuse with the plasma membrane and their contents are released into the cell wall (Fry 1987; Robinson *et al*. 1976).

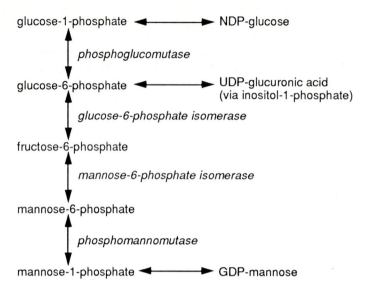

Fig. 7.8. Biosynthesis of NDP-sugars for hemicellulose.

The sugars are activated prior to polysaccharide synthesis by conversion to the nucleoside diphosphate (NDP) sugars, such as UDP (uridine diphosphate) and GDP (guanosine diphosphate) sugars (Feingold and Avigad 1980). The linkage for most D-sugars is an α-glycosidic bond and for L-sugars it is a ß-glycosidic, and in most cases for NDP-sugars, the sugar residue is in the pyranose form (Fry and Northcote 1983).

The starting point for the biosynthesis of NDP-sugars is a pool of hexose monophosphates which are in constant equilibrium (Fig. 7.8). Glucose-1-phosphate and mannose-1-phosphate form NDP-sugars directly, whilst glucose-6-phosphate forms UDP-glucuronic acid via inositol-1-phosphate (Loewus and Loewus 1980). These three NDP-sugars can act as precursors for the other NDP-sugars required in cell wall synthesis (Feingold and Avigad 1980). When [³H]-sugars are fed *in vivo*, labelled polysaccharides accumulate as soon as the corresponding NDP-sugar has become labelled, indicating that the NDP-sugar is the precursor of cell wall polysaccharides (Fry and Northcote 1983).

The enzymes involved in hemicellulose biosynthesis are only very poorly understood. Glycosyl transferases which transfer sugars to an acceptor molecule such as a growing polysaccharide have been found bound to the membrane of the Golgi body (Camirand *et al.* 1987). These enzymes are only poorly characterised and little is known about the specificity of sugar donors and receptors, or the number of enzymes involved in cell wall biosynthesis. Two enzymes identified are a ß-glucan synthetase (Thelen and Delmer 1986; Henry and Stone 1982) and a glucuronyl transferase which adds glucosamine residues to xylan (Waldron and Brett 1985).

Little else is known about hemicellulose synthesis. For instance, it is unclear whether the hemicellulose grows towards its reducing or non-reducing terminus, or whether the synthesis of backbone is coupled to side-chain synthesis. In the case of xyloglucans, there is some evidence that xylose residues are attached simultaneously with backbone synthesis (Hayashi and Matsuda 1981).

Sugar residues of polysaccharides are probably derivatised prior to polysaccharide secretion into the cell wall (Fry 1985; Fry 1987) and it appears that non-sugar groups are added to the polysaccharide directly rather than via the NDP-sugar. Methyl groups are provided by adenosyl-methionine (Krauss *et al.* 1967) and acetyl groups arise from acetyl-CoA (Fincher and Stone 1981). Sparse information is available concerning the donors of other groups such as monolignols.

Very little is also known about the transport of the polysaccharide in the vesicles. Once the vesicles arrive at the plasma membrane they discharge their contents into the cell wall, and *in vitro* studies have shown that fusion depends upon Ca^{2+} and a protein which may be a Ca^{2+}-dependant ATPase (Baydoun and Brett 1984).

Conclusions

This chapter has illustrated the importance of lignocellulose as a massive resource, so far under-exploited but with great potential as a raw material for conversion into both fuels and commodities. Additionally, and unlike many other currently important resources such as oil, it is renewable in the short-term and supplies are determined primarily by the ecologically sound management of forests and cereal crop residues. Additionally, lignocellulose-derived materials, including lignins and hemicelluloses from pulping, which are presently considered as wastes, are rapidly increasing supplements to this resource. Their utilisation would not only prevent wastage and increase the cost effectiveness of industry but would also reduce the environmental impact caused by their discharge or disposal.

The biosynthesis and structure of lignocellulose and the associations between the component chemicals are highly complex, the details being far from resolved. It is certainly true that the biotransformation of this substrate cannot be fully understood or exploited without a detailed knowledge of the structure. In the case of lignin, it was not until the structure had been described with some accuracy that major advances could be made in biodegradation research. This was especially true with respect to microbial degradation using lignin model compounds and DHP which have advanced the area dramatically over the past 10-15 years. However, work of this latter type does not describe the complete picture and intact polymers are still probaby the most important substrates when attempting to understand the degradation of the native chemicals.

The importance of lignocellulose is also illustrated in the number of reviews on its degradation in this book and references to structural details in these are numerous. It was for these reasons and to prevent duplication of information that this separate chapter on biosynthesis and structure of lignocellulose was written.

References

Adler E (1977) Lignin Chemistry. Past, present and future Wood Science and Technol. 11: 169-218

Aspinall GO (1980) Chemistry of cell wall polysaccharides in The Biochemistry of Plants, a comprehensive treatise Vol 3 Preiss J (ed) Academic Press pp 473-500

Attala RH, van der Hart DL (1984) Native cellulose: a composite of two distinct crystalline forms. Science 223: 283-285

Baydoun EA-H, Brett CT (1984) The effect of pH on the binding of calcium to pea epicotyl cell walls J Expt Bot. 35: 1820-1831

Blackwell J, Marchessault RH (1971) In: Bikales NM, Segal L (eds) Cellulose and cellulose derivatives, part 4. Wiley Interscience, New York pp 1-2

Blackwell J, Kolpak FJ, Gardner KH (1977) In: Arthur JC (ed) Cellulose chemistry and technology, ACS Symposium Series No 48. American Chemical Society, Washington pp 42-43

Bowles DJ, Northcote DH (1974) The amounts and rates of export of polysaccharides found in the membrane systems of maize root cells. Biochem J 142: 139-144

Buliga GS, Brant DA, Fincher GB (1986) The sequence statistics and solution confirmation of a barley (1 3, 1 4)-ß-D-glucan. Carbohydrate Res 157: 139-156

Camirand A, Brummell D, MacLachlan G (1987) Fucosylation of Xyloglucan. Plant Physiol. 84: 753-756

Crawford RL (1981) Lignin Biodegradation and Transformation. Wiley Interscience

Delmer DP (1987) Cellulose Biosynthesis. Ann. Revs. Plant Physiology 38: 259-290

Doyle CJ, Mason VC, Baker RD (1988) Straw disposal and utilisation: an economic evaluation of the end-uses for wheat straw in the UK. Biological Wastes 23:39-56

Eriksson K-EL, Blanchette RA, Ander P (1990) Biodegradation of cellulose. In: Microbial and enzymatic degradation of wood and wood components. Springer-Verlag, Heidelberg pp 89-177

Fan LT, Young-Hyun Lee, Gharpuray MM (1982) The nature of lignocellulosics and their pretreatments for enzymatic hydrolysis. Adv Biochem Eng 23:155-188

Feingold DS, Avigard G (1980) Sugar nucleotide transformations in Plants. In Biochemistry of Plants; A Comprehensive Treatise Vol 3 Preiss J (ed) Academic Press pp 101-170

Fengel D, Wegener G (1983) Wood: chemistry, ultrastructure, reactions. Walter de Gruyter, Berlin 613 pp

Fincher GB, Stone BA (1981) Metabolism of non-cellulosic polysaccharides in Plant Carbohydrates II Tanner W, Loewus FA (eds) Springer, Berlin pp 68-132

Freudenberg K (1965) Lignin: Its constitution and formation from p-hydroxy cinnamyl alcohols Science 148: 595-600

Freudenberg K (1968) The constitution and biosynthesis of Lignin. In: The constitution and biosynthesis of Lignin Freudenberg K, Neish AC (eds) Springer, Berlin pp 47-122

Fry SC (1985) Primary cell wall metabolism Oxford Surv. Plant Mol. Cell. Biol. 2: 1-42 Mifflin BJ (ed) OUP

Fry SC (1987) Intracellular feruloylation of pectin polysaccharides Planta 171: 205-211

Fry SC, Northcote DH (1983) Sugar-nucleotide precursors of the aribinofuranosyl, arabinopyranosyl and xylanopyranosyl residues of spinach polysaccharides. Plant Physiol. 73: 1055-1061

Gross GG, Jansen C, Estner EF (1977) Involvement of malate, monophenols and superoxide radicals in hydrogen peroxide formation by isolated cell walls from horse radish (Aromoraeia lapathifolium Gilib) Planta 136: 271-276

Gross GG (1985) Biosynthesis and Metabolism of phenolic acids and monolignols in Biosynthesis and degradation of wood components Higuchi T (ed) Academic Press

Harris PJ, Hartley RD (1980) Phenolic constituents of the cell walls of monocotyledons Biochem. Syst. Ecol. 8: 153-160

Hayashi T, Matsuda K (1981) Biosynthesis of xyloglucan in suspension-cultured soyabean cells. Plant Cell Physiol 22: 1571-1584

Henry RJ, Stone BA (1982) Solubilisation of ß-glucan synthases from the membranes of cultured ryegrass endosperm cells. Biochem J 203: 629-636

Higuchi T (1985) Biosynthesis of lignin. In: Higuchi T (ed) Biosynthesis and biodegradation of wood components Academic Press, San Diego pp 141-160

Higuchi T (1990) Lignin biochemistry: Biosynthesis and Degradation. Wood Sci Technol 24: 23-63

Hwang RH, Kennedy JF, Melo EHM, Paterson M, Jumel K (1990) Lignin structure: approach by conformational analysis. In: Kennedy JF, Phillips GO, Williams PA (eds) Cellulose sources and exploitation: industrial utilisation, biotechnology and physico-chemical properties, Ellis Horwood, England pp 497-504

Jeffries TW (1987) Physical, chemical and biochemical considerations in the biological degradation of wood. In: Kennedy JF, Phillips GO, Williams PA (eds) Wood and cellulosics: industrial utilisation, biotechnology, structure and properties. Ellis Horwood Limited, Chichester, England pp 213-230

Janshekar H, Fiechter A (1983) Lignin: Biosynthesis, Application and Biodegradation. Adv Biochem Eng Biotech 27 119-178

Kennedy JF (1988) Biotransformation of polysaccharides. A report prepared for the Biotransformation Club of the Government Chemist, UK pp 14-34

Kerr AJ, Goring DAI (1975) The ultrastuctural arrangement of the wood cell wall. Cellul Chem Technol 9: 563-573

Kirk TK (1983) Degradation and conversion of lignocellulose in The Filamentous Fungi Vol. IV Fungal Technology Smith NE, Berry DR, Kristiansen B (eds) pp 266-295

Kirk TK, Farrell RL (1987) Enzymatic "combustion": The Microbial Degradation of Lignin Ann Revs Microbiol 41: 464-505

Kirk TK, Fenn P (1982) Formation and action of the ligninolytic system in basidiomycetes. In: Swift MJ, Frankland J, Hedger JN (eds) Decomposer basidiomycetes, Br Mycol Soc Symp 4 Cambridge University Press, England pp 67-90

Krassig H (1985) Structure of cellulose and its relation to properties of cellulose fibres. In: Kennedy JF, Williams GO, Wedlock DJ, Williams PA (eds) Cellulose and its derivatives. Ellis Horwood Limited, Chichester, England pp 3-26

Krauss H, Swanson AL, Hassid WZ (1967) Biosynthesis of the methyl ester groups of pectin by transmethylation from S-adenosyl-L-methionine. Biochem Biophys Res Comm 26: 234-240

Loewus FA, Loewus MW (1980) myo-Inositol: Biosynthesis and metabolism in The Biochemistry of Plants, a comprehensive treatise Vol 3 Preiss J (ed) Academic Press pp 43-76

Lewis NG, Yamamoto E (1990) Lignin: occurrence, biogenesis and biodegradation. Ann Rev Plant Physiol Plant Mol Biol 41: 455-496

Lynch JM (1987) Utilisation of Lignocellulosic Wastes J Appl Bact Symp Suppl 71S-83S

McNeil M, Darvill AG, Fry SC, Albersheim P (1984) Structure and Function of the Primary Cell Wall of Plants Ann Revs Biochem 53: 625-663

Meier H, Buchs L, Buchala AJ, Homewood T (1981) (1 3)-ß-glucan is a probable intermediate in the biosynthesis of cellulose of cotton fibres Nature 289: 821-822

Nakamura Y, Higuchi T (1976) Ester linkages of p-coumaric acid in Bamboo Holzforsch 30: 187-191

Northcote DH (1972) Chemistry of the plant cell wall. Ann Rev Plant Physiol 23:113-132

Northcote DH, Pickett-Heaps JD (1966) A function of the Golgi apparatus in polysaccharide synthesis and transport in the root cap cells of wheat Biochem J 98: 159-167

Obst JR (1982) Frequency and alkali resistance of lignin-carbohydrate bonds in wood. Tappi 65 109-112

Reid JSG (1985) Structure and function in legume-seed polysaccharides. In: Plant Cell Walls Brett CT, Hillman JR (eds) CUP pp 259-268

Robinson DG, Eisinger WR, Ray PM (1976) Dynamics of the Golgi system in wall matrix polysaccharide synthesis and secretion by pea cells. Ber deutch Bot Ges 89: 147-161

Ross P, Weinhouse H, Aloni Y, Michaeli D, Weinberger-Ohang P, Mayer R, Braun S, de Vroom E, van der Marcl G, van Boem JH, Benziman M (1987) Regulation of cellulose synthesis in Acetobacter xylinum by cyclic diguanylic acid. Nature 325: 279-281

Ross P, Mayer R, Benziman M (1991) Cellulose biosynthesis and function in bacteria. Microbiological Reviews 55: 35-58

Sakakibara A (1983) Chemical structure of lignin related mainly to degradation products. In: Recent Advances in Lignin Biodegradation Research. Higuchi T, Chang H-M, Kirk TK. Tokyo: Uni Publishers Company Ltd pp 12-23

Sarkanen KV (1971) Precursors and their polymerisation. In: Lignins, occurence, formation sructure and reactions. Sarkanen KV, Ludwig CH (eds) p 95

Stephenson PJ (1987) Modern analytical methods - application to cellulose and its derivatives. In: Kennedy JF, Phillips GO, Williams PA (eds) Wood and cellulosics: industrial utilisation, biotechnology, structure and properties. Ellis Horwood Limited, Chichester, England pp 13-21

Tanahashi M, Aoki T, Higuchi T (1981) Dehydrogenative polymerisation of monolignols by peroxidase and H_2O_2 in a dialysis tube. Mokuzai Gakkaishi 27: 116-124

Tanaka K, Nakatsubo F, Higuchi T (1976) Reaction of guaiacyl-glycerol-ß-guaiacyl ether with sugars I Mokuzai Gakkaishi 22: 587-590

Tanaka K, Nakatsubo F, Higuchi T (1979) Reaction of guaiacyl-glycerol-ß-guaiacyl ether with sugars II. Mokuzai Gakkaishi 25: 653-659

Thelen MP, Delmer DP (1986) Gel Electrophoretic separation, detection and characterisation of plant and bacterial UDP-glucose glucosytransferases. Plant Physiol 81: 913-918

Waldron KW, Brett CT (1985) Interactions of enzymes involved in glucuronoxylan synthesis in pea (Pisum sativum) epicotuis. Biochem J 213 :115-122

Whitmore FW (1978) Lignin-protein complex catalysed by peroxidase. Plant Sci Lett 13: 241-245

Wood TM (1985) Aspects of the Biochemistry of Cellulose Degradation in Cellulose and its Derivatives. Kennedy JF, Phillips GO, Wedlock DJ, Williams PA (eds) 173-188 Ellis Horwood

Chapter 8

White-Rot Degradation of Lignin and Xenobiotics

H. E. Schoemaker, U. Tuor, A. Muheim, H. W. H. Schmidt and
M. S. A. Leisola

Introduction

Wood contains three important classes of biopolymers; cellulose, hemicelluloses and lignin. Lignin is a highly irregular, three-dimensional biopolymer composed of oxygenated phenylpropane units. It is synthesised by plants mainly to provide strength and protection. Lignin is formed via a peroxidase-catalyzed polymerisation of methoxy-substituted p-hydroxy-cinnamyl alcohols. The initially formed phenoxy-radicals randomly combine to form a variety of bonds of which the ß-O-4 interunit linkage is the most prevalent. Other representative bonds include ß-5 (phenylcoumaran), 5,5 (biphenyl), α-O-4 (α-arylether) and ß-1 (diarylpropane); α and ß refer to, respectively, the Cα and Cß carbon atoms of the phenylpropane units, O-4 indicates the oxygen atom of the p-hydroxy-group. The numbers refer to the carbon atoms in the aromatic ring, with C-1 carrying the propyl side chain. A schematic representation of the lignin structure is given by Dart *et al.* Chapter 7, this volume. The benzylic hydroxy groups are introduced via quinone methide intermediates (Higuchi 1990).

The white-rot fungus *Phanerochaete chrysosporium* has been widely used as a model system to understand the processes of lignin biodegradation. The isolation of the lignin peroxidase from ligninolytic cultures of this fungus (Tien and Kirk 1983; Glenn *et al.* 1983) and the subsequent elucidation of the mechanism of this enzyme (Schoemaker *et al.* 1985) have generated a widespread interest in the ligninolytic system of other white-rot fungi such as *Coriolus versicolor*, *Phlebia radiata*, *Bjerkandera adusta* etc. Moreover, due to the rather unspecific nature of the lignin peroxidase activity in combination with its remarkably strong oxidising power, the degradation of a number of persistent xenobiotics has also received considerable attention in recent years. Recently, a number of review papers on lignin biodegradation (Kirk and Farrell 1987;

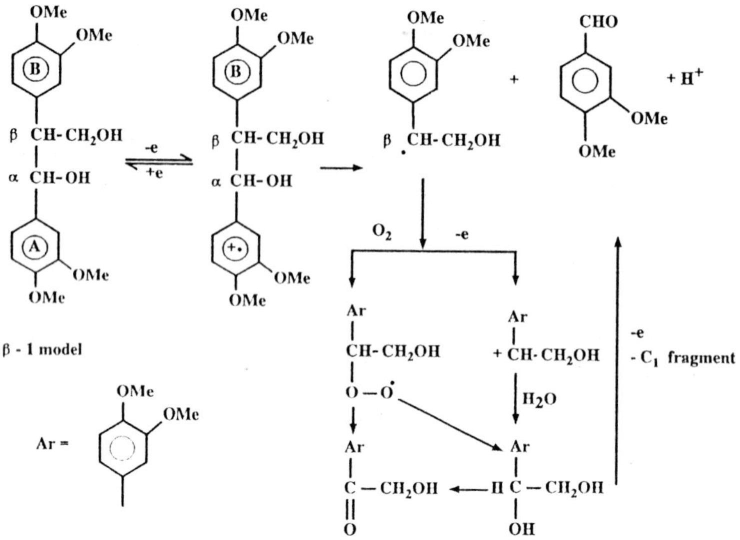

OMe OMe

β CH-CH₂OH
α CH-OH

OMe
OMe

β - 1 model

OMe
OMe

β CH-CH₂OH
α CH-OH

OMe
OMe

-e / +e

OMe
OMe

β ·CH-CH₂OH

+

CHO

OMe

+ H⁺

OMe

O₂ | -e

Ar
CH-CH₂OH
O—O·

Ar
+ CH·CH₂OH

H₂O

-e
- C₁ fragment

Ar
C—CH₂OH
‖
O

Ar
H C—CH₂OH
|
OH

OMe
OMe

Ar =

Scheme 8.1. Single electron transfer from the methoxylated aromatic ring to the oxidised forms of the iron-protoporphyrin IX containing active site of lignin peroxidase.

Tien 1987; Buswell and Odier 1987; Umezawa 1988; Schoemaker and Leisola 1990, Schoemaker 1990) and on the degradation of environmental pollutants (Bumpus and Aust 1987a) have appeared. Therefore, in this review only a general outline of the insights gained into this exciting field will be given. Attention will be focussed on some new data on the isolation of other enzyme systems from white-rot fungi and their possible role in the catabolism of lignin. Moreover, some recent results in the field of xenobiotic degradation will be highlighted.

Degradation of Lignin

Chemical Mechanism of Lignin Peroxidase Catalysis

In 1983 both Kirk (Tien and Kirk 1983) and Gold (Glenn et al. 1983) announced the isolation of a unique enzyme, ligninase, from ligninolytic cultures of the white-rot fungus *P. chrysosporium*, capable of oxidizing non-phenolic lignin and lignin models. Although first described as an H₂O₂-requiring oxygenase, in 1985 it was established that ligninase should be designated a peroxidase (Harvey et al. 1985; Kuila et al. 1985; Renganathan and Gold 1986). At present, the enzyme is generally referred to as lignin peroxidase (LiP). In fact, a number of isoenzymes with molecular weights of approximately 41 000 have been isolated from *P. chrysosporium* (Leisola et al. 1987). The physical and kinetic properties of these isoenzymes have been described (Farrell et al. 1989; Glumoff et al. 1990). Also, LiP has been crystallized (Glumoff et al. 1989). Due to the specific incorporation of 18O from dioxygen on the Cβ atom of a ß-1 dimer model compound upon ligninase-induced Cα-Cβ cleavage, it was thought at first that the ligninase was an oxygenase. Subsequent research, however, showed that this result

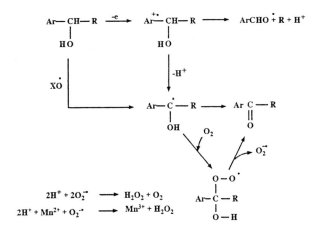

Scheme 8.2. Mechanism for oxidation of non-phenolic, electron rich aromatic compounds by single electron transfer and involving the formation of radical cations.

should be explained by the mechanism depicted in Scheme 8.1, in which single-electron transfer takes place from the methoxylated aromatic ring to the oxidized forms of the iron-protoporphyrin IX containing active site of the LiP, the so-called compound I and compound II.

The redox cycle of the enzyme is presently under active investigation in a number of laboratories (Marquez *et al.* 1988; Harvey and Palmer 1990; Cai and Tien 1989, 1990; Wariishi and Gold 1989, 1990). In its basic form the cycle can be represented as:

$$Enz\text{-}Fe^{III}P + H_2O_2 \qquad \rightarrow \qquad Enz\text{-}Fe^{IV}= O\ P^{+\cdot} + H_2O$$
$$\text{compound I}$$
$$Enz\text{-}Fe^{IV}= O\ P^{+\cdot} + H^+ + e \qquad \rightarrow \qquad Enz\text{-}Fe^{IV}= O\ P$$
$$\text{compound II}$$
$$Enz\text{-}Fe^{IV}= O\ P\ + H^+ + e \qquad \rightarrow \qquad Enz\text{-}Fe^{III}P + H_2O$$

Enz = apo-enzyme; P = protoporphyrin IX

Thus, LiP will oxidize non-phenolic, electron-rich aromatic compounds by a single-electron transfer mechanism that entails formation of radical cations. The ensuing reactions of the radical cations include (Cα-Cβ)-cleavage, demethoxylation and other ether bond cleaving reactions, hydroxylation of benzylic methylene groups, oxidation of benzylic alcohols, decarboxylation, formation of phenols and quinones and aromatic ring cleavage. In those processes reaction of oxygen with intermediate radicals will occur, resulting either in oxygen incorporation or in oxygen activation (i.e. reduction to superoxide anion). These reactions have been comprehensively reviewed (Schoemaker 1990 and references cited). In Schemes 8.2 and 8.3 the mechanistic base for the above mentioned reactions is given. Radical cation formation in substituted benzyl alcohols can either lead to Cα-oxidation or to Cα-Cβ cleavage, depending on the stability of the resulting radical R. Oxygen incorporation is the result of reaction of the radical R (or other radicals) with molecular oxygen. Oxygen activation can occur via reaction of the intermediate hydroxy-substituted benzyl radical

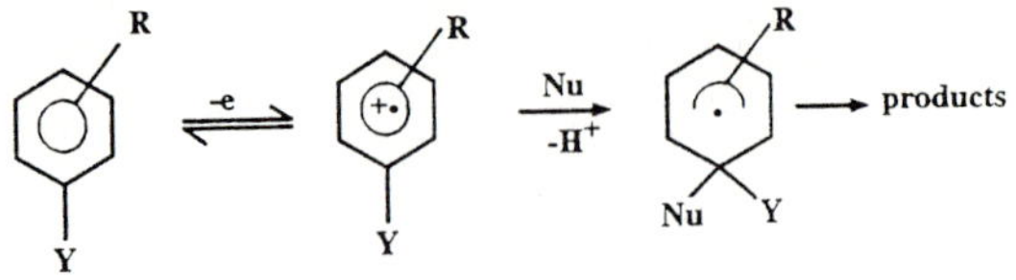

Scheme 8.3. Reaction with nucleophiles when labile bonds are absent in the ß-position relative to the radical cation.

with oxygen, upon which superoxide anion and the corresponding aldehyde or ketone is formed (Scheme 8.2). If no labile bonds in the position ß relative to the radical cation are present, reactions with nucleophiles can occur, e.g. reaction with the solvent water, leading to a cyclohexadienyl radical (Scheme 8.3). The fate of this radical can be rather complex depending on the substituents and the reaction conditions. The radical can react with molecular oxygen, or further oxidation to the corresponding carbonium ion can occur, followed by reaction with water. Both possibilities will be discussed in the paragraphs on veratryl alcohol oxidation and benzo[a]pyrene oxidation, respectively.

The Cα-Cß cleavage depicted in Scheme 8.1 represents one of the depolymerizing reactions observed in lignin biodegradation. Another major depolymerizing reaction is the ether cleavage occurring in ß-O-4 lignin models, where it is observed in competition with the Cα-Cß cleavage similar to the one decribed for the ß-1 model (see Scheme 8.4a and b). Note that during the cleavage-reaction phenols are generated as products. Phenols are well known substrates for peroxidases, their oxidation often giving rise to polymerisation.

Thus, from Scheme 8.4a and 8.4b it can be inferred that during LiP catalyzed oxidation of non-phenolic lignin (obtained from the natural phenolic lignin, e.g. by methylation) at first depolymerisation will be observed, but in the course of the depolymerising Cα-Cß or ether-bond cleavages, phenols will be formed, which can polymerise again. This effect is even more pronounced if the reaction is performed with the natural phenolic lignin. Indeed, upon incubation of this substrate with LiP, polymerisation is observed almost exclusively (Haemmerli *et al.* 1986b). Still, LiP stimulates the biodegradation of lignin (as monitored by the increase in formation of $^{14}CO_2$ from ^{14}C-labeled lignin) by ligninolytic cultures of *P. chrysosporium*. In the crucial experiment the extracellular LiP was first removed from the fungal pellets by a careful washing procedure and the formation of $^{14}CO_2$ was measured. Subsequently, purified LiP was added to the fungal pellets. Upon addition of LiP a strong increase in the formation of $^{14}CO_2$ was observed (Leisola *et al.* 1988). Obviously, LiP is only a part of the ligninolytic system of the white-rot fungus *P. chrysosporium*.

Oxidation of Veratryl Alcohol and Related Compounds

Lignin itself is a quite complicated system to study. Therefore mostly model systems are used to gain an insight into the reactivity of LiP. Evidently, extrapolation of the results obtained with such simple model compounds to the polymeric case should be undertaken with the utmost care.

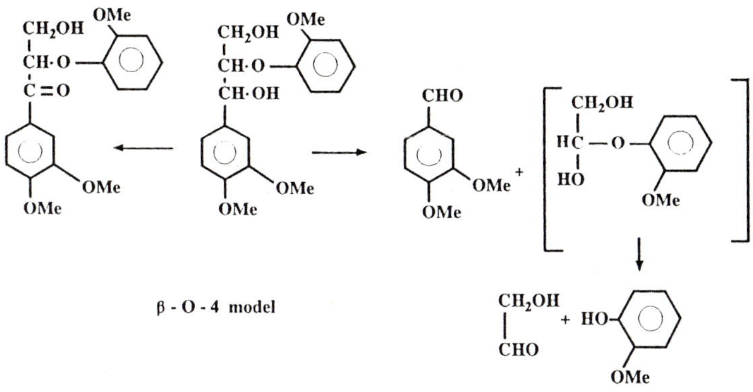

Scheme 8.4a. Cα–Cβ cleavage in ß-O-4 lignin models.

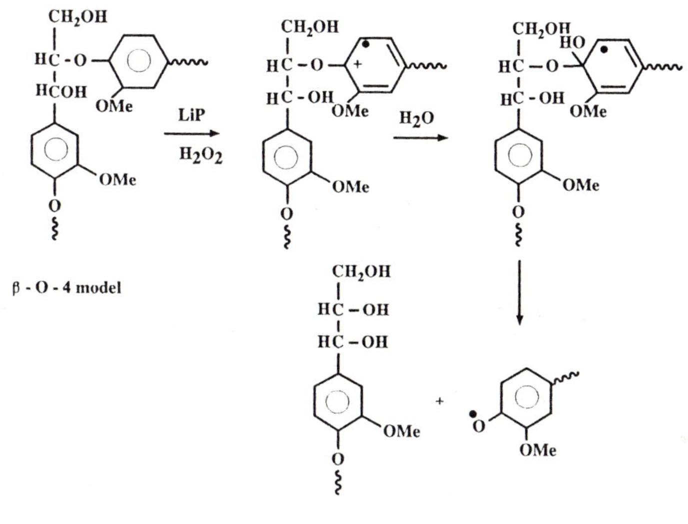

Scheme 8.4b. Ether cleavage in ß-O-4 lignin models.

As a very simple model system veratryl alcohol oxidation will be discussed. Veratryl alcohol plays a pivotal role in studies on lignin biodegradation. Veratryl alcohol is a secondary metabolite of the white-rot fungus *P. chrysosporium* but remarkably, veratryl alcohol is also metabolized by ligninolytic cultures of this organism. It is an inducer for lignin peroxidase and it seems to protect the enzyme against H_2O_2. In general, veratryl alcohol oxidation is used as an assay for lignin peroxidase activity.

At first it was believed that veratraldehyde was the only product and that oxygen did not play a role in the process. However, careful analysis of the reaction products and the stoichiometry of the reaction showed that dioxygen is both used as an electron acceptor and as a reagent. Molecular oxygen is incorporated in some of the reaction products. Also, dioxygen is converted to H_2O_2 via the intermediacy of superoxide

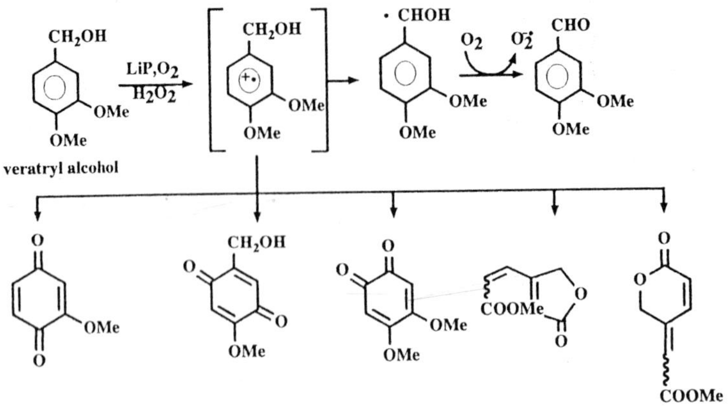

Fig. 8.1. Lignin peroxidase-catalysed oxidation of veratryl alcohol.

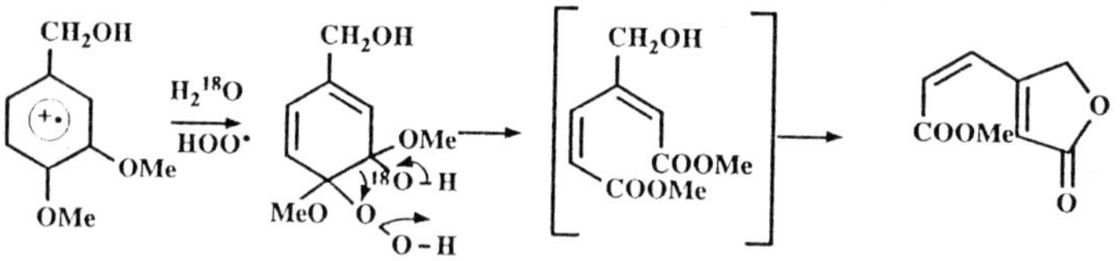

Scheme 8.5. Aromatic ring opening and quinone side products formed during lignin peroxidase-catalysed oxidation of veratryl alcohol.

anion. The H_2O_2 produced is then used in the redox cycle of the lignin peroxidase and thus reduced to H_2O.

In Figure 8.1 the products of the LiP-catalysed oxidation of veratryl alcohol are depicted. Veratraldehyde is the major product. Important features of the reaction are the formation of quinones as side products and the fact that aromatic ring opening occurs as depicted in Scheme 8.5. For a detailed discussion of the reaction mechanisms the reader is referred to other reviews (see Schoemaker 1990).

In the ring cleavage reaction the radical cation is formed first, followed by reaction with the nucleophile water. The resulting cyclohexadienyl radical then reacts with molecular oxygen or perhydroxyl radical, followed by ring opening with concomitant loss of water. The resulting muconic diester derivative subsequently cyclises to the observed lactone. The latter reaction can be inhibited if the methyl ether of veratryl alcohol is used as the substrate (Fig. 8.2). Interestingly, the methyl ester of veratric acid is observed as a minor product in the oxidation of veratryl alcohol methyl ether at pH3, but at pH5 it becomes a major product, together with veratraldehyde. This is the first time that a carboxylic acid derivative is observed in an LiP-catalysed reaction (Schmidt *et al.* 1989). Aromatic ring cleavage is not confined to monomeric compounds, also with dimeric and polymeric substrates this type of LiP-induced ring opening has been observed (Higuchi,1990; Gold *et al.* 1989; Schoemaker 1990).

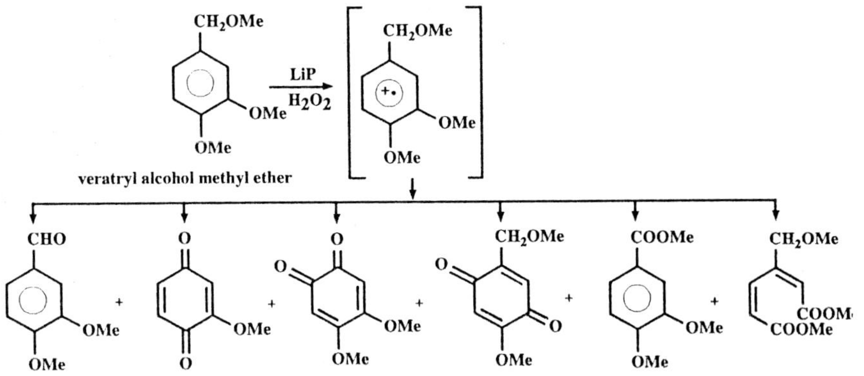

Fig. 8.2. Inhibition of lactone production with veratryl alcohol methyl ether.

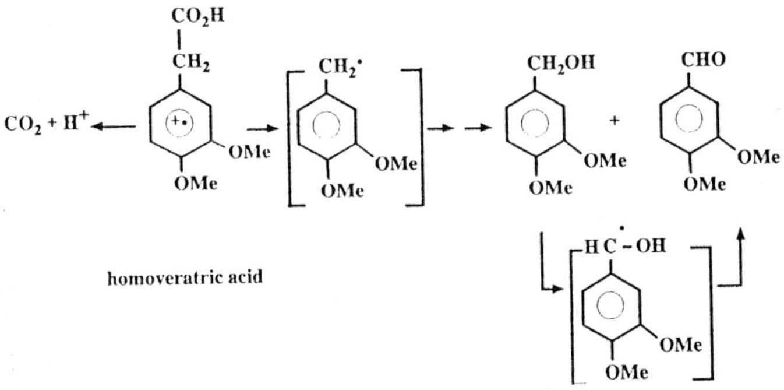

Scheme 8.6. Lignin peroxidase oxidation of homoveratric acid to veratraldehyde via formation of a radical cation.

Lignin Peroxidase Assay Systems

Veratryl alcohol oxidation is often used as an assay system for LiP activity in ligninolytic cultures of white-rot fungi, mainly because of its convenience, i.e. the reaction can be UV-monitored at 310 nm due to the formation of veratraldehyde. However, those data should be interpreted with care since formation of veratraldehyde does not necessarily imply that the radical cation of veratryl alcohol has been an intermediate. It should be stressed that it is in fact the ability of LiP to form radical cations from methoxylated aromatic rings that gives LiP its power to induce Cα-Cβ cleavage, ether bond cleavage (and aromatic ring opening) of non-phenolic systems, thereby inducing depolymerisation (Schemes 8.1 and 8.4). In contrast, veratraldehyde can be formed from veratryl alcohol via abstraction of the Cα H-atom followed by further oxidation (Scheme 8.1). A corollary of such a process is that no radical cation is formed (the enzyme involved is not LiP!) and consequently no quinone formation or aromatic ring opening will be observed and no Cα-Cβ cleavage or ether cleavage (thus no depolymerisation) will be induced. As an illustration of such a case the aryl alcohol

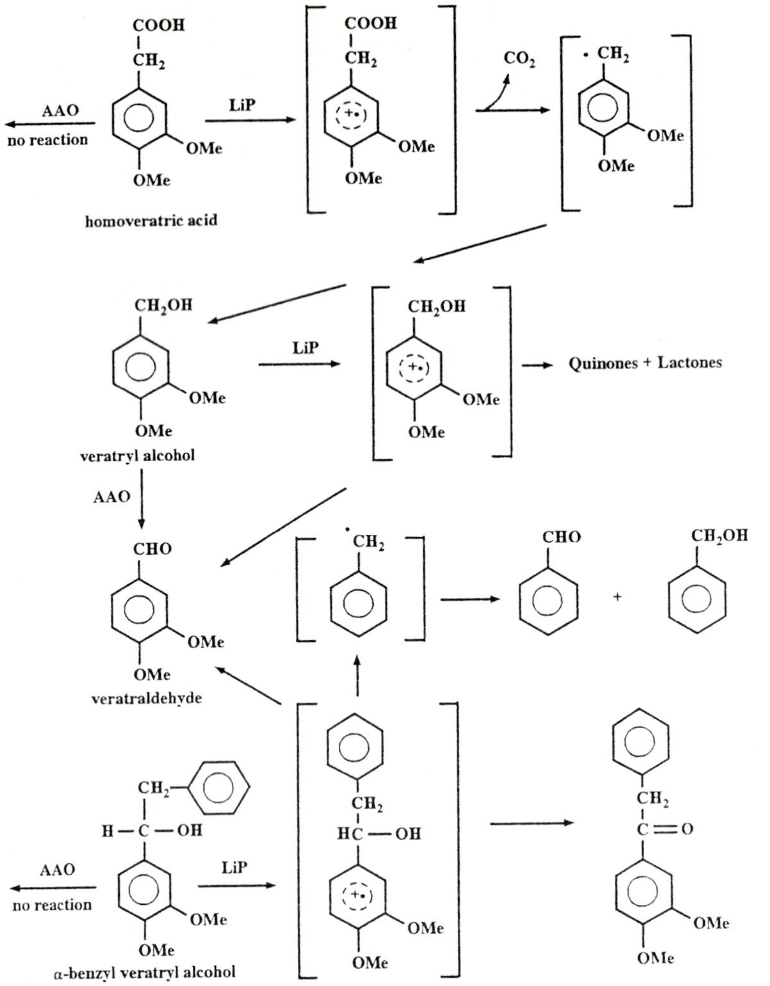

Scheme 8.7. Lignin peroxidase from *B. adusta* catalysing oxidation of homoveratric acid and cleavage of the Cα–Cß bond in α-benzyl veratryl alcohol.

oxidase from *B. adusta* will be discussed. This enzyme is capable of oxidising a number of aryl alcohols, including anisyl alcohol, veratryl alcohol, vanillyl alcohol and benzyl alcohol, under formation of H_2O_2 (Muheim *et al.* 1990a). The enzyme uses molecular oxygen as an electron acceptor. The enzyme, however, is not capable of oxidizing homoveratric acid (LiP will oxidize homoveratric acid to veratraldehyde via formation of the radical cation, decarboxylation and further oxidation of the resulting 3,4-dimethoxybenzyl radical, see Scheme 8.6). Moreover, the enzyme was also not capable of inducing Cα-Cß cleavage in α-benzyl veratryl alcohol, indicating that no radical cation was formed and that the enzyme indeed did not have the powerful depolymerising properties of LiP (Muheim *et al.* 1990b).

Remarkably, *B. adusta* also produces LiP, which has been purified to homogeneity. In contrast to the aryl alcohol oxidase (AAO) discussed above, this LiP from *B. adusta* had indeed the ability to oxidise homoveratric acid to veratraldehyde and to induce Cα-Cß cleavage in α-benzyl veratryl alcohol, indicating it has depolymerising properties (Scheme 8.7). It can be argued that since the aryl alcohol oxidase and the LiP use different electron acceptors it will be easier to distinguish between the two enzymes by doing the experiment under anaerobic conditions (only LiP will give veratraldehyde) than to use homoveratric acid (not very soluble in water) or α-benzyl veratryl alcohol (not readily accessible and slightly unstable) as assay systems.

However, a more serious problem arises if other H_2O_2-dependent enzymes are found that will oxidise veratryl alcohol via side-chain oxidation, a distinct possibility, as can be inferred from the fact that e.g. the chloroperoxidase from *Caldariomyces fumago* will dehydrogenate some benzyl alcohols to the corresponding aldehydes (Geigert *et al.* 1983). Thus, when screening for LiP activities in microbial cultures using the veratryl alcohol assay method, the LiP should eventually be checked further, either by looking at the side products (quinones and ring-opened products) of the veratryl alcohol oxidation using high performance liquid chromatography (HPLC) methods, or by using other assay systems like homoveratric acid, α-benzyl veratryl alcohol or similar compounds which indicate a radical cationic intermediate.

An alternative approach was developed by Palmer and co-workers (Harvey *et al.* 1986; Dodson *et al.* 1987) based on the so-called mediator effect. LiP will oxidise dimethoxylated aromatic rings rather readily. Monomethoxylated compounds, however, are notoriously poor substrates for LiP. Thus, veratryl alcohol is oxidised to veratraldehyde and dimethoxybenzene is oxidised to benzoquinone. In contrast, anisyl alcohol is hardly converted to anisaldehyde and in the LiP catalysed oxidation of 4-methoxymandelic acid only traces of anisaldehyde are formed. Surprisingly, it was found that the addition of catalytic amounts of dimethoxybenzene or veratryl alcohol to the 4-methoxymandelic acid oxidation, resulted in a markedly increased rate of anisaldehyde formation, whilst no benzoquinone or veratraldehyde was formed. Those results were interpreted as involving the formation of the radical cation of dimethoxybenzene or veratryl alcohol. These act as powerful one-electron oxidants, oxidising the abundant 4-methoxymandelic acid to the corresponding radical cation, which in a subsequent step is rapidly and irreversibly decarboxylated under formation of the corresponding hydroxy-substituted 4-methoxybenzyl radical. This is further oxidised to anisaldehyde. In this process dimethoxybenzene, respectively veratryl alcohol are regenerated again (Scheme 8.8).

Although this interpretation is still somewhat controversial and has met severe criticism (Cui and Dolphin 1989; Kirk and Farrell 1987), Palmer and co-workers have used this methodology to assay for an LiP isolated from ligninolytic cultures of *C. versicolor* (Dodson *et al.* 1987). This LiP also catalysed the oxidation of homoveratric acid and the ß-1 lignin model dimer 1,2-di(3,4-dimethoxyphenyl)-1,3-propanediol. More recently, the oxidation of ß-O-4 models by LiP from *C. versicolor* was also described (Kawai *et al.* 1990).

The basis for the criticism lies in the fact that the redox cycle of LiP is still poorly understood, despite a number of rapid scan stopped-flow spectroscopic studies. The addition of the dimethoxylated compounds seems to prevent the formation of the catalytically poorly active compound III (see Scheme 8.8) by converting the intermediate compound II back to native enzyme (Harvey *et al.* 1989a; Cai and Tien 1989, 1990). Alternatively it has been argued that veratryl alcohol converts compound III (or a modified form of compound III) back to native enzyme via a ligand

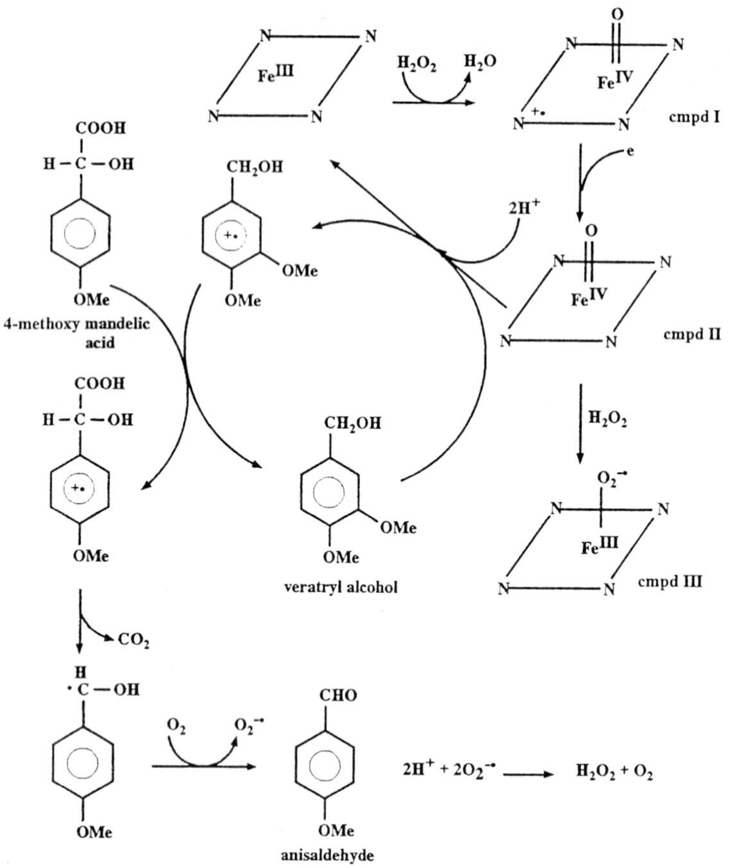

Scheme 8.8. Formation of the radical cation and regeneration of veratryl alcohol during conversion of 4-methoxy-mandelic acid to anisaldehyde.

displacement reaction (Wariishi and Gold 1989, 1990). A detailed discussion of this problem, however, would go beyond the scope of this review. Still, the mediator effect remains an interesting phenomenon and should be investigated in more detail.

Recently, the oxidation of methoxylated benzyl alcohols by laccase of *C. versicolor* in the presence of syringaldehyde was described (Kawai *et al.* 1989). Without syringaldehyde being present, laccase will not oxidise veratryl alcohol. The authors rationalised their results by assuming mediation by the radical cation of syringaldehyde as depicted in Scheme 8.9. However, laccase was not capable of inducing Cα-Cß cleavage in the non-phenolic ß-1 dimeric lignin model 1,2-di(3,4,5-trimethoxyphenyl)-1,3-propanediol in the presence of syringaldehyde. This indicates that no radical cation is formed and the proposed mechanism is clearly erroneous. More likely, veratryl alcohol is oxidised via abstraction of the Cα H-atom (cf. Scheme 8.1) and further oxidation of the hydroxy-substituted 3,4-dimethoxybenzyl radical. Most probably, the phenoxy radical of syringaldehyde is responsible for the hydrogen atom abstraction.

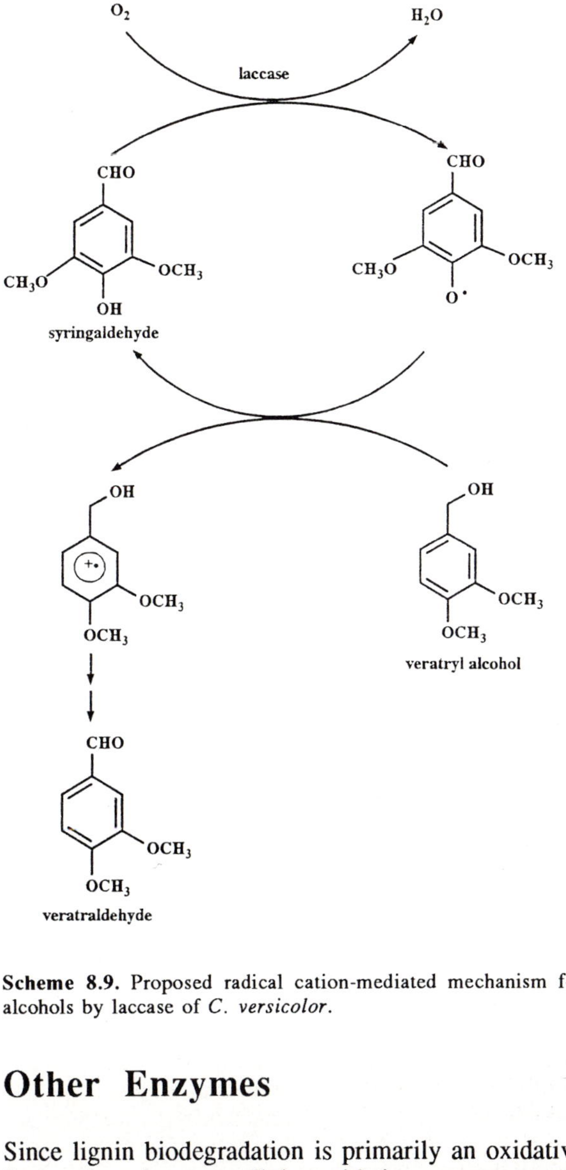

O_2

H_2O

laccase

CHO

CH_3O — OCH_3

OH

syringaldehyde

CHO

CH_3O — OCH_3

$O^{\bullet}$

OH

OCH_3

OCH_3

(+•)

CHO

OCH_3

OCH_3

veratraldehyde

OH

OCH_3

OCH_3

veratryl alcohol

Scheme 8.9. Proposed radical cation-mediated mechanism for oxidation of methoxylated benzyl alcohols by laccase of *C. versicolor*.

Other Enzymes

Since lignin biodegradation is primarily an oxidative process, attention has mainly focussed on the extracellular oxidative enzymes present in ligninolytic cultures of the white-rot fungi.

P. chrysosporium produces glyoxal oxidase, an extracellular H_2O_2-producing enzyme, which can use the C1-C3 fragments derived from the side-chains of the lignin building blocks after Cα-Cβ cleavage (Kersten and Kirk 1987)

In addition to LiP, *P. chrysosporium* also produces a set of other isoenzymes, the so-called Mn(II)-dependent peroxidases (MnP). These enzymes oxidise phenolic lignin and lignin models and require Mn(II) for their activity (Wariishi *et al.* 1989a, 1989b). A detailed discussion of these interesting enzymes would go beyond the scope of this review. A brief description can be found in Evans, chapter 9 this volume. As a first

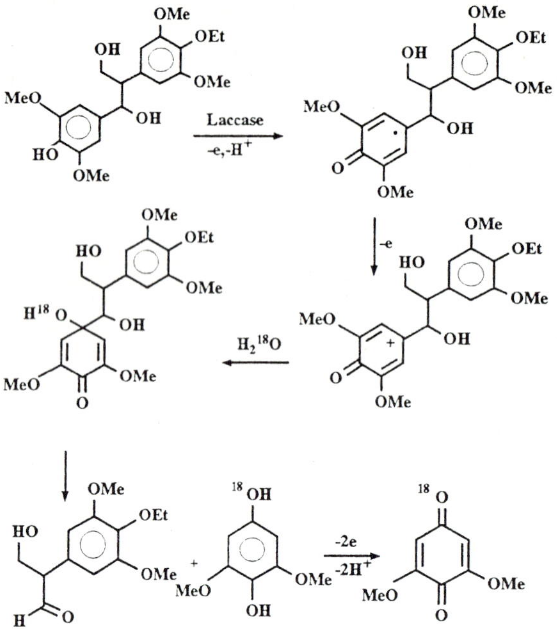

Scheme 8.10. Laccase-catalysed Cα-arene cleavage resulting in quinone/hydroquinone products.

tentative conclusion it can be stated that the activity of the Mn(II)-dependent peroxidase is quite similar to the activity of laccase (*vide infra*) present in other ligninolytic fungi like e.g. *C. versicolor* (Higuchi 1990) and *P. radiata* (Niku-Paavola *et al.* 1990). Laccase is a copper-containing enzyme that uses oxygen as the final electron acceptor. Evidently, the mechanisms of action of laccase and MnP are quite different. The function of MnP in *P. chrysosporium* is not yet known, but it can be envisaged that it protects LiP from phenolic substrates, which give rise to rapid inactivation of LiP (Harvey and Palmer 1990).

Laccase is the most important oxidative enzyme produced by *C. versicolor* and has been the subject of numerous studies which have been extensively reviewed (Higuchi 1990). In Scheme 8.10 an important laccase-catalysed Cα-arene cleavage is depicted, again a depolymerising reaction. As a result of this reaction quinones/hydroquinones are formed as products (*vide infra*).

As already mentioned LiP is also present in ligninolytic cultures of *C. versicolor*, *B. adusta* and *P. radiata*.

From the foregoing discussion it can be inferred that quinones are ubiquitous products of both non-phenolic (LiP-mediated) and phenolic (laccase or MnP-mediated) lignin model compound degradation. Therefore it is not surprising that *P. chrysosporium* produces a number of quinone reductases (Schoemaker *et al.* 1989). Also, aryl aldehyde reductases and aryl carboxylic acid reductases are produced by white-rot fungi like *P. chrysosporium* and *P. radiata*. The role of these enzymes is not yet clear at present, although their involvement in lignin biodegradation has been implied (Schoemaker *et al.* 1989; Schoemaker and Leisola 1990; Schoemaker 1990).

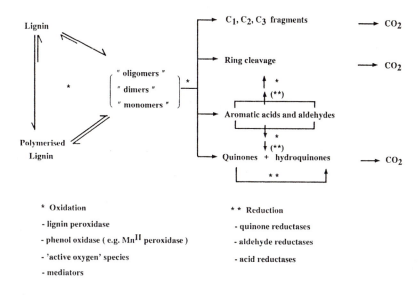

* Oxidation   ** Reduction

- lignin peroxidase   - quinone reductases

- phenol oxidase (e.g. Mn^{II} peroxidase)   - aldehyde reductases

- 'active oxygen' species   - acid reductases

- mediators

Fig. 8.3. Polymerisation/depolymerisation equilibrium during lignin catabolism.

Catabolism of Lignin

The mechanisms by which the fungus limits the peroxidase-induced polymerization of phenolic lignin have yet to be elucidated. It has been suggested that cellobiose quinone oxidoreductase (Westermark and Eriksson 1974) plays a role in this process, although contradicting evidence has been obtained in this respect (Odier *et al.* 1988; Ander *et al.* 1990).

The presence of carbohydrates and glycosidating enzymes has been implicated to prevent polymerization (Kondo *et al.* 1990). Leisola and Garcia also stressed the importance of carbohydrates in the depolymerising process (Leisola and Garcia 1989). We have suggested that by both peroxidase-induced polymerisation as well as peroxidase-induced depolymerisation a dynamic system is established (a so-called polymerisation/ depolymerisation equilibrium) which can be shifted towards degradation by fungal uptake of smaller fragments (Schoemaker *et al.* 1989; Schoemaker and Leisola 1990; Schoemaker 1990). This concept is schematically depicted in Figure 8.3. Harvey *et al.* have suggested that both spatial arrangement and charge transfer reactions are important elements in the process (Harvey *et al.* 1989b).

In conclusion, in recent years tremendous progress has been made in understanding the mechanism of fungal lignin biodegradation. However, due to the extreme complexity of the problem, a vast amount of research remains to be done in order to fully understand all the factors involved in the biodegradation process.

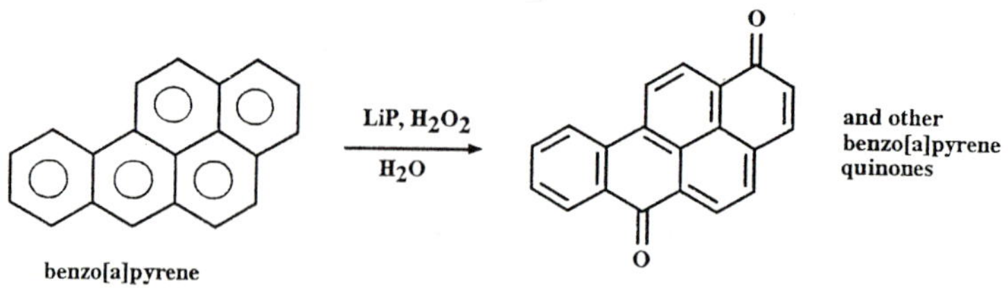

Fig. 8.4. Oxidation of benzo(a)pyrene by crude and purified extracellular lignin peroxidase preparations from *P. chrysosporium*.

Degradation of Xenobiotics

P. chrysosporium is able to degrade a broad spectrum of structurally diverse organic compounds to carbon dioxide. Well known examples are DDT (1,1-bis(4-chlorophenyl)- 2,2,2-trichloroethane), polychlorinated biphenyls, benzo[a]pyrene, 2,3,7,8-tetrachlorodibenzo-*p*-dioxin (Bumpus and Aust 1987a,1987b, Bumpus *et al.* 1985), chlorinated phenols (Hammel and Tardone 1988; Mileski *et al.* 1988; Lin *et al.* 1990), TNT trinitrotoluene (Fernando *et al.* 1990), crystal violet (Bumpus and Brock 1988) and other dyes (Cripps *et al.* 1990). Although the catabolic pathway is not yet known, evidence suggest that the ability to degrade these persistent chemicals is due, at least in part, to the lignin degrading system of *P. chrysosporium* and other white-rot fungi. In this paragraph some of the results obtained in this field are reviewed. Emphasis is placed on those examples in which LiP appears to play a role, i.e. polycyclic aromatic hydrocarbons, chlorinated phenols and dioxins.

The oxidation of benzo[a]pyrene by crude and purified extracellular LiP preparations from *P.chrysosporium* has been studied (Haemmerli *et al.* 1986b). The substrate was oxidised to three organic soluble products, namely benzo[a]pyrene 1,6-, 3,6-, and 6,12-dione (Fig. 8.4).

The mechanism presumably involves LiP-induced radical cation formation, followed by hydroxylation in the 6-position. Further oxidation then yields the mixture of diones. Analogously, the oxidation of pyrene yields a mixture of pyrene diones (Hammel *et al.* 1986). In Scheme 8.11 a hypothetical pathway for the formation of pyrene-1,6-dione is given. Note that in the product both oxygen atoms are derived from water, indicating that in contrast to the veratryl alcohol oxidation ring opening mechanism, the intermediate radical does not react with molecular oxygen. However the radical is further oxidized to the carbonium ion, followed by the addition of water. In the same paper the authors describe the detection of the radical cation of dibenzo[p]dioxin with ESR-spectroscopy. They also studied the oxidation of pyrene with whole fungal cultures. From those studies it can be inferred that the quinones formed in the LiP-mediated oxidation are transient intermediates, similar to the mechanism proposed for the catabolism of lignin. Bumpus recently showed that at least 22 polycyclic aromatic hydrocarbons are degraded by *P. chrysosporium* (Bumpus 1989).

LiP catalyses the oxidative 4-dechlorination of polychlorinated phenols (Hammel and Tardone 1988). The biodegradation of pentachlorophenol by *P. chrysosporium* has also been described (Mileski *et al.* 1988; Lin *et al.* 1990).

In conclusion, the ability of *P. chrysosporium* to degrade a large number of environmentally persistent chemicals has convincingly been demonstrated. However, a

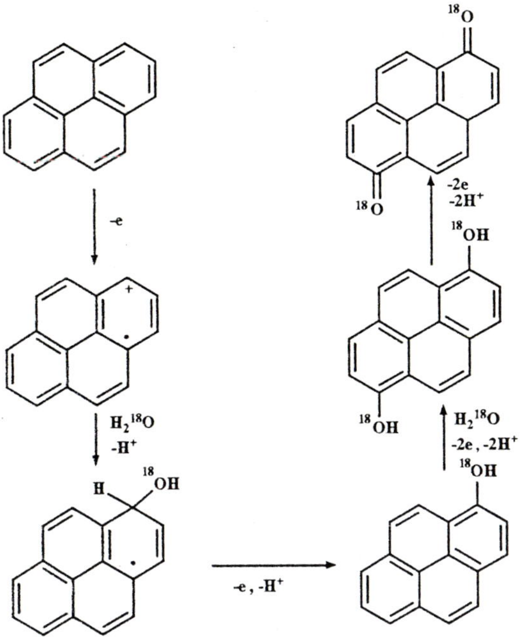

Scheme 8.11. Hypothetical pathway for the formation of pyrene-1,6-dione from pyrene involving formation of a lignin peroxidase-induced radical cation.

word of caution is required here. The oxidation of pyrene, an environmentally ubiquitous nonmutagenic component of combustion emissions, yields diones that are known mutagens (Hammel *et al.* 1986). Therefore, purified ligninase should be used with caution for applications such as waste water treatment. In whole cell cultures, these mutagenic quinones do not persist, but further studies are needed to elucidate the pathway of polycyclic aromatic hydrocarbon (quinone) degradation in *P. chrysosporium*.

Acknowledgements

Mr W Kortenoeven is gratefully acknowledged for his assistance in the preparation of the manuscript.

References

Ander P, Mishra C, Farrell RL, Eriksson KEL (1990) Redox reactions in lignin biodegradation: interactions between laccase, different peroxidases and cellobiose: quinone oxidoreductase. J Biotechnol 13:189-198

Bumpus JA (1989) Biodegradation of polycyclic aromatic hydrocarbons by *Phanerochaete chrysosporium*. Appl Environ Microbiol 55:154-158

Bumpus JA, Aust SD (1987a) Biodegradation of environmental pollutants by the white-rot fungus *Phanerochaete chrysosporium*: involvement of the lignin degrading system. BioEssays 6:166-170

Bumpus JA, Aust SD (1987b) Biodegradation of DDT (1,1,1-trichloro-2,2-bis(4-chlorophenyl)-ethane) by the white-rot fungus *Phanerochaete chrysosporium*. Appl Environ Microbiol 53:2002-2008

Bumpus JA, Brock BJ (1988) Biodegradation of crystal violet by the white-rot fungus *Phanerochaete chrysosporium*. Appl Environm Microbiol 54:1143-1150

Bumpus JA, Tien, Wright D, Aust SD (1985) Oxidation of persistent environmental pollutants by a white-rot fungus. Science 228:1434-1436

Buswell JA, Odier E (1987) Lignin biodegradation. CRC Critical Rev Biotechnol. 6:1-60

Cai D, Tien M (1989) On the reactions of lignin peroxidase compound III (isozyme H8). Biochem Biophys Res Comm 162:464-469

Cai D, Tien M (1990) Characterization of the oxycomplex of lignin peroxidase from *Phanerochaete chrysosporium*. Equilibrium and kinetic studies. Biochemistry 29:2085-2091

Cripps C, Bumpus JA, Aust SD (1990) Biodegradation of azo and heterocyclic dyes by *Phanerochaete chrysosporium*. Appl Environ Microbiol 56:1114-1118

Cui F, Dolphin D (1989) Biomimetic studies in lignin degradation. In: Lewis NG, Paice MG (eds) Plant cell wall polymers, ACS Symposium series 399, Washington pp 519-528

Dodson PJ, Evans CS, Harvey PJ, Palmer JM (1987) Production and properties of an extracellular peroxidase from *Coriolus versicolor* which catalyses $C\alpha$-$C\beta$ cleavage in a lignin model compound. FEMS Microbiol Letters 42:17-22

Farrell RL, Murtagh KE, Tien M, Mozuch MD, Kirk TK (1989) Physical and enzymatic properties of lignin peroxidase isoenzymes from *Phanerochaete chrysosporium*. Enzyme Microb Technol 11:322-328

Fernando T, Bumpus JA, Aust SD (1990) Biodegradation of TNT (trinitrotoluene) by *Phanerochaete chrysosporium*. Appl Environ Microbiol 56:1666-1671

Geigert J, Dalitoes DJ, Neidleman SL, Lee TD, Wadsworth J (1983) Peroxide oxidation of primary alcohols to aldehydes by chloroperoxidase catalysis. Biochem Biophys Res Comm 114:1104-1108

Glenn JK, Morgan MA, Mayfield MB, Kuwahara M, Gold MH (1983) An extracellular H_2O_2-requiring enzyme preparation involved in lignin biodegradation by the white-rot basidiomycete *Phanerochaete chrysosporium*. Biochem Biophys Res Comm 114:1077-1083

Glumoff T, Winterhalter KH, Smit JDG (1989) Monoclinic crystals of lignin peroxidase. FEBS Letters 257:59-62

Glumoff T, Harvey PJ, Molinari S, Frank G, Palmer JM, Smit JDG, Leisola MSA (1990) Lignin peroxidase from *Phanerochaete chrysosporium*. Molecular and kinetic characterization of isozymes. Eur J Biochem 187: 515-520

Gold MH, Wariishi H, Valli K (1989) Extracellular peroxidases involved in lignin degradation by the white-rot basidiomycete *Phanerochaete chrysosporium*. In: Biocatalysis in Agricultural Biotechnology. Whitaker JR, Sonnet PE (eds) ACS Symposium series No. 389, Washington pp 127-140

Haemmerli SD, Leisola MSA, Fiechter A (1986a) Polymerisation of lignins by ligninases from *Phanerochaete chrysosporium*. FEMS Microbiology Letters, 35:33-36

Haemmerli SD, Leisola MSA, Sanglard D, Fiechter A (1986b) Oxidation of benzo[a]pyrene by extracellular ligninases from *Phanerochaete chrysosporium*. J Biol Chem 261:6900-6903

Haemmerli SD, Schoemaker HE, Schmidt HWH, Leisola MSA (1987) Oxidation of veratryl alcohol by the lignin peroxidase of *Phanerochaete chrysosporium*: involvement of activated oxygen. FEBS Letters 220:149-154

Hammel KE, Kalyanaraman B, Kirk TK (1986) Oxidation of polycyclic aromatic hydrocarbons and dibenzo[p]dioxins by *Phanerochaete chrysosporium* ligninase. J Biol Chem 261:16948-16952

Hammel KE, Tardone PJ (1988) The oxidative 4-dechlorination of polychlorinated phenols is catalyzed by extracellular fungal lignin peroxidase. Biochemistry 27:6563-6568

Harvey PJ, Schoemaker HE, Bowen RM, Palmer JM (1985) Single-electron transfer processes and the reaction mechanism of enzymic degradation of lignin. FEBS Letters 183:13-16

Harvey PJ, Schoemaker HE, Palmer JM (1986) Veratryl alcohol as a mediator and the role of radical cations in lignin biodegradation by *Phanerochaete chrysosporium*. FEBS Letters, 195:242-246

Harvey PJ, Palmer JM, Schoemaker HE, Dekker HL, Wever R (1989a) Pre-steady-state kinetic study on the formation of compound I and II of ligninase. Biochim Biophys Acta 994:59-63

Harvey PJ, Gilardi GF, Palmer JM (1989b) Importance of charge transfer reactions in lignin degradation. In: Coughlan MP (ed) Enzyme systems for lignocellulose degradation. Elsevier, London pp 111-120

Harvey PJ, Palmer JM (1990) Oxidation of phenolic compounds by ligninase. J Biotechnol 13:169-179

Higuchi T (1990) Lignin biochemistry: biosynthesis and biodegradation. Wood Sci Technol 24:23-63

Kawai S, Umezawa T, Higuchi T (1989) Oxidation of methoxylated benzyl alcohols by laccase of *Coriolus versicolor* in the presence of syringaldehyde. Wood Research 76:10-16

Kawai S, Shoji S, Nabeta K, Okuyama H, Higuchi T (1990) Degradation of non-phenolic ß-O-4 ligin substructure model compounds by lignin peroxidase from *Coriolus versicolor*. Mokuzai Gakkaishi 36:126-132

Kersten P, Kirk TK (1987) Involvement of a new enzyme, glyoxal oxidase, in extracellullar H_2O_2 production by *Phanerochaete chrysosporium*. J Bacteriology 169:2195-2201

Kirk TK, Farrell RL (1987) Enzymatic "combustion": the microbial degradation of lignin. Ann Rev Microbiol 41:465-505

Kondo R, Iimori T, Imamura H, Nishida T (1990) Polymerization of DHP and depolymerization of DHP-glucoside by lignin oxidizing enzymes. J Biotechnol 13:181-188

Kuila D, Tien M, Fee JA, Ondrias MR (1985) Resonance raman spectra of extracellular ligninase: Evidence for a heme active site similar to those of peroxidases. Biochemistry 24:3394-3397

Leisola MSA, Kozulic B, Meussdoerffer F, Fiechter A (1987) Homology among multiple extracellular peroxidases from *Phanerochaete chrysosporium*. J Biol Chem 262:419-424

Leisola MSA, Haemmerli SD, Waldner R, Schoemaker HE, Schmidt HWH, Fiechter A (1988) Metabolism of a lignin model compound, 3,4-dimethoxybenzyl alcohol by *Phanerochaete chrysosporium*. Cellulose Chem Technol 22:267-277

Leisola MSA, Garcia S (1989) The mechanism of lignin degradation. In: Coughlan MP (ed) Enzyme systems for lignocellulose degradation. Elsevier, London. pp 89-99

Lin JE, Wang HY, Hickey RF (1990) Degradation kinetics of pentachlorophenol by *Phanerochaete chrysosporium*. Biotechnol Bioeng 35:1125-1134

Marquez L, Wariishi H, Dunford HB, Gold MH (1988) Spectroscopic and kinetic properties of the oxidized intermediates of lignin peroxidase from *Phanerochaete chrysosporium*. J Biol Chem 263:10549-10552

Mileski GJ, Bumpus JA, Jurek MA, Aust SD (1988) Biodegradation of pentachlorophenol by the white-rot fungus *Phanerochaete chrysosporium*. Appl Environ Microbiol 54:2885-2889

Muheim A, Waldner R, Leisola MSA, Fiechter A (1990a) An extracellular aryl alcohol oxidase from the white-rot fungus *Bjerkandera adusta*. Enzyme Microb Technol 12:204-209

Muheim A, Leisola MSA, Schoemaker HE (1990b) Aryl alcohol oxidase and lignin peroxidase from the white-rot fungus *Bjerkandera adusta*. J Biotechnol 13:159-167

Niku-Paavola ML, Karhunen E, Kantelinen A, Viikari L, Lundell T, Hatakka A (1990) The effect of culture conditions on the production of lignin modifying enzymes by the white-rot fungus *Phlebia radiata*. J Biotechnol 13:211-221

Odier E, Mozuch MD, Kalyanaraman B, Kirk TK (1988) Ligninase-mediated phenoxy radical formation and polymerization unaffected by cellobiose:quinone oxidoreductase. Biochimie 70:847-852

Renganathan V, Gold MH (1986) Spectral characterization of the oxidized states of lignin peroxidase, an extracellular heme enzyme from the white-rot basidiomycete *Phanerochaete chrysosporium*. Biochemistry, 25:1626-1631

Schmidt HWH, Haemmerli SD, Schoemaker HE, Leisola MSA (1989) Oxidative degradation of 3,4-dimethoxybenzyl alcohol and its methyl ether by the lignin peroxidase of *Phanerochaete chrysosporium*. Biochemistry 28:1776-1783

Schoemaker HE, Harvey PJ, Bowen RM, Palmer JM (1985) On the mechanism of enzymatic lignin breakdown. FEBS Letters 183:7-12

Schoemaker HE, Meijer EM, Leisola MSA, Haemmerli SD, Waldner R, Sanglard D, Schmidt HWH (1989) Oxidation and reduction in lignin biodegradation. In: Lewis NG, Paice MG (eds) Biogenesis and biodegradation of plant cell polymers. ACS Symposium series Vol 399, Washington pp 454-471

Schoemaker HE, Leisola MSA (1990) Degradation of lignin by *Phanerochaete chrysosporium*. J Biotechnol 13:101-109

Schoemaker HE (1990) On the chemistry of lignin biodegradation. Recl Trav Chim Pays-Bas 109:255-272

Tien M, Kirk TK (1983) Lignin-degrading enzyme from the Hymenocyte *Phanerochaete chrysosporium* Burds Science, 221:661-663

Tien M (1987) Properties of ligninase from *Phanerochaete chrysosporium* and their applications. CRC Critical Rev Microbiol 15:141-168

Umezawa T (1988) Mechanisms for chemical reactions involved in lignin biodegradation by *Phanerochaete chrysosporium*. Wood Research 75:21-79

Wariishi H, Gold MH (1989) Lignin peroxidase compound III, formation, inactivation and conversion to the native enzyme. FEBS Letters 243:165-168

Wariishi H, Gold MH (1990) Lignin peroxidase compound III. J Biol Chem 265:2070-2077

Wariishi H, Dunford HB, MacDonald ID, Gold MH (1989a) Manganese peroxidase from the lignin-degrading basidiomycete *Phanerochaete chrysosporium*. J Biol Chem 264:3335-3340

Wariishi H, Valli K, Gold MH (1989b) Oxidative cleavage of a phenolic diaryl propane lignin model dimer by manganese peroxidase from *Phanerochaete chrysosporium*. Biochemistry 28:6017-6023

Westermark U, Eriksson KEL (1974) Cellobiose:quinone oxidoreductase, a new wood degrading enzyme from white-rot fungi. Acta Chem Scand B28:209-214

Chapter 9

Enzymes of Lignin Degradation

C. S. Evans

Lignin Structure

Lignin occurs in the matrix of plant cell walls. It is a complex heterogeneous polymer which in association with cellulose and hemicellulose provides strength and rigidity to plant cells. In supporting the plant cell structure, it gives shape and form to the whole plant. Although lignin is found in the middle lamellae between cells, it is most abundant in the secondary walls of plant cells, laid down after the cells have differentiated and ceased growing.

Lignin is synthesised by free radical polymerisation of phenylpropanoid monomers initiated by the enzyme peroxidase (Fig. 9.1). In the middle lamella a three dimensional network forms within the hemicellulose and pectic matrix. In the secondary walls of wood cells the polymer is more two-dimensional with the aromatic rings lying in parallel to each other and to the cellulose microfibrils (Goring 1989).

There is no single repeating bond within the polymer but several different linkages, the most favoured of which is an ether bond between the ß-carbon of the side chain and the phenolic group on C_4 of the aromatic ring. Other frequently formed bonds are α-O-4 , C_3 or C_5 aryl-O-4 linkages and biphenyl linkages (Fig. 9.1). Differing degrees of methoxy substitution on the aromatic rings determines the type of lignin as guaiacyl, predominantly in the soft woods of gymnosperms, or syringyl, characteristic of the hard woods of angiosperms. Modifications of the side chains include cinnamyl alcohols, aldehydes, and hydroxyl groups on the α and ß carbons. Such a high proportion of ether bonds in lignin gives the strong, resistant polymer its unique structure.

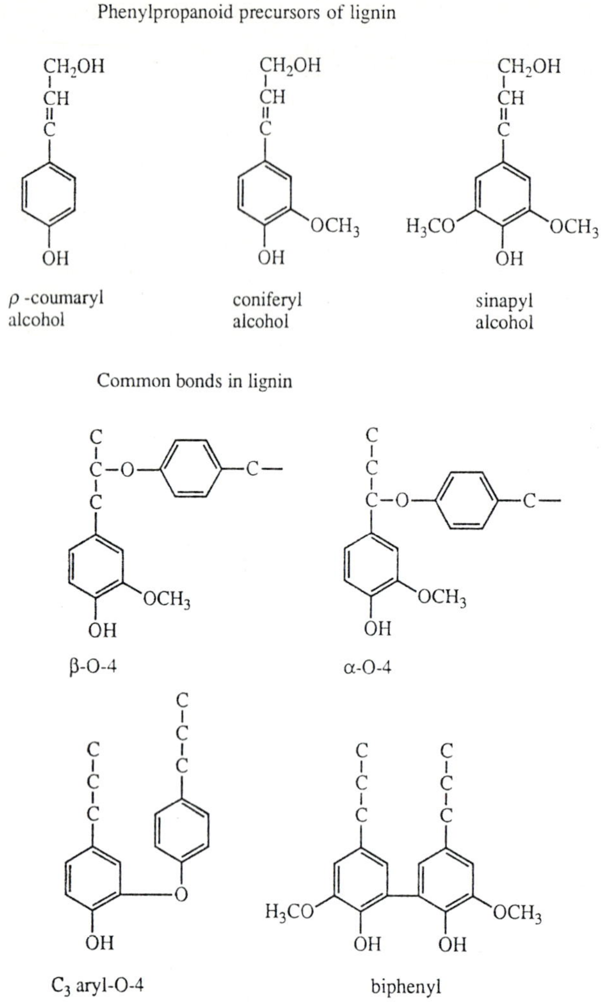

Phenylpropanoid precursors of lignin

p -coumaryl
alcohol

coniferyl
alcohol

sinapyl
alcohol

Common bonds in lignin

β-O-4

α-O-4

C₃ aryl-O-4

biphenyl

Fig. 9.1. Monomeric structures of lignin, and the dominant bond linkages within the lignin polymer.

Biodegradation of Lignocellulose

Plants convert carbon dioxide from the atmosphere into organic carbon, a large part of which is converted to lignocellulose. In order to return this fixed carbon back to the atmosphere lignocellulose must be degraded. Wood is destroyed by higher organisms such as man and insects, causing major mechanical damage to living plants, timbers and products manufactured from wood. However the most successful organisms at mineralising lignocellulose in nature are micro-organisms. The most efficient are basidiomycete fungi which cause white- and brown-rot decay of wood, so called by the colour of the degraded wood after fungal attack. Other fungi, some ascomycetes and fungi imperfecti, also attack wood causing soft-rot decay, while many bacterial species colonise and degrade various components of lignocellulose.

Micro-organisms attack lignocellulose by the secretion of enzymes. Because of the complexity of the lignocellulosic matrix of plant cell walls, a wide range of proteins with different yet complementary activities are produced. Virtually all infecting microbes secrete hydrolytic cellulases and glycosidases, but relatively few secrete enzymes capable of degrading lignin. The most highly characterised of these lignin-degrading enzymes are from the white-rot fungi, in particular *Phanerochaete chrysosporium* Burds. (Kirk 1988, Lewis and Yamamoto 1990). As the lignocellulosic substrate for these enzymes is complex, so are the interactions between the enzymes degrading the individual components.

Lignin-degrading Enzymes

Laccase

The first protein implicated as a lignin-degrading enzyme was laccase, a copper-containing polyphenol oxidase produced extracellularly and isolated from the white-rot fungus *Trametes versicolor* (also designated *Coriolus*, *Polyporus*, or *Polystictus versicolor*). Mutants without laccase activity were unable to degrade lignin until laccase was added to the cultures, leading to the suggestion that laccase controlled the secretion of lignin- and cellulose-degrading enzymes (Ander and Eriksson 1976). The primary role of laccase was considered to be polymerisation of phenolics, although there were indications that under specific conditions such as in the presence of hydrogen peroxide, or in organic media some depolymerisation of lignin occurred (Dordick *et al.* 1986, Evans 1985). It is now clear that although laccase polymerises phenols readily, it can also act in the reverse direction to degrade phenolic lignin model compounds, though evidence of degradation of polymeric lignin is still unclear (Kawai *et al.* 1987). The conditions controlling the direction of the reaction *in vivo*, producing synthesis or depolymerisation, are still not fully understood.

Not all white-rots secrete laccase. Studies with *P. chrysosporium* showed that other enzymes were effective in degrading lignin model compounds, as this species did not produce any polyphenol oxidases.

Lignin-peroxidase

Peroxidases which degrade lignin-model compounds have been characterised from several white-rot fungi. First isolated from *P. chrysosporium* (Tien and Kirk 1983, Glenn *et al.* 1983), they are produced as extracellular enzymes in the secondary phase of growth following carbon or nitrogen limitation. In culturing *P. chrysosporium* for production of peroxidases it is essential that the agitation rate of the cultures is carefully controlled at a low speed, and that the oxygen tension is maintained at a high level. Although mycelial growth proceeds rapidly in aerated cultures, the production of lignin-peroxidase is greatly stimulated at 100% oxygen levels. Thick mycelial growth and extracellular mucilage secretion reduce the amount of oxygen reaching the hyphae, so high oxygen levels added to cultures compensate for oxygen deficiency of the hyphae when grown in air. The yield of lignin-peroxidase from cultures is low, rising to a maximum of 25mg/l under optimised conditions (Leisola *et al*.1985).

The enzyme can be assayed by the oxidation of veratryl alcohol to veratraldehyde, the formation of which is monitored by its absorbance at 310nm (Tien and Kirk 1983). Catalytic amounts of hydrogen peroxide are needed to oxidise the iron in the protoporphyrin haem prosthetic group of the enzyme, to enable the enzyme to oxidise its substrate. Excess hydrogen peroxide over-oxidises the iron resulting in an inactive enzyme (Leisola and Waldner 1988).

Veratryl alcohol, a secondary metabolite produced in cultures of *P. chrysosporium* is thought to be involved in the induction of the ligninolytic enzymes, a property that can be used to stimulate production of the enzymes in culture (Lundquist and Kirk 1978). It also acts as a substrate for the enzyme. The mechanism of oxidation involves a one-electron transfer with the formation of a radical cation in the substrate molecule (Schoemaker and Leisola 1990). This cation can then react as an electron transfer oxidant producing radical cations in remote and insoluble lignin structures. It has been postulated that the radical cation of veratryl alcohol can act as a mediator by effecting oxidation of lignin rather than its conversion to veratraldehyde (Harvey *et al*. 1986). Lignin peroxidase has a higher oxidation potential than other known peroxidases such as horse-radish peroxidase which enables it to oxidise non-phenolic lignin molecules directly. Oxidation can result in cleavage of the $C\alpha$-$C\beta$ bond, the aryl-$C\alpha$ bond, aromatic ring opening, phenolic oxidation and demethoxylation. These reactions occur *in vitro* with lignin-model compounds, though demonstration of the degradation of polymeric lignin has not been so straightforward. Evidence of repolymerisation of lignin fragments has shown that the reactions are reversible, but the factors controlling the equilibrium are unknown (Haemmerli *et al*. 1986).

There are many isomers of lignin-peroxidase with molecular weights of 40 kDa-47 kDa. Up to 15 isomers have been separated by iso-electric focusing techniques (Leisola and Waldner 1988). The differences between isomers may be in the level of glycosylation of the protein moiety rather than any major changes in amino acid number or composition. Lignin-peroxidase has now been isolated from several other white-rot fungi such as *T. versicolor* and *Phlebia radiata* (Dodson *et al*. 1987, Hatakka *et al*. 1989). These proteins basically have the same characteristics as the protein from *P. chrysosporium* though slight modifications of culture conditions are required to produce equivalent yields.

Manganese-dependant Peroxidases

Several isomers of a peroxidase which requires manganese as a cofactor have also been isolated from *P. chrysosporium* (Paszczynski *et al*. 1985, Renganatham *et al*. 1985). The substrate for these enzymes requires a free phenolic group on the aromatic ring as they cannot directly oxidise non-phenolic lignin model compounds or veratryl alcohol. The assay for these peroxidases uses guaiacol as substrate instead of veratryl alcohol but also requires trace amounts of hydrogen peroxide. In the absence of hydrogen peroxide, reduced compounds such as glutathione, dithiothreitol and NADPH are oxidised. The oxidation potential is lower than for lignin-peroxidase. Not all white-rots produce these peroxidases.

If a fungus is to degrade lignin successfully, it must have the capacity to attack both phenolic and non-phenolic lignin components. It seems probable that lignin-peroxidases are the major enzymes produced by white-rots to degrade non-phenolic lignins, with different species secreting either laccase or manganese dependant peroxidases for the oxidation of phenolic lignins. For example, *T. versicolor* secretes lignin-peroxidase and laccase whereas *P. chrysosporium* secretes lignin-peroxidase and the manganese dependant peroxidase. Although lignin-peroxidase, Mn dependant peroxidase, and laccase can all degrade specific lignin model compounds, the evidence for degradation of polymeric lignin is less clear.

Identification of Fungal Enzymes

A rapid means of identifying ligninolytic enzymes produced by a fungus is by their cross-reactivity with specific antibodies. Using Western blotting techniques crude fungal protein extracts can be separated into individual protein bands on polyacrylamide gels and blotted against the antibody to a specific protein. All white-rot fungi tested in this way in our laboratory have proved positive for lignin-peroxidase, with at least one protein band cross-reacting with the antibody raised to an isomer of lignin-peroxidase of molecular weight 43 kDa from *P. chrysosporium*. Table 9.1 shows species of basidiomycetes whose proteins cross-react with this antibody.

Similar experiments with antibodies raised to laccase purified from *T. versicolor* have shown there is cross-reactivity with proteins from some white-rot species but unlike lignin-peroxidase, not all species tested showed the presence of cross-reacting proteins (Table 9.1).

Table 9.1. Immunoreactivity of fungal proteins with antibodies to lignin-peroxidase and antibodies to laccase

	Species	Lignin-peroxidase	Laccase
White-rots	*Trametes versicolor*	+	+
	Ganoderma applanatum	+	-
	Heterobasidion annosum	+	+
	Lentinus lepideus	+	nd
	Phanerochaete chrysosporium	+	-
	Poria contigua	+	+
Brown rots	*Serpula lacrymans*	+	-
	Coniophora puteana	-	nd
	Fibroporia vaillenti	-	+
	Agaricus bisporus	-	+

+   positive immunoreactivity on Western blot
-   negative immunoreactivity on Western blot
nd immunoreactivity not determined

Localisation of Lignin-degrading Enzymes

Studies on the biochemistry of lignin degradation have elucidated many aspects of the process, but over the last few years electron microscopists have made valuable contributions to our knowledge of *in vivo* processes of wood decay. Many ultrastructural studies have demonstrated the sequence of events following colonisation of wood cells by white-rots (Ruel *et al. 1981*, Messner and Stachelberger 1984, Blanchette 1984). In the last few years, using new techniques of immunocytochemical labelling of ultra-thin sections of fungal hyphae it has been possible using transmission electron microscopy, to localise specific enzyme molecules within the hyphal cells. These techniques depend on the interaction between an individual enzyme molecule and its antibody. In post-embedding labelling, the sections of hyphae are treated with diluted primary antibody (up to 1:500 dilution) with subsequent washing of the sections in a secondary antibody-gold complex which binds to the primary antibody. Individual protein molecules can therefore be located by the presence of the electron opaque gold particles visible under the transmission electron microscope (Horisberger *et al.* 1975).

Localisation of Lignin-Peroxidase

In hyphae of both *P. chrysosporium* and *T. versicolor*, lignin-peroxidase has been localised intracellularly, close or attached to the plasma membrane of the cell. The protein was also labelled in the extracellular wall layers and in the mucilage layer surrounding the hyphae (Srebotnik *et al.* 1988, Daniel *et al.* 1989). In wood colonised

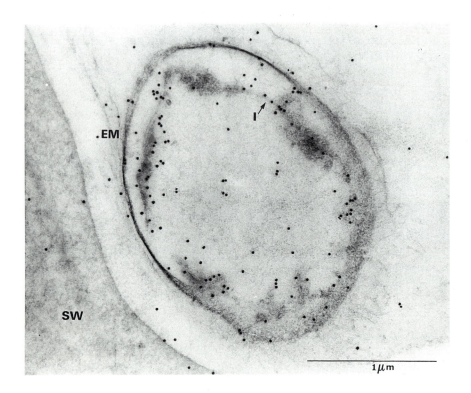

Fig. 9.2. Localisation of lignin-peroxidase in a section of a hypha of *T. versicolor* in beech heartwood.
SW   secondary wood cell wall
EM   extracellular mucilage layer around hypha
I   inner membrane, probably the plasmalemma

by white-rot fungi (beech, birch and pine woods have been the infected woods studied), lignin-peroxidase was found closely associated with the fungal hyphae. There was some evidence that it bound slightly to the lumen surface of the secondary wood cell wall in the initial stages of decay, but was most abundant in the cell lumen close to areas of decay within the extracellular mucilage layers around hyphae (Fig. 9.2). It did not diffuse into the secondary wall or into the middle lamella region between wood cells unless the wood was already highly degraded (Srebotnik *et al.* 1988, Daniel *et al.* 1989). This localisation suggests that lignin-peroxidase attacks fragments of lignin released from the secondary wood wall rather than binding to polymeric lignin in the intact secondary wall of the wood cell. Initiation of decay is most probably by a small molecular weight molecule which can diffuse readily into the wood cell wall. Such a molecule could be the cation radical of veratryl alcohol which may initiate the decay process in lignin at a distance from the fungal hypha (Harvey *et al.* 1986). Lignin-peroxidase then degrades released lignin fragments. Localised decay in the wood cell wall immediately adjacent to the hypha could be caused by the action of lignin-peroxidase on lignin in the secondary cell wall close to the lumen surface.

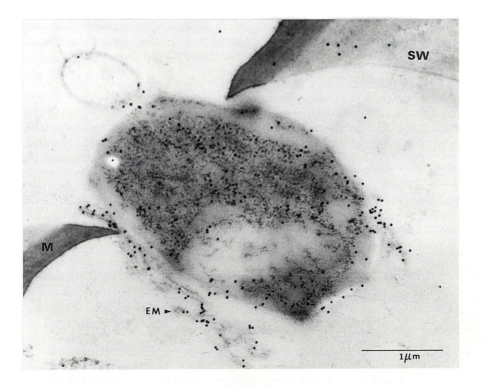

Fig. 9.3. Localisation of laccase in a section of a hypha of *T. versicolor* in beech heartwood. Laccase in the degraded secondary wood cell wall is labelled.
SW   secondary wood cell wall
M   middle lamella
EM   extracellular mucilage

Localisation of Laccase

Immunogold labelling of laccase in hyphae of *T. versicolor* has shown it is localised primarily in the cell wall and extracellular mucilage layer around the hyphae. A little intracellular labelling was observed which was not highly associated with any specific membrane or organelle (Gallagher *et al.* 1989). The antiserum used for these studies was a polyclonal serum raised in rabbits to a purified laccase of molecular weight 64 kDa. from *T. versicolor*.

Labelling of laccase in the wood cell wall in beech heartwood degraded by *T. versicolor* only occurred in already highly degraded regions of the secondary wall, and was not labelled in the middle lamella. Diffusion of laccase away from the hyphae through the mucilage layer into the cell lumina was observed (Fig. 9.3). The mode of action of laccase as a depolymerising enzyme within wood cells appears to be similar to that of lignin-peroxidase in that little evidence was found of binding of laccase to polymeric lignin in the undecayed secondary wood cell wall.

Hydrogen Peroxide Producing Enzymes

Extracellular hydrogen peroxide required for the action of the lignin peroxidases is thought to be produced enzymatically. Various enzymes can give rise to hydrogen peroxide, including glucose-1-oxidase and glucose-2-oxidase, both of which are primarily intracellular enzymes (Kelley and Reddy 1986, Eriksson *et al.* 1986). As all fungi have catalase activity associated with their cell walls it is unlikely that hydrogen peroxide produced intracellularly, then transported out of the hyphae, would avoid destruction by catalase (Veness and Evans 1989). Glyoxal oxidase is an extracellular hydrogen peroxide-producing enzyme, which has been isolated and characterised from *P. chrysosporium* (Kersten 1990). Provided that the liberated hydrogen peroxide did not come into contact with hyphal-bound catalase, sufficient peroxide would be produced as cofactor for lignin peroxidase. The regulatory controls on the production of hydrogen peroxide are not known, but may result from a specific co-alignment of lignin peroxidase and glyoxal oxidase within the extracellular mucilage layer. Such a spatial molecular arrangement is still hypothetical.

Enzymes Linking Lignin and Cellulose Degradation

Many of the cellulases produced by white-rot fungi are hydrolytic endo- and exoglucanases and ß-glucosidases. In addition enzymes have been isolated that are involved in the oxidation of cellulose and its breakdown products. Cellobiose-quinone oxidoreductase was first isolated from cultures of *T. versicolor* (Westermark and Eriksson 1974) and cellobiose oxidase from cultures of *P. chrysosporium* (Ayers *et al.* 1978, Morpeth and Jones 1986). In the oxidation of cellobiose (an end-product of cellulase activity) to glucose via the intermediate cellobionic acid, quinones are reduced to quinols. Quinones liberated from lignin by the action of lignin peroxidase or laccase would be reduced to phenols by these cellobiose oxidases. These enzymes may exert some control over the rate of both lignin and cellulose biodegradation.

Conclusions

Lignin-peroxidases and laccases are enzymes capable of degrading non-phenolic and phenolic lignin-model compounds respectively. It is not yet clear whether these enzymes attack polymeric lignin in wood cell walls, as there is evidence of both polymerisation and depolymerisation activities by these proteins. All white-rot fungi tested produce lignin-peroxidases but only some produce the polyphenol oxidase, laccase whereas other ligninolytic fungi such as the common mushroom, *Agaricus bisporus*, produce laccase but not lignin-peroxidase. It is possible that there are other undiscovered proteins which have lignin-degrading activities, maybe of small molecular size which would enable them to penetrate into the wood cell walls. There is also support for the theory of a low molecular weight mediator acting in the transfer of a radical cation to polymeric lignin. These hypotheses need to be substantiated by experimental evidence before we can fully understand the complex interactions of lignin degradation in nature.

Acknowledgements

I wish to thank Dr IM Gallagher for the electron micrographs and SERC for the award of a CASE research studentship for this work (in collaboration with IHR, Littlehampton).

References

Ander P, Eriksson KE (1976) The importance of phenoloxidase activity in lignin degradation by the white-rot fungus *Sporotrichum pulverulentum*. Arch Microbiol 109:1-8

Ayers AR, Ayers SB, Eriksson KE (1978) Cellulose-oxidase, purification and partial characterisation of a hemoprotein from *Sporotrichum pulverulentum*. Eur J Biochem 90:171-181

Blanchette RA (1984) Screening wood decayed by white-rot fungi for preferential lignin degradation. Appl Environ Microbiol 48:647-653

Daniel G, Nilsson T, Pettersson B (1989) Intra- and extracellular localisation of lignin-peroxidase during the degradation of solid wood and wood fragments by *Phanerochaete chrysosporium* by using transmission electron microscopy and immuno-gold labeling. Appl Environ Microbiol 55: 871-881

Dodson PJ, Evans CS, Harvey PJ, Palmer JM (1987) Production and properties of an extracellular peroxidase from *Coriolus versicolor* which catalyses $C\alpha$-$C\beta$ cleavage in a lignin model compound. FEMS Microbiol. Letts 42:17-22

Dordick JS, Marletta MA, Klibanov AM (1986) Peroxidases depolymerise lignin in organic media but not in water. Proc Natl Acad Sci 83:6255

Eriksson KE, Pettersson B, Volc J, Musilek V (1986) Formation and partial characterisation of glucose-2-oxidase, a hydrogen peroxide producing enzyme in *Phanerochaete chrysosporium*. Appl Microbiol Biotechnol 23:257-262

Evans CS (1985) Laccase activity in lignin degradation by *Coriolus versicolor in vivo* and *in vitro* studies. FEMS Microbiol Letts 27:339-343

Gallagher IM, Fraser MF, Evans CS, Atkey PT, Wood DA (1989) Ultrastructural localisation of lignocellulose-degrading enzymes. In: Plant cell wall polymers: Biogenesis and biodegradation Lewis NG, Paice MG (eds) , Am Chem Soc, chapter 31, 426-442

Glenn JK, Morgan MA, Mayfield MB, Kuwahara M, Gold MH (1983) An extracellular H_2O_2-requiring enzyme preparation involved in lignin biodegradation by the white-rot basidiomycete *Phanerochaete chrysosporium*. Biochem Biophys Res Comm 114:1077-1083

Goring DAI (1989) In: Lignin: Properties and Materials, Chapter 1, 2-10, Am Chem Soc, Washington USA

Haemmerli SD, Leisola MSA, Fiechter A (1986) Polymerisation of lignins by ligninases from *Phanerochaete chrysosporium*. FEMS Microbiol Letts 35: 33-36

Harvey PJ, Schoemaker HE, Palmer JM (1986) Veratryl alcohol as a mediator and the role of radical cations in lignin biodegradation by *Phanerochaete chrysosporium*. FEBS Letts 195:242-246

Hatakka AI, Lankinen VP, Lundell TK, Hietanen P, Fabricius BO, Pellinen J (1989) The ligninolytic system of white-rot fungi and potential applications in the treatment of bleach plant effluents. In: Cellulose Sources and Exploitation, Kennedy JF, Phillips GO, William PA (eds) publ Ellis Horwood Ltd 149-154

Horisberger M, Rosset J, Bauer H (1975) Colloidal gold granules as markers for cell surface receptors in the scanning electron microscope. Experientia 31:1147-1149

Kawai S, Umezawa T, Higuchi T (1987) *p*-Benzoquinone monoketals, novel degradation products of ß-O-4 lignin model compounds by *Coriolus versicolor* and lignin peroxidase of *Phanerochaete chrysosporium*. FEBS Letts 210:61-65

Kelley RL, Reddy CA (1986) Identification of glucose oxidase activity as the primary source of H_2O_2 production in ligninolytic cultures of *Phanerochaete chrysosporium*. Arch Microbiol 144:248-253

Kersten PJ (1990) Glyoxal oxidase of *Phanerochaete chrysosporium:* its characterisation and activation by lignin peroxidase. Proc Natl Acad Sci 87:2936-2940

Kirk TK (1988) Lignin degradation by *Phanerochaete chrysosporium*. ISI Atlas of Science: Biochemistry 1:71-76.

Leisola M, Waldner R (1988) Production, characterisation and mechanism of lignin peroxidases. In Treatment of lignocellulosics with white-rot fungi, Zadrazil F, Reiniger P, Elsevier 37-42

Leisola MSA, Thanei-Wyss U, Fiechter A (1985) Strategies for production of high ligninase activities by *Phanerochaete chrysosporium*. J Biotechnol 3:97-107

Lewis NG, Yamamoto E (1990) Lignin: Occurrence, biogenesis and biodegradation, Ann Rev Plant Physiol Plant Mol Biol 41:455-496

Lundquist K, Kirk TK (1978), *De novo* synthesis and decomposition of veratryl alcohol by a lignin-degrading basidiomycete. Phytochem 17:1676

Messner K, Stachelberger H (1984) TEM observations of white-rot caused by *Trametes hirsuta* with respect to osmiophilic particles. Trans Br Mycol Soc 83:209-216

Morpeth FF, Jones GD (1986) Resolution, purification and some properties of the multiple forms of cellobiose quinone dehydrogenase from the white-rot fungus *Sporotrichum pulverulentum*. Biochem J 236: 221-226

Paszczynski A, Huynh VB, Crawford RL (1985) Enzymatic activities of an extracellular manganese dependant peroxidase from *Phanerochaete chrysosporium*. FEMS Microbiol Letts 29:37-41

Renganatham V, Miki K, Gold MH (1985) Multiple molecular forms of diarylpropane oxygenase, an H_2O_2 - requiring, lignin-degrading enzyme from *Phanerochaete chrysosporium*. Arch Biochem Biophys 241:304-314

Ruel K, Barnoud F, Eriksson KE (1981) Micromorphological and ultrastructural aspects of spruce wood degradation by wild-type *Sporotrichum pulverulentum* and its cellulase-less mutant Cel 44 Holzforschung 35:157-171

Schoemaker HE, Leisola MSA (1990) Degradation of lignin by *Phanerochaete chrysosporium*. J Biotechnol 13:101-109

Srebotnik E, Messner K, Foisner R, Pettersson B (1988) Ultrastructural localisation of ligninase of *Phanerochaete chrysosporium* by immunogold labeling. Current Microbiol 16: 21-227

Tien M, Kirk TK (1983) Lignin degrading enzyme from the hymenomycete *Phanerochaete chrysosporium* Burds. Science 221:661-663

Veness RG, Evans CS (1989) The role of hydrogen peroxide in the degradation of crystalline cellulose by basidiomycete fungi. J Gen Microbiol 135:2799-2806

Westermark U, Eriksson KE (1974) Cellobiose quinone oxidoreductase, a new wood-decaying enzyme from white-rot fungi. Acta Chem Scand 28:209-214

Chapter 10

Actinomycete Enzymes and Activities Involved in Straw Saccharification

A. J. McCarthy and A. S. Ball

Introduction

Agricultural residues such as grass lignocelluloses represent large renewable resources for which enzymic generation of fermentable sugars is one of a number of alternative strategies currently under investigation. Wheat straw is a widely available substrate and its disposal also presents an environmental problem. It is essentially lignocellulose microfibrils embedded in a matrix of lignocarbohydrate comprising polyphenolic lignin covalently bound to hemicellulose. The suitablity of wheat straw for bioconversion processes is enhanced by its low lignin content (<20% w/w) and high content of readily hydrolysable hemicellulose (Ladisch *et al.* 1983). Both cellulose and hemicellulose require the action of a range of enzymes for complete degradation; the former because it is physically complex and the latter because it is chemically heterogeneous. In fact, hemicellulose is a class of polysaccharides of which the xylans are the most common form. Depolymerisation is largely achieved through the action of endoxylanases (Biely 1985), but the importance of debranching enzymes and various esterases is now being examined (Biely *et al.* 1986; MacKenzie *et al.* 1987; Johnson *et al.* 1988).

Actinomycetes are widely distributed in natural environments such as soils and composts where they make an important contribution to nutrient recycling and humification. They are therefore a potentially useful source of lignocellulose-degrading enzymes and activity against all three major components (cellulose, xylan and lignin) has been identified in various strains (McCarthy 1987). The enzymology of lignocellulose degradation by actinomycetes remains poorly understood, but it is likely that a concerted enzyme action against all substrate components is involved. Such cooperative action between enzymes has been observed for fungal cellulases and xylanases (Biely *et al.* 1986; Wood and McCrae 1978).

Actinomycete cellulases and xylanases are inducible extracellular enzymes, often produced simultaneously (Kluepfel and Ishaque 1982; Van Zyl 1985). Endoglucanase and exoglucanase components of the cellulose-degrading system have been identified in a number of species including *Thermomonospora fusca* (Hägerdal *et al.* 1978; Calza *et al.* 1985) and *Microbispora bispora* (Bartley *et al.* 1984). Fewer studies on actinomycete xylanase activity have been reported, but endoxylanases have been purified from *Streptomyces* strains (Nakajima *et al.* 1984; Morosoli *et al.* 1986). Disaccharide-hydrolysing components of cellulase and xylanase systems (ß-glucosidase and ß-xylosidase) are generally cell-associated in actinomycetes, but monomeric xylose can nevertheless be generated directly from lignocellulosic substrates by treatment with culture supernatants (Van Zyl 1985; McCarthy *et al.* 1985).

Lignin is the most recalcitrant component of plant biomass, being composed of repeating phenylpropane units linked by an array of non-hydrolysable linkages (Betts *et al.* chapter 7 this volume). Research on lignin degradation by actinomycetes has primarily been concerned with obtaining evidence for activity and this has now been achieved for several species. The primary activity exhibited by actinomycetes appears to be lignin solubilisation (McCarthy 1987), the principal product being a soluble, acid precipitable lignocarbohydrate complex (APPL) (Crawford *et al.* 1983). The agents of lignin degradation are largely unknown but their extracellular nature has been demonstrated (McCarthy *et al.* 1986; Mason *et al.* 1988). Enzymes such as phenol oxidase, cellulase and xylanase have been implicated and other enzymes may be involved in the disruption of lignin-carbohydrate cross-links and in the introduction of limited oxidations, leading to solubilisation. In the same way that cellulases have primarily been studied in a cellulolytic fungus, *Trichoderma*, so the model organism for research on lignin degradation is the wood-rotting fungus, *Phanerochaete chrysosporium*. In this species a range of extracellular hydrogen peroxide-requiring peroxidases have been positively identified as the primary agents of lignin depolymerisation (Farrell *et al.* 1989).

Against this background of limited work on the actinomycetes, as a source of hydrolytic and oxidative enzymes for plant biomass conversion, we initiated studies in which enzymic saccharification of straw was the primary objective. The initial aim was to screen actinomycete strains, to identify both common and individual features of their enzymology and to follow this with a detailed examination of enzymes produced by a range of strains including thermophiles. Studies on novel oxidative enzymes involved in attack on the lignin component were also initiated and clarification of the relationship between lignin solubilisation and degradation achieved. Improvements in sugar yields from straw by using combinations of enzymes and components from different strains was the ultimate objective.

Materials and Methods

Culture Conditions and Enzyme Preparations

A collection of over 200 strains, including 60 fresh isolates from compost samples, was maintained as suspensions of spores and hyphal fragments in 20% (v/v) glycerol at -70°C. Environmental isolates were obtained by the Andersen sampler/sedimentation chamber method described previously (McCarthy and Broda 1984). Strains were routinely cultured on L-agar plates (Hopwood *et al.* 1985) and distilled water suspensions of sporulating growth used to inoculate shake flasks containing basal salts medium plus 0.1% (w/v) yeast extract (McCarthy and Broda 1984), supplemented with 0.2% (w/v) ball-milled wheat straw. Cultures were incubated for 72 h at 200 rpm at 30°C or 37°C for mesophilic strains, and 50°C for thermophiles.

Cultures were centrifuged at 10 000 g for 10 min at 4°C and the supernatants appropriately diluted in 0.1 M-potassium phosphate buffer (pH 7.0) for enzyme assays. The harvested pellets were used to determine intracellular protein concentration. Where necessary, residual reducing sugar was removed by dialysis against buffer. Enzyme preparations were stored with added sodium azide (0.03%, w/v) at -20°C. Intracellular enzyme activities were assayed in culture extracts prepared by sonication in an ice bath (3 x 30 s at 18 μ peak to peak) of washed culture pellets.

For determining the utilisation of lignin related compounds, similar conditions were used except that ball-milled straw was replaced in culture media with the appropriate substrate at 0.01% (w/v). A range of aromatic compounds were used as substrates and comprised commercially available monomers, the polymeric dye Poly R, fractionated Kraft lignin and dimer model compounds (Fig. 10.3) kindly supplied by Dr WB Betts, University of York, UK.

Assay Procedures

Enzyme preparations were assayed for the release of reducing sugar from the following substrates: oat spelt xylan (Sigma Chemical Company), ball-milled wheat straw, carboxymethylcellulose (CMC; low viscosity, BDH Limited) and cellulose powder (CF11, Whatman Limited). Some enzyme preparations were also assayed for the release of reducing sugar from vibratory ball-milled straw (kindly supplied by Dr W Zimmerman, UMIST, Manchester, UK). The assay is based on the spectrophotometric detection of reducing sugar and a scaled-down procedure for rapid application in microtitre plates was developed. The detailed procedure has been published (Ball and McCarthy 1988). Enzyme activities were related to microbial biomass to permit meaningful comparison of different strains as enzyme producers and this was achieved by spectrophotometric determination of the intracellular protein concentration in harvested cell pellets (for detailed procedure see Ball and McCarthy 1988). Measurement of the following activites was based on spectrophotometric determination of nitrophenol released from the appropriate model compounds and again is detailed elsewhere (Ball and McCarthy 1988): ß-glucosidase; ß-xylosidase; acetyl esterase; cellobiosidase; arabinofuranosidase. Peroxidase activity was assayed by recording the formation of dopachrome pigment (A_{470}) from L-DOPA (Deobald and Crawford 1987). The ability of a range of strains to utilise lignin-related compounds as growth substrates was determined using several methods. These have already been published (Ball et al. 1989) and include: measurement of decrease in specific absorbance of monomeric substrates; appearance of absorbance peaks corresponding to expected products; changes in absorbance ratios; and direct measurement of growth by determining dry weight yields. Lignin-solubilising activity was determined in cultures containing wheat straw as growth substrate. Yield of acid precipitable material in the culture supernatant was the criterion used and the detailed procedure has been published (Ball et al. 1989).

Product Analysis

The products of wheat straw and xylan saccharification by actinomycete culture supernatants and enzyme preparations were further analysed by ascending thin layer chromatography (TLC). This enabled specific identification of monomeric and oligomeric sugars produced and monitoring with time provided insights into basic mechanisms of enzyme action. The detailed procedure has been published (McCarthy *et al.* 1985). Saccharified straw samples were also analysed for their specific glucose content using the glucose oxidase method described previously (Kunst *et al.* 1984).

In order to determine the pathway by which dimeric lignin model compounds were degraded, appropriate culture supernatants were analysed by both TLC and HPLC. Culture supernatants were acidified to pH 2 with HCl, extracted twice with ethyl acetate, evaporated to dryness and dissolved in a small volume of acetone. Silca TLC plates were developed in either toluene/methanol/ethyl acetate (90:16:8), toluene/ethyl acetate (90:10) or chloroform/methanol (97:3), aromatic compounds were visualised under short wave ultraviolet light. For HPLC, products were separated on a CN column eluted with methanol/water/acetic acid (20:79:1) and detected by absorbance at 254 nm.

Temperature, pH and Inhibition Kinetics

Temperature and pH are important parameters in enzyme processes. The former is related to the thermostability of the enzymes which determines to what degree they can be recycled and thus directly influences cost. Inhibition kinetics produce information on susceptiblity to end-product inhibition which again has bearing on enzyme addition rates and costs. pH relationships provide information on the robustness of the enzymes and dictate substrate pretreatments and hydrolysis conditions. Temperature and pH effects were determined in relation to straw saccharification as well as xylanase activity. Inhibition kinetics were determined on xylan hydrolysis only.

The effect of pH was determined by assaying for the release of reducing sugar in reaction mixtures buffered to provide pH values in the range 3.0-11.0. Thermostability of straw saccharifying enzymes and xylanases was assessed by preincubating enzyme preparations for 5 min at temperatures in the range 55°C-90°C, followed by assays for reducing sugar as described. The kinetics of xylanase activity was determined by incubating culture supernatants with a range of xylan concentrations. Inhibition was identified by including a range of concentrations of xylose, arabinose, glucose or cellobiose - all potential products of enzymatic straw saccharification. In addition, inhibition experiments were also performed in which dilution series of xylan hydrolysis products from previous experiments were added to identify and quantify general end-product inhibition *per se*. The detailed procedures for the experiments on kinetics have been published (Ball and McCarthy 1989).

Straw Saccharification

The development of a microtitre plate assay technique enabled the rapid screening of over 200 actinomycete strains for the production of enzymes capable of releasing reducing sugar from ball-milled wheat straw. A summary of the results obtained is presented in Table 10.1.

Thermomonospora and *Streptomyces* strains were the most active against all substrates but considerable variation between individual strains was evident. Activities against crystalline cellulose were low (<1.0 unit mg^{-1} intracellular protein) in all strains examined. The yields of reducing sugar were generally higher from xylan, although some strains of *Thm. chromogena* and *Micromonospora* were as active against straw in relative terms.

Table 10.1. Enzyme activities of culture supernatants from actinomycetes

Taxa	No. of strains tested	Range of enzyme activities[+] against:			
		Straw	Xylan	CMC	Cellulose
Micromonospora	10	0-4	0-3	0-2	0
Nocardia	6	0	0-1	0-1	0
Saccharomonospora viridis (T)	10	0-1	0-3	0-1	0
Streptomyces					
Mesophiles	61	0-4	0-66	0-3	0-1
Thermophiles (T)	14	0-4	1-54	0-5	0-1
Thermoactinomycetes (T)	12	0-1	1-4	0-1	0
Thermomonospora					
alba	7	0-3	1-11	0-1	trace
chromogena (T)	20	0-2	0-7	0-3	trace
curvata (T)	17	0-2	1-5	0-1	trace
fusca	27	0-4	1-54	0-3	0-1

*   xylan (oat-spelt, Sigma); CMC, carboxymethylcellulose (low viscosity, BDH); cellulose (fibrous CF11, Whatman); straw, ball-milled wheat straw.
(T) denotes thermophilic strains
     Results from each strain are the means of three replicates
+   Enzyme activity expressed in units (μmol reducing sugar released per min) per mg intracellular protein.

Table 10.2. Enzyme activity of culture supernatants from selected actinomycete strains

Taxa	Strain	Growth temp	Enzyme activity against:			
			Straw	Xylan	CMC	Cellulose
Microbispora bispora	DSM43038	50°C	4.9 (0.7)	8.9 (1.3)	3.1 (0.5)	4.0 (0.6)
Micromonospora	LL23	30°C	3.3 (0.2)	2.9 (0.1)	1.5 (<0.1)	<0.1 (<0.1)
Streptomyces	EC1	30°C	3.3 (0.6)	69.1 (12.4)	1.0 (0.2)	0.8 (0.1)
Streptomyces	EC3	30°C	3.6 (0.6)	67.0 (11.8)	2.2 (0.4)	0.8 (0.1)
Streptomyces	EC22	50°C	4.6 (0.8)	53.6 (9.4)	4.6 (0.8)	0.5 (0.1)
Thermomonospora chromogena	MT808	50°C	3.0 (0.3)	3.3 (0.4)	1.7 (0.2)	<0.1 (<0.1)
Thermomonospora fusca	M100	50°C	3.7 (0.6)	53.5 (8.3)	3.0 (0.5)	1.1 (0.2)

Enzyme activity expressed in units (μmol reducing sugar released per min) per mg intracellular protein.
Results from each strain are the means of three replicates.
Standard deviations were all within 15% of the mean values presented.
Activity ml^{-1} culture supernatant given in brackets.
CMC - carboxymethylcellulose.

The effect of pretreatment on straw saccharification by actinomycete enzyme preparations was investigated by comparing straw milled in a conventional rolling ball-mill with that prepared in a vibratory ball-mill. Although both substrates appeared identical in gross morphological appearance, the vibratory ball-milled straw was always more readily saccharified. In a comparison involving 48 strains, sugar yields from ball-milled straw were 50% ($\pm$8%) of those from vibratory ball-milled straw. Scanning electron microscopy (Fig. 10.1) suggested that susceptibility to increased hydrolysis was not due to an increase in available surface area because of decreased particle size, but rather to the production of straw particles of a more amorphous and less crystalline appearance by the vibratory action of the ball-mill. Straw which had received no

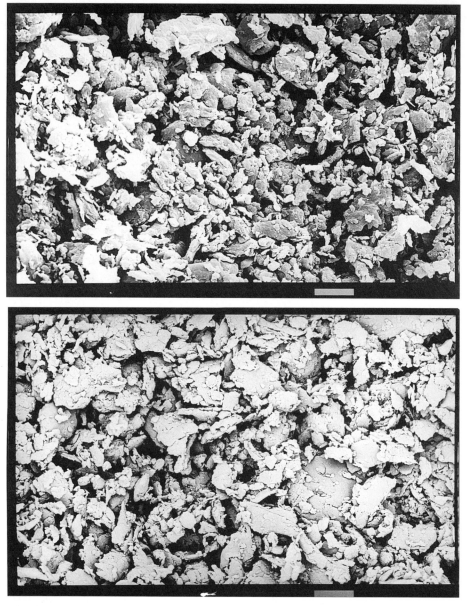

Fig. 10.1. Scanning electron micrographs of non-vibratory ball-milled straw (**a**) and vibratory ball-milled straw (**b**)

pretreatment other than being finely chopped, yielded 24% (±7%) of the sugar obtained from the enzymic hydrolysis of vibratory ball-milled straw.

Seven strains were selected for further study and comprised representative mesophilic and thermophilic streptomycetes, strains of *Thm. chromogena* and *Micromonospora* alluded to above, the most active strain of *Thm. fusca*, and the type strain of *Microbiospora bispora* which was the most cellulolytic strain in the collection. Their extracellular activity against straw and related substrates is presented in Table 10.2.

One important point which emerges from these data is the fact that the enzyme activity of slow-growing strains eg micromonosporas is seriously underestimated when growth yields are not considered and this is a common misconception.

The representative strains were also examined for several other enzyme activities involved in straw saccharification although not in themselves depolymerising enzymes. These included: ß-glucosidase, ß-xylosidase and cellobiosidase enzymes which complete saccharification and relieve end-product inhibition; acetyl esterase which modifies acetyl xylan and potentially expedites xylanase action; arabinofuranosidase which probably has a role in disrupting the lignocarbohydrate complex as well as specific synergistic action with endoxylanase.

Table 10.3. Activities of acetylesterase, arabinofuranosidase, cellobiosidase, ß-glucosidase and ß-xylosidase in cell extracts and culture supernatants of the selected strains

Taxa	Strain	Enzyme activity:									
		Acetyl esterase		Arabinofur- anosidase		Cellobio- sidase		ß-glucosi- dase		ß-xylosi- dase	
		I	E	I	E	I	E	I	E	I	E
Microbispora bispora	DSM 43038	79	74	27	151	ND	ND	20	1	20	0
Streptomyces	EC1	44	114	73	250	34	67	32	2	99	16
Streptomyces	EC3	27	123	58	250	12	25	31	2	50	0
Streptomyces	EC22	24	166	20	245	46	200	37	4	28	0
Thermomonospora chromogena	MT808	45	100	16	67	24	17	18	2	25	0
Thermomonospora fusca	MT100	123	143	35	120	25	25	36	2	88	38

Results are expressed in μmols 4-nitrophenol released min^{-1} mg^{-1} intracellular protein and are the means of three determinations.
(I) denotes cell extract activities; (E) denotes extracellular activities; (ND) = not determined.
Standard deviations were all within 15% of the mean values presented.

The results (Table 10.3) show that no single strain is the best source of all these activities. However, production of extracellular cellobiosidase activity by *Streptomyces* strain EC22 was found to be significantly higher than for any other strain. In common with other bacterial systems, the dimer hydrolases ß-glucosidase and ß-xylosidase were cell-associated activities in all of the actinomycetes studied here.

The pH optimum for straw saccharification was in the range 7.0-9.0 for all enzyme preparations examined. There was some variation in pH profiles between strains primarily in the proportion of activity exhibited outside the optimum pH range. Maximum release of sugar from straw within the confines of the 15 min assay reaction occurred at 70°C, for enzyme preparations from thermophilic strains, and at 60°C for those from mesophiles. Thermal inactivation curves are more meaningful and demonstrate the clear difference in thermostability of enzymes from thermophiles and mesophiles (Fig. 10.2).

The products of straw saccharification by culture supernatants were analysed by Thin Layer Chromatography (TLC). In all cases, xylobiose and oligmeric xylose, clearly generated by attack on the xylan component, were the dominant products. Monomeric xylose appeared later in the reaction (3 h-24 h) and its concentration increased with time. Hexoses were not detected by TLC, but glucose was determined using the glucose oxidase assay and estimated as constituting 6%-9% of the total reducing sugar generated.

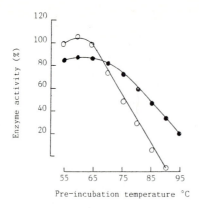

Fig. 10.2. Thermostability curves for straw saccharification by enzyme preparations from *Thermomonospora mesophila* (o) and *Thermomonospora fusca* (•). Activity is expressed as a percentage of the value for untreated enzyme. All samples were assayed at 55°C.

Characterisation of Xylanase Activity

It was clear from the results of screening procedures that actinomycetes in general are a rich source of xylanase activity. Furthermore, the analysis of straw saccharification revealed that the xylan-degrading system accounted for most of the sugar released from straw by actinomycete culture supernatants. The principal depolymerising enzymes in this system are the endoxylanases and these were further investigated.

The production of xylanase activity was found to be growth associated in all strains examined, such that maximum extracellular xylanase activity was detected at the end of the exponential growth phase and remained stable throughout the subsequent stationary phase. Intracellular xylanase activity was detected in all strains but accounted for only 15% (± 2.4%) of the total xylanase. As expected from the work on straw saccharifying enzymes, xylanase activity was optimal in the pH range 6.0-9.0. Again, thermophilic strains produced thermostable activity (half-life at 70°C, 1 h-4 h) compared to mesophiles (half-life at 70°C, 13 m-40 m). Studies on the kinetics of xylanase activity revealed significant variation between strains with respect to their enzymes' affinity for the xylan substrate. In all strains however, enzyme activity was regulated by competitive end product inhibition. This was probably effected by the oligomeric products of xylan degradation since neither xylose nor arabinose had any effect on xylanase activity. The failure of cellobiose or glucose to inhibit xylan hydrolysis supported the contention that specific xylanases, rather than cellulases with xylan hydrolysing activity, were responsible. These kinetic data and associated arguments have been published in detail (Ball and McCarthy 1989).

Experiments on the identification of specific proteins responsible for endoxylanase activity demonstrated that multiple forms are often produced by individual strains. Separations by isoelectric focussing and polyacrylamide gel electrophoresis detected the same number of endoxylanases in each case and there was some evidence for a direct relationship between good xylanase activity and the presence of multiple forms of endoxylanase (Table 10.4).

None of the separated endoxylanases exhibited endoglucanase (cellulase) activity and, in some strains, distinct endoglucanases were identified directly on gels.

Table 10.4. Identification of endoxylanases from selected actinomycetes

Taxa	Strain number	Endoxylanase-specific activity (IU mg^{-1} extra-cellular protein	No. of xylanase bands identified by IEF[1] and native PAGE[2]	Isoelectric point (pI)
Amycolata autotrophica	DSM43099	0.9	1	7.3
Micromonospora sp	LL23	6.2	5	4.4-8.8
Streptomyces badius	252	1.7	1	7.2
Streptomyces sp	EC1	33.3	4	4.6-8.7
Streptomyces sp.	EC22	24.1	4	5.2-8.6
Thermomonospora fusca	MT100	24.6	6	5.2-8.6

[1] Isoelectric focussing
[2] Polyacrylamide gel electrophoresis

Solubilisation of a Straw Lignocarbohydrate Complex by Actinomycetes

Release of a soluble, acid precipitable lignocarbohydrate (APPL) complex into the supernatant of actinomycete cultures growing on straw has been described (McCarthy *et al.* 1986). We found that production of APPL was common amongst actinomycetes, although yields varied (12 mg-65 mg APPL g^{-1} straw in a sample of 20 strains). All strains solubilised ligno-carbohydrate during primary growth and maximum yields were obtained at the end of this growth phase (three days-ten days).

It is established that APPL also contains protein, probably extracellular protein of microbial origin, which has complexed with lignocarbohydrate during the acid precipitation step. We compared APPL recoveries determined by dry weight with those estimated by routine protein analysis using the Lowry assay and found that the latter could indeed be used as a rapid and simple method of monitoring APPL production. Protein accounted for 20%-50% of the APPL product and in all cases it appeared to be intimately associated with lignocarbohydrate since <5% could be removed by repeated washing. An interesting and potentially exploitable development from this work was our observation that this protein component included active enzymes. Six representative actinomycete strains were investigated for three hydrolytic and two oxidative extracellular enzymes. In all cases, enzyme specific activities were appreciably higher in APPL compared to culture supernatants. The oxidative enzymes peroxidase and veratryl oxidase could be detected only in APPL while the hydrolytic enzymes endoglucanase, endoxylanase and arabinofuranosidase although concentrated in APPL, were recovered with efficiencies varying from 33%-111% (Ball *et al.* 1990). Thus acid precipitation of actinomycete culture supernatants on straw provides concentrated crude enzyme preparations which may also be in a more stabilised form. Stabilisation of enzyme activity within APPL can be envisaged in theoretical terms but has yet to be substantiated experimentally.

Degradation of Lignin-Related Compounds by Actinomycetes

The lignin component of straw is an important factor limiting its saccharification. The structural complexity and variability of lignin is such that studies on its degradation rely heavily on the use of model compounds containing structures prevalent within

Table 10.5. Degradation of lignin and related compounds by selected actinomycetes

Taxon	Strain	APPL production from straw (mg dry weight g^{-1} straw)	Ferulic acid (OD282) substrate present after 7d growth	Growth (7d) on fractionated Kraft lignin (mg dry wt culture)	Poly R decolourisation (change in ratio OD518/346 per day)	Veratraldehyde (OD310) produced after 7d growth on veratryl alcohol
Amycolata autotrophica	DSM43099	12*(±3)	0.1*(±0)	10(±10)	0	1.2*(±0.2)
Streptomyces badius	252	20*(±7)	0.6*(±1)	130*(±40)	0.2*(±0)	0
Streptomyces cyaneus	MT813	55*(±12)	0.1*(±0)	0	0	0
Streptomyces sp	EC1	50*(±7)	0.5*(±.1)	0	0	0.4*(±.1)
Streptomyces sp	EC22	40*(±8)	0.7(±.1)	10(±10)	0.1*(±0)	0
Thermomonospora mesophila	DSM43048	20*(±3)	0.1*(±0)	110*(±30)	0.1*(±0)	0.1*(±0)
Control	-	8(±2)	0.7(±1)	0	0	0

Standard deviations from three experiments given in brackets
* indicates results significantly different from control

native lignins. Twenty actinomycete strains selected to represent taxonomic diversity, good straw saccharifiers and strains, reported as being capable of attack on lignin, were examined for their ability to decolourise the polymeric dye, Poly R. Only three strains gave significant positive results and their activity was identified as being extracellular, although the amount of decolourisation was considerably lower than that observed with growing cultures. There was a poor correlation between this activity and veratryl alcohol oxidation, the other assay routinely used for lignin-degrading fungi. Only three strains exhibited veratryl alcohol oxidation of which only one, *Thm. mesophila*, could also decolourise Poly R. Again, evidence that this was an extracellular activity was obtained. Ferulic acid, one of a group of methoxylated aromatic monomers from which plants synthesise lignin, served as a growth substrate for three strains, including *Thm. mesophila*. However, two other compounds of this type, syringic and coumaric acids, were not utilised by any of the strains examined. The most complex lignin-related compound tested was fractionated kraft lignin. kraft lignin is the by-product of the kraft pulping process used by the paper industry and is a heterogeneous and complex mixture of low and high molecular weight compounds derived from lignin. We used this material as a more meaningful model by subjecting it to fractionation so that only high molecular weight (>100 kD) compounds remained. Two strains could grow on this material, again including *Thm. mesophila*. All of this evidence that a few strains, especially *Thm. mesophila*, could directly attack the lignin component of straw or other plant material bore no relationship to the solubilisation of lignin as APPL discussed in the previous section. Some of the data pertaining to utilisation of lignin-related compounds by actinomycetes are summarised in Table 10.5.

The next stage in this investigation of evidence for the ability of actinomycetes to degrade lignin was to ascertain whether intermonomer bonds could be attacked, thus indicating that lignin could be depolymerised. The predominant bond type in native lignin is the ß-aryl ether bond and synthesised models containing this bond were used.

Growth of several strains on a model dimer (compound I, Fig. 10.3) was assessed and three strains identified as able to significantly utilise compound I as a carbon source. However, while TLC analysis of products revealed that many strains could

Compound I

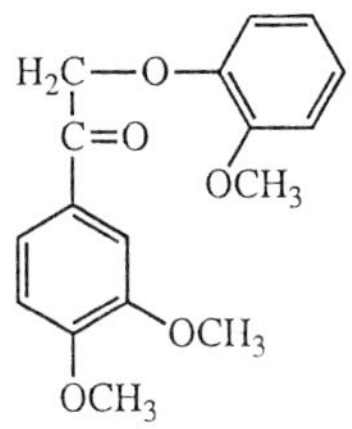

Compound II

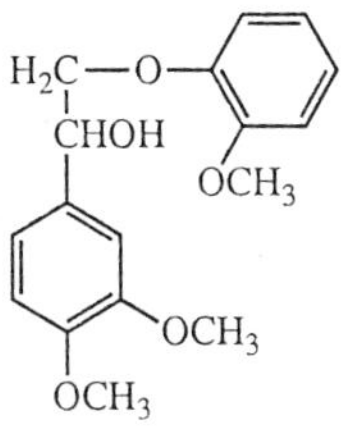

Fig. 10.3. Structural formulae of the model compounds used in this study.

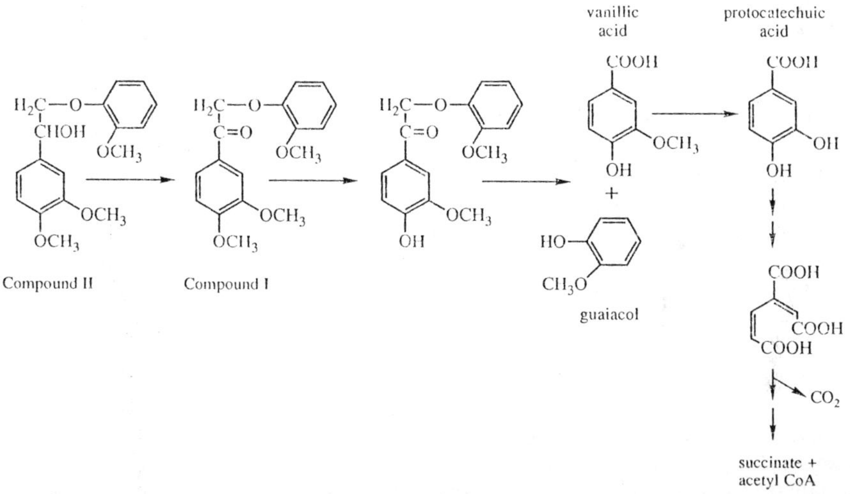

Fig. 10.4. Degradation pathway for the utilisation of compound I by *Stm. badius* and *Thm. mesophila*.

demethoxylate the compound, only two, *Thm. mesophila* and *Stm. badius*, cleaved the intermonomer bonds. When these experiments were repeated with analysis of products by the more sensitive high performance liquid chromatography (HPLC) technique, evidence that some other strains could also carry out this reaction was obtained. Further analysis of the degradation products from compounds I and II by reverse phase HPLC enabled the construction of a rudimentary degradation pathway as used by *Thm. mesophila* and *Stm. badius* (Fig. 10.4).

General Discussion

This investigation of actinomycetes as a novel source of enzymes for lignocellulose saccharification proceeded from an initial broad screening programme for straw saccharifying activity to more detailed analyses of the enzymes involved. Throughout the programme the diversity of actinomycete strains was maintained so that both general and specific observations could be made. It was established that pentoses were invariably the main product of straw saccharifications and this corresponded to the widespread detection of high xylanase activity in this group of microorganisms. This further emphasises the importance of developing pentose fermentation technology (Ladisch *et al.* 1983), one of a number of factors currently limiting efficient utilisation of lignocellulosic material for fermentation. At an early stage in the project we also paid some attention to substrate pretreatment another major bottleneck in the development of economic technology for bioconversion. It was clear that vibratory ball-milling of straw improved sugar yields from enzyme hydrolysis but we were surprised at the magnitude of the improvement over conventional ball-milling. Electron microscopic analysis suggested that this greater susceptibility to enzyme attack was due to disruption of the lignocarbohydrate matrix rather than any further decrease in particle size. A wide range of physical, chemical and biological pretreatments for lignocellulose have been developed, each with their own supporting technical and economic arguments. Our only contribution to this debate is to support other data (Rivers and Emert 1987) which illustrate the limitations of particle size as an indicator of potential conversion efficiencies or yields.

All of the actinomycete enzymes examined here acted optimally at neutral to alkaline pH values. This now appears to be a feature of enzymes from these microorganisms (McCarthy 1987), in marked contrast to fungal enzymes which generally exhibit acidic pH optima. Thus actinomycete saccharifying enzymes may offer advantages for processes which use alkali-treated lignocellulose as the substrate. Furthermore, within the actinomycete group we identified many thermophilic strains producing enzymes which were thermostable. These could have an application in saccharification processes coupled to fermentation and ethanol recovery at high temperature (Sonnleitner and Fiechter 1983).

Enzymes other than the primary depolymerising enzymes, endoxylanase and endoglucanase, were also found to be widespread amongst actinomycetes. These included acetylesterases and arabinofuranosidases which deacetylate native straw xylan and hydrolyse arabinose branch points to increase the amount of substrate accessible to endoxylanase. Synergistic relationships between these enzymes, leading to significant increases in sugar yields, have been reported (Biely *et al.* 1986; Greve *et al.* 1984) and we have also observed such effects in actinomycete enzyme systems (Bachmann and McCarthy, unpublished data). Considerable variation in the amount of different enzymes was detected between strains (Tables 10.1-10.3) and this supports our hypothesis that the most efficient straw saccharifying enzyme systems will comprise components from more than one source.

The predominance of pentose sugars in straw saccharification products directed us towards a more detailed characterisation of xylanase activity in actinomycetes. Almost every strain analysed possessed some degree of xylanase activity, but *Thermomonospora* and *Streptomyces* strains were consistently the most active. In all cases, extracellular xylanase activity was limited by end product inhibition which could be relieved by the addition of intracellular ß-xylosidase activity since the ultimate product, D-xylose, was not inhibitory. Analysis of degradation products confirmed that all of the strains produced endoxylanases which by definition attacked the polymer chain at random to yield a mixture of oligomeric products. The most active xylanolytic strains produced multiple endoxylanases, up to six, which may be due to modification reactions and/or requirements for binding and hydrolysis at different sites on the xylan chain. This was not further investigated but the possible relationship to endoglucanase activity was pursued. There is considerable debate concerning the specificity of these enzymes with some workers reporting the ability to attack both xylan and cellulose by individual enzymes (Ramachandra *et al.* 1987). We found that all of the actinomycete enzymes examined during this investigation produced distinct enzymes specific for each substrate, based on both electrophoretic separations and inhibition kinetics.

Like xylanase activity, the ability to solubilise an acid precipitable lignocarbohydrate complex (APPL) from straw was found to be widespread amongst actinomycetes. Actinomycete-mediated generation of this material has been described before (Crawford *et al.* 1983; McCarthy *et al.* 1986) but has always been assumed to be a special feature of a small number of strains which attack lignin. We have now demonstrated that this is not true and that activity against lignin-related aromatic compounds is not a prerequisite.

Furthermore, we have developed a simple and reproducible method for measuring production of this compound, based on the demonstrated correlation between quantitative yields of APPL and its associated protein. The most interesting aspect of this work is the discovery that the protein component of APPL is in fact active enzymes now present, and recoverable, in concentrated form. Both oxidative and hydrolytic enzymes were concentrated and application of this observation may not be restricted to lignocellulose saccharification processes but extend to commercial enzyme production in general.

Finally, our attention was drawn to the production of some substantial evidence for direct attack on the lignin component of plant biomass by actinomycetes. We were particularly interested to determine if indicators of ligninolytic activity developed in fungi could be applied to actinomycetes. The correlation between these indicators was poor so that no individual test could be used to demonstrate ligninolytic activity. However one strain, *Thm. mesophila*, was positive for all of the tests and further studies showed that it could cleave the common lignin intermonomer linkage (the ß-aryl ether bond). Thus, *Thm. mesophila* can be identified as an actinomycete candidate to be included in further studies towards the development of biological delignification processes.

Acknowlegements

We are grateful to Dr WB Betts, University of York, for lignin model compounds and kraft lignin samples and Dr George Sharples, Liverpool Polytechnic for the electron microscopy work. The technical assistance of Joanne Harrison is gratefully acknowledged. We would also like to thank Dr MJ Penninckx, Dr B Godden and colleagues at the Microbiology Department, University of Brussels for valuable discussions and exchange of data and strains.

This research was funded by the EEC Non-Nuclear Energy Programme.

References

Ball AS, McCarthy AJ (1988) Saccharification of straw by actinomycete enzymes. J Gen Microbiol 134:2139-2147

Ball AS, McCarthy AJ (1989) Production and properties of xylanases from actinomycetes. J Appl Bacteriol 66:439-444

Ball AS, Betts WB, McCarthy AJ (1989) Degradation of lignin-related compounds by actinomycetes. Appl Environ Microbiol 55:159-162Ball AS, Godden B, Helvenstein P, Penninckx MJ, McCarthy AJ (1990) Lignocarbohydrate solubilisation from straw by actinomycetes. Appl Environ Microbiol 56:3017-3022

Bartley T, Waldron C, Eveleigh D (1984) A cellobiohydrolase from a thermophilic actinomycete *Microbispora bispora*. Appl Biochem Biotechnol 9:337-338

Biely P (1985) Microbial xylanolytic systems. Trends in Biotechnol 3:286-290

Biely P, Puls, J, Schneider H (1985) Acetyl xylan esterase in fungal cellulolytic systems. FEBS Lett. 186:80-84

Biely P, MacKenzie CR, Puls J, Schneider H (1986) Co-operativity of esterases and xylanases in the enzymatic degradation of acetyl xylan Biotechnol 4:731-733

Calza RE, Irwin DC, Wilson DB (1985) Purification and characterisation of two ß-1,4-endoglucanases from *Thermomonospora fusca*. Biochem 24:7797-7804

Crawford DL, Pommetto III AL, Crawford RL (1983) Lignin degradation by *Streptomyces viridosporus*: isolation and characterisation of a new polymeric lignin degradation intermediate. Appl Environ Microbiol 45:898-904

Deobald LA, Crawford DL (1987) Activities of cellulase and other extracellular enzymes during lignin solubilisation by *Streptomyces viridosporus* Appl Environ Microbiol 26:158-163

Farrell RL, Murtagh KE, Tien M, Mozuch MD, Kirk TK (1989) Physical and enzymatic properties of lignin peroxidase isoenzymes from *Phanerochaete chrysosporium*. Enz Microb Technol 11:322-328

Greve LC, Labavitch JM, Hungate RE (1984) α-L-Arabinofuranosidase from *Ruminococcus albus* 8: purification and possible role in hydrolysis of Alfafa cell wall. Appl Environ Microbiol 47:1135-1140

Hgerdal BGR, Ferchak JD, Pye EK (1978) Cellulolytic enzyme system of *Thermoactinomyces* sp grown on microcrystalline cellulose. Appl Environ 73 Microbiol 36:606-612

Hopwood DA, Bibb MJ, Chater KF, Kieser T, Bruton CJ, Keiser HM, Lydiate DJ, Smith CP, Ward JM, Schrempf H (1985) Genetic Manipulation of *Streptomyces*. A Laboratory Manual. The John Innes Foundation: Norwich

Johnson KG, Harrison BA, Schneider H, MacKenzie CR, Fontana JD (1988) Xylan hydrolying enzymes from *Streptomyces* spp. Enzyme Microb Technol 10:403-409

Kluepfel D, Ishaque M (1982) Xylan-induced cellulolytic enzymes in *Streptomyces flavogriseus*. Dev in Ind Microbiol 23:389-395

Kunst A, Draegar B, Ziegenhorn J (1984) Colorimetric methods with glucose oxidase and peroxidase. In Methods of Enzymatic Analysis, 3rd edn, vol VI:178-185 Bergmeyer HU, Bergmeyer J, Grassi M (eds) Weinheim: Verlag Chemie

Ladisch MR, Lin KW, Voloch M, Tsao GT (1983) Process considerations in the enzymatic hydrolysis of biomass. Enzyme and Microb Technol 5:82-102

MacKenzie CP, Bilous D, Schneider M, Johnson KG (1987) Induction of cellulolytic and xylanolytic enzyme systems in *Streptomyces* spp. Appl Environ Microbiol 53:2835-2839

Mason JC, Richards M, Zimmerman W, Broda P (1988) Identification of extracellular proteins from actinomycetes responsible for the solubilisation of lignocellulose. Appl Microbiol Biotechnol 28:276-280

McCarthy AJ (1987) Lignocellulose-degrading actinomycetes. FEMS Microbiol Rev 46:145-163

McCarthy AJ, Broda P (1984) Screening for lignin-degrading actinomycetes and characterisation of their activity against [14C] lignin-labelled wheat lignocellulose. J Gen Microbiol 130:2905-2913

McCarthy AJ, Peace E, Broda P (1985) Studies on the extracellular xylanase activity of some thermophilic actinomycetes. Appl Microbiol Biotechnol 21:238-244

McCarthy AJ, Paterson A, Broda P (1986) Lignin solubilisation by *Thermomonospora mesophila*. Appl Microbiol Biotechnol 24:347-352

Morosoli R, Bertrand JL, Mondou F, Shareck F, Kluepfel D (1986) Purification and properties of a xylanase from *Streptomyces lividans*. Biochem J 239:587-592

Nakajima T, Tsukamoto K, Watanabe T, Kainuma K, Matsuda K (1984) Purification and some properties of an endo-1,4-ß-D-xylanase from *Streptomyces* sp Fermen Technol 62:269-276

Ramachandra M, Crawford DL, Pometto III AL (1987) Extracellular enzyme activities during lignocellulose degradation by *Streptomyces* spp: A comparative study of wild type and genetically manipulated strains. Appl Environ Microbiol 53:2754-2760

Rivers DB, Emert GH (1987) Lignocellulose pretreatment; A comparison of wet and dry ball attrition. Biotechnol Lett 9:365-368

Sonnleitner B, Fietcher A (1983) Advantages of using thermophiles in biotechnological processes: expectations and reality. Trends in Biotechnol 1:74-80

Van Zyl WH (1985) A study of the cellulases produced by three mesophilic actinomycetes grown on bagasse as substrate. Biotechnol Bioeng 27; 1367-1373

Wood TM, McCrae SI (1978) The cellulase of *Trichoderma konningii*. Biochem J 171:61-72

Chapter 11

Uses and Potential of Lignocellulose

R. K. Dart and W. B. Betts

Introduction

Lignocellulose is the most abundant source of organic chemicals on earth, accounting for approximately 50% of the world's biomass which has been estimated at 3×10^{11} tonnes (Lynch 1987). The biosynthesis and structure of the component molecules have been discussed by Betts *et al.*, chapter 7 this volume, (1991). Kirk and Fenn (1982) have calculated the annual production rate of lignocellulose at $20\text{-}50 \times 10^9$ tonnes, of which 4×10^9 tonnes could be made available on an annual basis. Glasser and Kelly (1987) suggested that the waste lignin derived from the pulp and paper industry is of the order of $30\text{-}50 \times 10^6$ tonnes per year.

Lignocellulose has attracted considerable attention as an alternative feedstock and energy resource due to the large quantities available and also its renewable nature. Actual and potential outlets for lignocellulose are as pulp and paper, food (animal and human), fuel, chemicals and construction materials. Whichever option is chosen, the processing of low value forestry or agricultural wastes must be justified by a significant increase in value. The relationship between price and size of the market has been shown by Dunhill (1983) and Wood (1985) who concluded that lignocellulose is probably best suited for conversion into low value bulk products. Details showing the availability, profitability and constraints on a number of products were provided by Wood (1985). However, it should be pointed out that the situation is not a simple one and factors such as the negative value placed on effluents obtained from lignocellulose processing must be taken into account. This will vary from country to country depending on local legislation.

The quantities of waste lignin and hemicellulose from paper pulping are vast and any application making significant use of these must also be on a large scale. Whilst there is obviously a place for small scale, "high-tech" operations, these can make only minor inroads into the quantities of substrate available. The pulp and paper industries generally regard lignin and hemicelluloses as waste products rather than a resource and some of the waste and effluent problems of these industries could be changed by a more imaginative approach.

In addition to the problems mentioned by Wood (1985) there are also problems caused by the collection of large bulk, low value lignocellulosic materials such as straw, which may be high in water content. The seasonal nature of such of the lignocellulosic wastes is a further problem.

The final fate of the lignocellulose, e.g. production of specialised chemicals, edible biomass or biogas will determine the initial treatment. If either the second or third option is required then it is not necessary to separate the components of the lignocellulose.

Substrates from the Pulp and Paper Industry

Celluloses, hemicelluloses and lignin will be discussed independently later in this section, but, first, substrates from the pulp and paper industry will be considered. This is because the industry is so large compared with other lignocellulose technologies and the pollution problems it causes so serious, that it tends to dominate all discussions on lignocellulose.

The pulp and paper industry is the major commercial user of lignocellulose, most of which is derived from wood, although in some countries such as Denmark significant quantities of straw are used. The industry produces large quantities of material regarded as waste and also causes serious effluent and pollution problems.

Two major pulping technologies are found, mechanical and chemical. In mechanical pulping the wood is debarked and ground between rotating discs which separate the individual fibres. Chemical pulping requires wood to be treated with chemicals, and high temperatures and pressures, to labilise or dissolve the lignin holding the cellulose fibres together. Mechanical pulps give high yields (>95% of raw material) but the pulp has poor strength, whilst chemical pulps are stronger although the yield is lower.

There are two major chemical pulping methods in current use. The kraft (sulphate) process uses a mixture of sodium hydroxide and sodium sulphide and accounts for the majority of chemically produced pulp. The sulphite process uses aqueous sodium sulphite, and as a commercial process is diminishing rapidly.

At the end of the cooking stage, the kraft black liquor contains dissolved lignin, numerous sugar derivatives from degraded hemicelluloses, partially degraded cellulose and reacted/unreacted cooking chemicals. Major constituents include a variety of isosaccharinic acids derived from sugars. Approximately 95% of the kraft black liquor produced is concentrated and used as fuel to provide heating or power. The heating value of lignin per kg approximates to 0.6 kg of heavy oil (Lindberg et al. 1988). The inorganic fraction falls to the floor of the furnace and is recovered.

Lignocellulose which is high in silica (e.g. straw) causes problems at this stage. When straw is pulped by conventional kraft pulping desilication may be carried out by bubbling flue gases through the black liquor and under the correct conditions silica is precipitated. It is claimed that lignocellulose high in silica can be handled by using the appropriate type of furnace. One process, known as the Rinman process, has been suggested as ideally suited to straw as it can be carried out on a small scale (<100 tonnes day^{-1}). This enables it to make use of local supplies, thus removing much of the high cost of transporting low value, low density and high volume material in bulk. The process produces chemicals such as solvents and oils from the lignin fraction of wood and straw in addition to recovering the digesting chemicals and is, therefore, environmentally sound.

The concentrated kraft black liquor is treated with a mixture of calcium and barium oxides which converts the liquor into a powder. When this powder is treated with superheated steam it produces hydrogen and a range of chemicals. These include acetone, methanol, isopropyl alcohol, methylethyl ketone, secondary butyl alcohol, various higher alcohols, ketones and hydrocarbons, light and heavy oils. Ammonium sulphate can also be obtained by scrubbing with sulphuric acid. A large portion of the sodium hydroxide can be recovered and recycled into the digestion process, whilst the calcium and barium can be recovered as the insoluble carbonates to be converted back to the oxides. In the sulphite pulping method the major by-products are lignosulphonates and pentose sugars.

Both kraft and sulphite pulping can cause serious pollution due to the sulphur content of the pulping chemicals and alternative methods are in use or are under investigation to reduce this problem. These include the use of NaOH and anthraquinone in the Soda-AQ process which does not contain any sulphur, solves many of the problems of black liquor production and allows the recovery of 80% of the NaOH. High pressure oxygen delignification has also been used for pulping in the so-called NACO process which does not use sulphur or chlorine containing compounds, and is claimed to be cheaper and less polluting than other methods. Oxygen at high alkalinity and pressure has also been used as a method of extending delignification in a secondary process. A number of uses for the waste lignins are known and will be considered later.

Options Using Fractionated Lignocellulose

It is generally true that the purer the fractions isolated from any heterogeneous system, the greater the value of each component. It is therefore necessary to separate the various components of lignocellulose if its economic potential is to be optimised. The most easily removed component should be separated first, as this reduces the size of plant required at subsequent stages.

The value of fermentation products depends to a great extent on the cost of the raw materials. Lignocellulose frequently has a negative cost offering a cheap fermentation source. The major requirements to realise this potential are:

1   the use of all three components;
2   effective and economical pretreatments maximizing the glucose yield from cellulose;
3   the negative value (i.e. how much does disposal of lignocellulose cost?);
4   the cost of alternative feedstocks;
5   any political or strategic considerations.

There are a number of possible uses for the component fractions of lignocellulose. Pentose sugars derived from hemicellulose can be converted into the solvent furfural, reduced to the sweetener xylitol, fermented to ethanol, used for single cell protein (SCP) production or converted into a variety of fine chemicals. The polymeric cellulose fraction can be used for paper, board, viscose, fabrics, cellulose esters, cellulose ethers, or saccharified to yield glucose. The lignin fraction can be used as a polymeric material giving surfactants, adhesives, asphalt substitutes and numerous other uses, or cracked to form a variety of chemicals including phenols, cyclohexane derivatives and fuel oils.

There are numerous difficulties associated with the use of lignocellulose as a feedstock. These include the commercial problem that most products obtainable from lignocellulose can presently be derived less expensively from a petrochemical based feedstock processed chemically. This would include both ethanol and animal feeds. Other major problems include the recalcitrance of lignin (and to a lesser extent cellulose) to enzyme attack, the time scale involved in bioconversions and scale up problems of solid-state fermentations. In the case of lignin, a further problem is that it contains several types of monomeric substructures with a wide variety of chemical bonds joining them (Betts *et al.* chapter 7 this volume). Therefore any method of breaking down lignin will produce a plethora of products, most present in small quantities. The cost of separation and purification frequently becomes prohibitive.

Several alternative strategies to kraft and sulphite pulping have been proposed recently for the fractionation of lignocellulose. Phenol is totally miscible with water at 100°C and atmospheric pressure, and if added to lignocellulose under these conditions, lignin is dissolved and hemicelluloses are hydrolysed. Separation of cellulose can then be achieved by filtration. The phenolic portion with the dissolved lignin separates from the aqueous phase containing the pentose sugars when the system is cooled. Residual phenol in the aqueous phase can be recovered with solvent and the pentoses also remaining in this phase can be separated for subsequent fermentation. The lignin fraction can then be hydrocracked replacing phenol lost that is in the process, and a fuel oil is also formed.

It is claimed that the process would be viable on a much smaller scale than conventional pulping processes. The use of ethyl acetate/acetic acid (ester pulping) has been described by Young *et al.* (1985), and Edel (1984) has discussed the use of methanol and sodium hydroxide to produce organosolv lignin.

The major advantage of these methods would be the removal of sulphur from pulping systems, as many countries are increasing restrictions on the emission of sulphur-containing compounds from both kraft and sulphite pulping mills.

Hemicelluloses

Hemicelluloses are the most easily removed component of lignocellulose and are hydrolysed rapidly by dilute acids into their monomers. The chemical conditions used for hydrolysing cellulose to glucose also hydrolyse hemicelluloses to their constituent monomers and convert the xylose fraction to furfural. Furfural is toxic to microorganisms and has to be removed by steam stripping at considerable expense if the hydrolysate is to be used for fermentation. Thus, hemicelluloses must be removed before any attempts are made to hydrolyse cellulose.

Tubb (1984) has searched for mutants with an increased resistance to furfural and hydroxymethylfurfural. There have been a number of investigations into methods of utilizing the sugars, especially the pentoses found in the hemicellulose fraction. The major problem is the wide variety of hemicelluloses obtained from different sources, and the range of monomers they produce.

Concentration of the hemicellulose fraction from sulphite pulping gives a concentrate resembling molasses which can be used as an animal feed supplement. It has also been used in the Pekilo process, described later. Enzymatic degradation of hemicellulose is only poorly understood, although a number of exo- and endohemicellulases, and enzymes splitting disaccharides have been described. Xylanases attack hemicelluloses in two ways, one in which the side chain substituents are removed and the second where the backbone is cut to give a mixture of small branched chain oligosaccharides. Dekker (1985) and Reilly (1981) have reviewed the enzymes involved.

The substrate normally used to assay xylanases is an arabinoglucuronoxylan. This is not necessarily the best choice, but is used because of its solubility. Generally xylanases are much more active than the corresponding cellulases and in contrast to cellulases which have only been shown to be inducible, both inducible and constitutive hemicellulases have been found.

Enzymatic removal of hemicelluloses has been shown to decrease the energy requirements for pulping. There has been little industrial interest in the use of hemicellulases for sugar production due to the ease of chemical hydrolysis methods, although enzymes have been used in the brewing industry for improving pumping and filtering.

The main pentose of hemicelluloses is xylose, an aldopentose which is not fermented by yeasts such as *Saccharomyces cerevisiae* or *Schizosaccharomyces pombe*, although they can produce ethanol from ketopentoses such as xylulose. The growth of *Saccharomyces* spp. on hydrolysed sugar mixtures has been suggested as a method to remove the hexose fraction, leaving xylose. *Fusarium* and *Mucor* spp. have also been suggested as these can ferment xylose and *F. oxysporium* has received considerable attention. A problem with these groups is the formation of acetate and large quantities of mycelium. Additionally, some species are toxigenic.

Mixed fermentations of xylose in which ethanol is the major end-product are also carried out by bacteria such as *Bacillus* and *Clostridium* species although these groups show low ethanol tolerance. Two pathways of xylose metabolism exist; the first in bacteria isomerises xylose to xylulose, whilst the second found mainly in fungi, reduces xylose to xylitol and reoxidises it to xylulose. Xylulose enters the pentose phosphate and Embden Meyerhof pathways, in which three molecules of xylulose are converted to five molecules of ethanol (Enari and Suihko 1984). No financially viable processes have been developed for the production of ethanol from hemicelluloses.

Gene cloning strategies are being used to improve pentose fermentation. The gene for xylose isomerase which converts xylose into xylulose has been cloned into *S. cerevisiae*. The advantage of this is questionable as xylose is transported by the same system as glucose, and in the presence of both glucose and xylose the transport of glucose is strongly favoured. The cloning of genes for β-xylosidase from *Bacillus cereus* into *S. cerevisiae* has been attempted, and the incorporation of both hemicellulases and isomerase into yeasts could provide a one step fermentation from hemicellulose to ethanol. The wide variety of hemicelluloses would be the main problem. Xylanase production in *Streptomyces* has been improved by recombinant DNA technology (Iwasaki *et al.* 1986).

Theoretically the most advantageous products from xylose are xylitol and xylonic acid. Several bacteria form xylonic acid by oxidation using xylose dehydrogenase (e.g. *Pseudomonas fragi*) and this product could replace glucuronic acid for some applications.

Other products may also be synthesised by fermentation of pentoses. One possibility is 2,3-butanediol (2,3-butylene glycol). Commercial interest in this compound centres around its conversion to the solvent, methylethyl ketone and to diacetyl (a food additive). Also it can be esterified yielding precursors of polyurethane foams, used as an octane booster in lead free petrol and the D(-) isomer used as antifreeze (Yu and Saddler

1985). The main organisms producing 2,3-butanediol are bacteria and the most interest has been shown in *Klebsiella pneumoniae* which produces high yields and *Bacillus polymyxa* which forms only the D(-) isomer. The subject has been reviewed by Magee and Kosaric (1987).

Shepard *et al.* (1987) have suggested several other chemicals which could be formed from the polysaccharide components. These include lactic acid (lactic acid polymers and acrylics) but commercial production will require considerable improvements in lactic acid separation and purification. Another suggestion is levulinic acid which has a rather chequered history (Herrick 1977).

A further large scale possibility is fermentation to acetic acid, and the use of the calcium/magnesium (CMA) salts as non-corrosive agents for de-icing roads.

A major problem with hemicelluloses is their conversion to large quantities of isosaccharinic acids during kraft pulping and, although not toxic, relatively few microorganisms are able to grow on them. The major one found is gluco-isosaccharinic acid formed by the peeling of cellulose. The growth of bacteria on kraft black liquor could remove the isosaccharinic acids and increase the combustible value of the black liquor. It might also be possible to utilise the biomass formed (Bailey 1987).

Cellulose

The use of cellulose can be divided into two areas: directly as a polymeric material; and indirectly following pretreatment and saccharification to form glucose.

Uses of Polymeric Cellulose

Cellulose with the greatest economic value is in the form of a high quality fibre and numerous uses are known as reviewed by Reveley (1985) and Philips (1989). Whilst some of these uses are obviously large scale e.g. paper, board and viscose, many of the more recent uses are small scale, highly specialised and involve cellulose derivatives. They require chemical rather than biological modification.

The principal industrial uses of cellulose and its derivatives, depend on their ability to form films and fibres, which are capable of being processed with a variety of other compounds, such as plasticisers and dyestuffs.

Cellulose derivatives fall into two groups, ethers and esters. These molecules are characterised by a number of factors which define their usage, including the degree of polymerisation (DP), the degree of substitution (DS) which has a maximum value of three, based on the number of free hydroxy groups found on each glucose residue, and the molar substitution (MS). MS can have a value of greater than three because when cellulose is reacted with a compound such as an alkylene oxide new reactive hydroxyl groups are added. In addition to these factors, the degree of cross-linking and choice of side-chain substituents will also influence the behaviour of the polymer.

The ethers include non-ionic compounds such as hydroxyethyl cellulose and ionic structures such as carboxymethyl cellulose. Cellulose ethers have a wide range of uses, e.g. in paints (where they control stability, viscosity and water retention), in the oil industry (viscosity agents), in foods, cosmetics and pharmaceuticals (low calorie additives, thickeners, plasticity and film forming agents). Other uses are as antiredeposition agents in detergents, as adhesives and in products requiring moisture adsorption. The major cellulose ester is cellulose acetate which is widely used in the formation of surface films, photographic film, lacquer coatings, membranes and filter tips for cigarettes. Applications of cellulose ethers have been discussed by Felcht (1985).

There is a great deal of interest in the use of different solvent systems in cellulose technology and this has been reviewed by Johnson (1985).

Pretreatment

The objective of pretreatment is to improve the accessibility of cellulose to enzymes with the intention of increasing hydrolytic dissimilation. Pretreatment is generally regarded as either physical or chemical but there is considerable overlap.

Physical grinding of lignocellulose is effective in improving accessibility for enzymes but the particle size must be reduced to 50 µm to maximise the effect. The energy costs become prohibitive at particle sizes of 200 µm (Datta 1981).

There is considerable industrial interest in steam explosion methods which saturate the lignocellulose with steam and then allow it to undergo explosive decompression. This treatment releases acids which make a significant contribution to the disruption process (Overend and Chornet 1987).

Chemical pretreatments of several types may be found, including the use of alkalis such as NaOH or NH_3 which swell the lignocellulose and have been used to increase the accessibility of straw for fodder. The use of acids for pretreatment overlaps with saccharification which can be divided into two types, chemical and enzymatic.

Saccharification

Chemical saccharification has been carried out with acids, both dilute and concentrated, but their use is problematic. Theoretically, the formation of glucose from cellulose by acids is only the first step in the formation of furan derivatives and, significant quantities of these and other by-products may arise. Other problems found in the use of acids include the recycling of catalyst and low yields. A method developed at ICI (Ragg and Fields 1987) utilises HCl and $CaCl_2$ and is claimed to give glucose yields of greater than 85%. The use of anhydrous HCl and HF have also been suggested.

The application of enzymes to cellulose hydrolysis confers both advantages and disadvantages. The major advantage is the specificity of the reaction and the lack of by-products. Disadvantages are the long time-scales involved and the cost of the process.

Numerous microorganisms have been shown to contain cellulase, the best studied being the fungus, *Trichoderma reesei*. The problems of assaying cellulase, however, are considerable. These include the physical heterogeneity of the substrate, alteration of the substrate during the course of the reaction and complexity of the enzyme. A large number of assays using ill-defined substrates and arbitrary units of activity are found. These have made it extremely difficult to compare results obtained in different laboratories (Wood and Bhat 1988).

In most fungi, cellulase consists of three major enzyme components. The first is endo-1:4-ß-glucanase (EC 3.2.1.4) which hydrolyses internal glycosidic bonds in the amorphous zone of cellulose, creating new sites for the next enzyme to attack. Endoglucanases account for up to 20% of extracellular protein when *T. reesei* is grown on cellulose.

The second enzyme component is cellobiose hydrolase (EC 3.2.1.91) or exo-glucanase. This attacks cellulose at the non-reducing end cleaving off cellobiose and accounts for 35%-85% of the extracellular protein when *T. reesei* is grown on cellulose. The enzyme from some species shows activity against crystalline cellulose. They act synergistically with endoglucanases, the endoglucanase cutting the polysaccharide in the middle of the chain, to be followed immediately by cellobiose hydrolase which removes a molecule of cellobiose. This prevents the re-closure of the scission which would be highly probable in a crystalline system. The action of these two enzymes converts cellulose into a mixture of short chain soluble oligosaccharides, cellobiose and glucose. Exo-glucanases of some fungi also attack xylan.

The third enzyme component of the cellulase complex is cellobiase (ß-glucosidase; EC 3.2.1.21). This converts cellobiose into two molecules of glucose and also slowly attacks short chain oligosaccharides releasing glucose. It accounts for less than 1% of the extracellular protein in *T. reesei*. Although not strictly cellulases, cellobiases are important as low ß-glucosidase activity means poor saccharifying powers due to the build-up of cellobiose, which acts as an inhibitor of endo-glucanase and cellobiohydrolase.

These three enzymes are occasionally joined by a fourth, glucohydrolase (EC 3.2.1.71), which removes glucose from the non-reducing end of cellulose. All these enzymes are basically inactive against crystalline cellulose when used individually.

Considerable reference may be found in older literature to the C_1C_x system based on the work of Reese *et al.* (1950). Interpretation of much of the early work is difficult, but C_x seems to be analogous to endoglucanase and C_1 is similar to cellobiohydrolase (Kirk 1983). Occasional reference is also found to C_b which corresponds to cellobiase.

Multiple forms of the three enzymes are found, differing in their relative activities on various substrates and with varying degrees of synergism, which are not fully understood. In *T. reesei* functionally and immunologically distinct forms of cellobiose hydrolase have been shown. One possible explanation is that they attack the different stereoisomers of the terminal cellobiose group of glucose (Eriksson and Wood 1985).

The system is also complicated in other species. For example, in *Clostridium thermocellum* ten genes have been identified as involved with cellulase activity. Modified cellulases appear in some cultures and are thought to be caused by exposure to proteolytic enzymes.

These problems have caused considerable confusion and have hindered the use of cellulase in the development of commercial saccharification processes as it has frequently proved impossible to compare quantitative data obtained from different sources. A number of standardised procedures have been published by The Commission on Biotechnology in an attempt to clear up the confusion.

Production of cellulases is expensive, contributing up to 60% of the cost of hydrolysing cellulose and as a result there has been considerable research on improving the yields of the enzymes. Cellulases have very low specific activities, being approximately 1% as active as amylases attacking a similar sized starch molecule. Extensive screening has seen only relatively small improvements in the cellulase activities of *T. reesei*, suggesting this is not a fruitful area of research.

Other possibilities include screening for catabolite repression resistant strains, i.e. strains giving high yields when grown on glucose or cellobiose, which normally repress cellulase synthesis even when an inducer is present.

Further suggestions include screening thermophilic organisms and anaerobes. Organisms associated with compost heaps, for example, the thermophilic actinomycete *Microbispora*, possess cellulases with a very wide pH range, which are relatively resistant to end-product inhibition by glucose. In anaerobes the relative cost of protein synthesis is high, and there has probably been evolutionary pressure for the selection of high specific activity cellulases. The anaerobic rumen fungus *Neocallimastic frontalis* contains a cellulase several times more active than a cellulase from one of the best *T. reesei* mutants.

Little evidence is available indicating high levels of cellulolytic activity in bacteria, although *Cl. thermocellum* possesses activity similar to that of *T. reesei*.

There has been a great deal of interest recently in cellulolytic activity in Actinomycetes (McCarthy 1987; McCarthy and Ball, chapter 10 this volume) with attempts at strain improvement. Cellulase genes have been cloned from cellulolytic bacteria including the mesophile *Cellulomonas fimi* and the thermophile *Cl. thermocellum* (Beguin *et al.* 1988).

A major barrier to cellulase action is end-product inhibition and several methods have been suggested to overcome this problem. These include adding *Aspergillus niger* ß-glucosidase to cellulases from *T. reesei* to enhance overall hydrolysis, as this ß-glucosidase is less sensitive to end-product inhibition.

One stage fermentations from cellulose to ethanol have been proposed including the use of the fungus *Monilia* (Gong *et al.* 1981). Two phase aqueous systems have been suggested which form when two different water soluble polymers are mixed. The catalyst is confined to one phase whilst the products may be preferentially partioned thus reducing product inhibition and toxicity (Lilly 1982).

Any successful commercial enzymatic hydrolysis of cellulose will have to compete with several chemical and physical methods and will depend on a much cheaper source of cellulases than presently available, with recovery and re-use of the enzymes.

Lignin

Many possibilities for dealing with lignin are technically viable but most are not economic at present (Little, chapter 12 this volume). These include the use of lignin as a polymer and also its conversion to monomers. They are also small scale conversions compared with the quantities available.

Lignin can be converted into a variety of chemicals using techniques such as pyrolysis and hydrogenation. It can also be converted to compounds such as vanillin, vanillic acid, syringaldehyde, dimethyl sulphide and dimethyl sulphoxide. Lignin and lignosulphonates are used for asphalt substitutes, cement binders, oil well drilling fluids, binders for pelletising ores, surfactants, soil binders, adhesives, dispersal agents and slow release agents for fertilisers and pesticides. The major problem is that many of these preparations are variable, producing unreliable results in use.

Ligninases (lignin-degrading enzymes) are non-specific with regard to substrate and chirality and, as the substrate is heterogeneous, it is obvious that attempts at bioconversion will generate large volumes of a non-uniform population of chemicals. The costs of separation and purification will also be very high. The breakdown of lignin by peroxidase in non-polar solvents forming quantities of compounds such as ferulic acid and vanillin was described by Dordick *et al.* (1986). However, Lewis *et al.* (1987) could not repeat these results and there have been no further claims in this area to date.

It has been suggested that ligninases will find major uses in the paper industry for biopulping and biobleaching and in the treatment of organic pollutants. The use of white-rot fungi (the most efficient lignin-degrading organisms) for biomechanical pulping has been proposed. The energy requirements for pulping were reduced by 30% for wood treated with *Phanerochaete chrysosporium* (Eriksson and Vallander 1982). Cellulase deficient mutants were used which degrade lignin at the expense of hemicellulose and thus reduce pulp loss. Other species such as *Trametes (Polyporus, Coriolus) versicolor* have also been used (Evans, chapter 9 this volume). The problems associated with biopulping include the long incubation periods (several weeks), a decrease in the brightness of the product and enzymatic oxidation of phenols causing a brown colour.

The use of fungi to degrade and decolourise the effluent streams of kraft mills has been suggested. These high concentrations of effluents containing partially degraded brown/black lignins, some of which are chlorinated from the bleaching processes, present a considerable hazard. Methods of cleaning up discharges such as oxygen bleaching and ultrafiltration are prohibitively expensive on the scales involved.

The MYCoR process (mycelial colour removal) uses an immobilised pure culture of *P. chrysosporium* for effluent improvement. Glucose is added as a carbon source and control of nitrogen levels are critical to maintain the fungus in the secondary metabolic state (Chang *et al.* 1983). The colour of the effluent is reduced, the chemical oxygen demand (COD) falls and some chlorinated materials are removed (Huynh *et al.* 1985). Veratryl alcohol, an easily degraded aromatic compound is formed although this is also known to be a secondary metabolite involved as a radical carrier in lignin dissimilation (Evans, chapter 9 this volume). Similar results have been obtained with other white-rot fungi such as *T. versicolor* (Reid *et al.* 1989).

The use of Actinomycetes to decolourise kraft lignins has been investigated (McCarthy and Ball, chapter 10 this volume; Betts *et al.* 1991). The advantage of these bacteria is that they will utilise lignin in the absence of a supplementary carbon source and do not need to be maintained in the secondary metabolic state.

The ligninase of *P. chrysosporium* has several unusual properties compared with other enzymes - it attacks a solid substrate, is non-specific and is non-chiral. Also it degrades several recalcitrant organohalides including DDT, polychlorinated biphenyls, polychlorinated dibenzo(p)dioxins and lindane. Many of these compounds are only poorly soluble and will be absorbed onto particulate matter restricting their susceptibility to microbial attack. Ligninase may be able to function under these conditions as it is extracellular and it normally attacks an insoluble molecule. Several researchers (Bumpus and Aust 1987; Buswell and Odier 1987) have suggested that this fungus could be used for the removal of xenobiotics, such as the chloroaniline herbicides and other organic wastes from the environment.

The use of lignin-degrading enzymes to deal with problems such as biopulping, biodecolourisation and degradation of recalcitrant compounds will depend on development of hyper-lignolytic strains. Comparison of the genetics of *P. chrysosporium*, with simpler, prokaryotic systems is difficult because of the complexity of the enzymes involved. Ligninase genes have been cloned into *Escherichia coli* but the optimum hosts for expression are *Aspergillus* species (Kirk and Farrell 1987).

Options Using Intact Lignocellulose

Mushroom Fermentation

Mushroom cultivation is a technically demanding solid-state fermentation that is practiced world-wide. It is the most financially viable of all the technologies dealing with waste lignocellulose due to a number of factors. These are:

1   the use of low or negative value substrates;
2   little or no investment in technology to avoid microbial contamination (the use of open systems varies in complexity depending on the type of mushrooms being grown. It is highest in *Agaricus bisporus* and minimal in *Lentinus edodes*). Growth of *A. bisporus* uses a two stage process in which wheat straw is composted with manure or some other nitrogen rich additive. The mushroom compost formed is highly selective for *A. bisporus* if correctly prepared. Cut oak logs inoculated with wood already colonised by fungus are used for the growth of *Lentinus;*
3   finally, the use of the product as human food produces a premium price.

A. bisporus is the main mushroom cultivated in the UK using about 300 000 tonnes of wheat straw annually, representing about 5% of that available. The composting process is aerobic and all the components are attacked with an overall weight loss of about 25%.

It has been estimated that the annual weight of mushrooms grown world-wide approaches 1.2×10^6 tonnes, *A. bisporus* accounting for the highest production at 750×10^3 tonnes and *L. edodes* being next at 180×10^3 tonnes. Consumption of *A. bisporus* is universal whereas the use of most other species is confined mainly to Asia although they are spreading. It is difficult to place a value on this type of technology due to local conditions and prices, but it has been estimated to exceed US4×10^9 annually and to be increasing by approximately 10% per annum.

Improvements are possible in several areas. Only about ten different fungi are grown commercially out of the estimated 2000 edible fungi available. Those grown commercially are *Basidiomycetes* which have a wide range of genetic systems and life cycles. Some are relatively simple, which allows the preparation and manipulation of desirable mutants and hybrids. However, *A. bisporus* does not have simple genetics and work on this species is more difficult. Several areas have been targeted for improvement, including pesticide resistance and genes controlling enzymes such as tyrosinase, which influence post-harvest quality.

The preparation of compost involves mixing lignocellulose with animal waste and allowing a solid-state fermentation to take place. Mesophilic organisms dominate in the first stage, raising the temperature and allowing thermophiles to grow. Attempts have been made to increase the rate of composting by recycling compost but these have not been very successful because of the complex succession of organisms involved in the process.

Chemical pretreatment of substrates to render them more available, an area closely studied in the upgrading of animal feeds, is virtually untouched in mushroom technology. Also, attempts at liquid culture have not been very successful to date.

Traditionally, horse manure is used for compost, although there have been studies on other types. Although these are not as good due to problems such as excess moisture content, in view of the manure and slurry mountains building up in the EEC from animals such as pigs and cattle, more extensive examination of this problem is overdue.

Single Cell Protein (SCP)

Another possibility for the use of intact lignocellulose is the production of single cell protein (SCP). It is obviously advantageous to use an organism generally accepted for food use e.g. *S. cerevisiae* or *Candida (Torula) utilis*.

Two techniques are possible, the first of which uses relatively intact lignocellulose and a non-sterile system to upgrade it to food level. It is difficult to ensure that the desired microorganism dominates the system to give product acceptability. The process can be run under sterile conditions but only at a considerable increase in operating costs. This approach was used with *Chaetomium cellulolyticum* (Tautoras and Chalmers, 1984) and it has been shown that mixed cultures of *C. cellulolyticum* and *Candida lipolyticum* have a higher protein content than mono-cultures.

Milstein *et al.* (1986) showed that conversion of straw to protein was higher in solid-state systems than in liquid culture using a number of fungi with straw as substrate.

The second approach (which is usually the one adopted) is to carry out a pretreatment step causing the hydrolysis of the lignocellulose to sugars which can then be converted to SCP. Crop residues are hydrolysed with dilute acid at approximately 120°C without separation of the products. This converts the hemicelluloses into sugars (Han 1978). Hydrolysis of the cellulose fraction at higher temperatures is of no advantage, as the pentose sugars from the hemicelluloses are converted to insoluble resins and furfural, which is toxic to microbial growth.

Spent sulphite liquor (available as a by-product of paper pulping) is widely used as a carbohydrate source and contains about 3% fermentable sugars. Nitrogen, phosphate and potassium sources must be added to allow the growth of the yeast, *C. utilis*. Washing produces an animal grade feed containing about 10% lignosulphonic acids which can be reduced by more extensive washing. The microfungus *Paecilomyces varoti* is grown on waste sulphite liquor (the "Pekilo" process) for use as animal feed in Finland.

These processes have two major advantages - the production of a saleable commodity and the reduction of a waste product capable of causing a serious pollution problem. The figures for the release of lignosulphonates from Swedish pulping mills into the Gulf of Bothnia were 160×10^3 tonnes in 1975 (Salkinoja-Salonen and Sundman 1980).

C. utilis is also used for the production of fodder and has a number of advantages. It is able to use a wide range of nitrogen sources and sugars, including pentoses. It also grows at low pH thus inhibiting bacterial growth, produces a high protein concentration, is easily adapted to industrial scale fermentations and can grow on sulphite liquor, and wood and straw hydrolysates (Coombs 1987). However, it is unsuitable for human consumption due to the high levels of nucleic acids, removal of which can only be achieved at considerable expense.

Other organisms have been used for SCP, including the bacteria *Cellulomonas* and *Lactobacillus*, the moulds *Penicillium*, *Aspergillus* and *Polyporus*, the yeasts *Saccharomyces* and *Rhodotorula* and the algae *Spirulina*, *Scenedesmus* and *Chlorella*. A major problem of *Saccharomyces*, a widely accepted food yeast, is that it is unable to grow on pentoses. A recent paper has suggested that some strains of *S. cerevisiae* are able to utilise the pentose sugar xylose under certain conditions (Van Zyl *et al.* 1989).

There has been renewed interest in SCP with considerable efforts, particularly in the US, to utilise waste carbohydrate (fruit and vegetable), pulp and paper waste and agricultural waste to grow yeasts for supplementing animal feed.

Methane Production

There is considerable interest in biogas production from lignocellulose in landfill sites, for reasons relating to both methane production and safety. Recently, there have been several cases of landfill sites, which were full and had been landscaped, exploding due to methane formation. There is also an interest in developing countries to develop a low technology method of producing alternative fuels to wood. Biogas is a mixture of methane (50% - 80%) and carbon dioxide (15% - 45%) with about 5% water and variable traces of H_2S. The energy available depends on the carbon dioxide content and can be altered by scrubbing out the CO_2. Methane which is much less soluble in aqueous systems will only be slightly reduced.

Methanogenesis, unlike composting, is anaerobic and therefore the oxidation state of the starting material influences the products and can effect the relative amounts of methane and carbon dioxide formed.

Methane is a gas at temperatures when biogas formation takes place and is only sparingly soluble in water. It therefore escapes spontaneously from any fermentation system so that recovery is not associated with significant costs. This is an advantage compared with ethanol but is so obvious that it is frequently overlooked. Another major advantage of methane production is that, because the system is anaerobic, it does not need expensive aeration systems. However, the gaseous nature of methane at room temperature causes serious problems over storage and transport, and generally the best option for utilizing biogas is combustion on site for heating or electricity generation. Evans (1977) divided the process of methanogenesis into several steps:

1   Solubilisation and hydrolysis of polymeric material.
2   Fermentation or acidogenesis.
3   Acetogenesis.
4   Methanogenesis.

Some authors claim the rate limiting step is depolymerization and breakdown of the starting material, whilst others claim it is the conversion of acetate and CO_2/H_2 to methane. Materials high in lignin cause severe rate limitation and polymeric lignin is not significantly degraded under anaerobic conditions. Therefore chemical or physical pretreatments may be necessary at considerable expense (Pauss et al. 1987).

The second stage involves the breakdown of monomers to short chain volatile fatty-acids (VFA) such as acetic, butyric and propionic acids and numerous other compounds. Considerable amounts of CO_2 and H_2 are also formed in this stage. The third stage is the conversion of all VFA's to acetic acid. The methanogenic bacteria from the kingdom Archaebacteria are the final component converting acetic acid to methane.

Radiolabelling experiments show that approximately 73% of the methane comes from the methyl group of acetate, the rest originating from CO_2. The methanogens use ammonia for their nitrogen source even though complex nitrogenous organic compounds may be present.

There is a sharp optimum near neutral pH and any conditions leading to a build-up of acetic acid cause a fall in methane production. A rise in acetic acid is frequently the first indication that problems are imminent and, once detected, the system usually crashes rapidly. The influence of temperature is complicated. Thermophilic methanogens with temperature optima in excess of 65°C have been isolated, but the reduced solubility of carbon dioxide at elevated temperatures reduces the level of substrate available to them.

Compounds such as chloroform and DDT poison the system. Also, sulphate reduces methane formation because of competition between methanogens and sulphate reducers for hydrogen.

Industrial methanogenesis depends on being able to control the complex mixed system which is frequently solid-state e.g. landfill sites. Generally systems are unreliable with ineffective treatment of dilute wastes, poor efficiencies at low temperatures and low resistance to shock loadings and changing flow rates. Methanogenesis has been reviewed by Kirsop (1984).

Fodder

Treatment of straw with alkali has been used for many years to increase the nutritional value for livestock. Early treatments involved soaking and heating in dilute alkali followed by washing (wet treating). Later processes used alkali sprays and no washing (dry process). Both ammonia and NaOH have been used, the former has the advantage that it is milder and can be removed by evaporation, but is less effective than the latter.

Protein enrichment of straw has also been suggested using cellulolytic species which will grow at low moisture content (Milstein *et al.* 1986) making a useful alternative to SCP.

Electrolysis, Pyrolysis, Hydrogenation and Gasification

Electrolysis of lignin in a solution of sodium hydroxide can give good yields of phenolics (spruce lignins producing 4-hydroxybenzaldehyde and eucalyptus lignins forming syringaldehyde). Lignins could be substituted before cleavage to form aromatics with useful substitution patterns.

The chemistry of lignin pyrolysis is extremely complex and the products vary depending on the temperature. At lower temperatures monomers predominate and at high temperatures a synthesis gas is found. Phenols, charcoal and tars are also found. The results are not reliable especially when variable feedstocks are being used.

Hydrogenation of lignin in the presence of various catalysts produces a mixture of phenols, cyclohexane derivatives, light and heavy oils. The products can be altered over a wide range by changing the temperature, catalysts and solvents systems used.

Biomass can be gasified and converted to synthesis gas (hydrogen and carbon monoxide) by heating with steam and oxygen. These can in turn be converted to methanol. The quality of the gas formed is better than synthesis gas formed from coal as it is higher in carbon monoxide and lower in sulphur compounds.

Conclusions

The previous discussion has depended upon the results of research over a considerable number of years and yet the vast resource of lignocellulose remains under-exploited. It is particularly important to recognise the environmental soundness of biotechnological approaches as compared to chemical technologies. Several areas require special attention before an extensive use can be made of the worlds lignocellulose and related substrates:

1   Alternative methods to sulphite and kraft pulping technologies are required (it is likely that this will be assisted by environmental pressure to replace them or to clean up their effluents).
2   A less expensive source of cellulase must be found, without which the commercial use of this enzyme to hydrolyse cellulose will not be economically attractive.
3   There should be full exploitation of white-rot fungi and other suitable microbes for biobleaching, biopulping and the bioremediation of effluents.
4   Pentose and hemicelluloses must be utilised efficiently through the development of suitable processes.
5   Uses for the isosaccharinic acids produced from kraft pulping must be found whilst this process continues.

However, recent developments have provided new insights into the mechanisms of biotransformation of lignocellulose components and applications of this knowledge are beginning to appear.

References

Bailey MJ (1987) A comparison of the bacterial strains growing on glucoisosaccharinic acid In: Wood and Cellulosics Kennedy J F, Phillips G O, Williams P A (eds) Ellis Horwood pp 331-337
Beguin P, Millet J, Grepinet O, Navarro A, Juy M, Amit A, Poljak R, Aubert J-P (1988) The *cel* (cellulose degradation) genes of *Clostridium thermocellum* In: Biochemistry and Genetics of Cellulose Degradation. Aubert J-P, Beguin P, Millet J Academic P pp 267-282
Betts WB, Pedlar LS, Dart RK (1991) A recirculating bioreactor conatining *Thermomonospora mesophila* for the purposes of lignin decolourisation VIth International Symposium on Wood and Pulping Chemistry, Melbourne Australia (in press)
Bumpus JA, Aust SD (1987) Degradation of environmental pollutants by the white-rot fungus *Phanerochaete chrysosporium*: involvement of the lignin degrading system. Bioessays 6:166-170
Buswell JA, Odier E (1987) Lignin biodegradation. CRC Crit Revs Biotech 6:1-61
Chang H-M, Joyce, TW, Campbell AG, Gerrard ED, Huynh V-B, Kirk TK (1983) Fungal decolourisation of bleach plant effluents. In: Recent Advances in Lignin Biodegradation Research Higuchi T, Chang H-M, Kirk TK (eds) Uni Press pp 257-268
Coombs J (1987) Carbohydrate feedstocks: availability and utilisation of malasses and whey. In: Carbon Substrates in Biotechnology Stockwell JD, Beardsmore AJ, Keevil CW, Woodward JR (eds) IRL Press pp 29-44
Datta R (1981) Energy requirements for lignin pretreatment processes Process Biochem 16:15-19
Dekker RFH (1985) Biodegradation of the hemicelluloses. In: Biosynthesis and Biodegradation of Wood Components Higuchi T (ed) Academic Press pp 505-533
Dordick JS, Marletta MA, Klibanov AM (1986) Peroxidases depolymerise in organic media but not in water Proc Nat Acad Sci US 83:6255-6257
Dunhill P (1983) The future of biotechnology Biochem Soc Symp 48:9-23
Edel E (1984) The MD organosolv process Papierwirtschaft 1:39
Enari T-M, Suihko M-L (1984) Ethanol production by fermentation of pentoses and hexoses from cellulosic materials Crit Revs Biotechnol 1: 229-240
Eriksson K-E, Vallander L (1982) Biomechanical Pulping In: Lignin Biodegradation, Microbiology, Chemistry and Potential Applications Kirk TK, Higuchi T, Chang H-M (eds) CRC Press Vol II pp 213-224
Eriksson K-E, Wood T (1985) Biodegradation of wood In: Biosynthesis and Biodegradation of Wood Components Higuchi T (ed) Academic Press pp 469-503
Evans WC (1977) Biochemistry of the bacterial catabolism of aromatic compounds in anaerobic environments. Nature 270:17-20

Evans R, Wallis AFA, Wearne RH (1987) Influence of additives on the alkaline degradation of cellulose In: Wood and Cellulosics Kennedy JF, Phillips GO, Williams PA (eds) Ellis Horwood pp 65-172

Fan LT, Lee Y-H, Gharpuray MM (1982) The nature of lignocellulosics and their pretreatment for enzymatic hydrolysis. Adv Biochem Eng 23:155-188

Felcht U-H (1985) Cellulose ethers - synthesis, applications and analytical aspects In: Cellulose and its Derivatives Kennedy JF, Phillips GO, Wedlock DJ, Williams PA (eds) Ellis Horwood pp 273-284

Glasser WG, Kelly SS (1987) Light stability of polymers. In: Encyclopedia of Polymer Science and Engineering Kroschwitz JJ, Salvatore A, Klingsberg A, Piccininni R (eds) pp 795-852

Gong Ch-S, Chen LF, Tsao GT, Flickinger MC (1981) Biosynthesis, purification and mode of action of cellulases of *Trichoderma reesei*. Adv Biochem Eng 20:93-118

Han YW (1978) Microbial utilisation of straw. Adv Appl Microbiol 23:119-153

Herrick FW (1977) Utilisation of chemicals from wood: retrospect and prospect Recent Adv Phytochem 2:443-512

Huynh V-B, Chang H-M, Joyce TW (1985) Dechlorination of chloro-organics by a white-rot fungus. Tappi 68:98-102

Iwasaki A, Kishida H, Okanishi M (1986) Molecular cloning of a xylanase gene from Streptomyces spp. No. 36a and its expression in Streptomyces J Antib 39:985-993

Johnson DC (1985) Solvents for cellulose In: Cellulose Chemistry and its Applications Nevell TP, Zeronian SH (eds) Ellis Horwood pp 181-201

Kirk TK (1983) Degradation and conversion of lignocellulose In: The Filamentous Fungi Smith JE, Berry DR, Kristiansen B (eds) vol 4 Edward Arnold pp 266-295

Kirk TK, Farrell RL (1987) Enzymatic "combustion": the microbial degradation of lignin. Ann Revs Microbiol 4:465-505

Kirk TK, Fenn P (1982) Formation and action of the lignolytic system in basidiomycetes In: Decomposer Basidiomycetes Frankland JC, Hedger JN, Swift MJ (eds) Cambridge Univ Press pp 67-90

Kirsop BH (1984) Methanogenesis Crit Revs Biotechnol 1:109-159

Lewis NG, Razal RA, Yamanoto E (1987) Lignin degradation by peroxidase in organic media: a reassessment Proc Nat Acad Sci US 84:7925-7927

Lilly MD (1982) Two liquid phase biocatalyst reactions J Chem Tech Biotechnol 32:162

Lindberg JJ, Levon K, Kuusela T (1988) Modification of lignin Acta Polymerica 39:47-49

Lynch JM (1987) Utilisation of lignocellulosic wastes. J Appl Bact Symp Suppl 71S-83S

Magee RJ, Kosaric N (1987) Microbial production of 2,3-butanediol Adv Appl Microbiol 32:89-161

McCarthy AJ (1987) Lignocellulose-degrading actinomycetes. FEMS Microbiol Reviews 46:145-163

Messner K, Ertler G, Jaklin-Farcher S (1989) Treatment of Bleach Pulp Effluents by the Mycopor Process. In: Proc 4th Int Symp Biotechnol Pulp and Paper Industry pp 67-68

Milstein O, Vered Y, Sharma A, Gressel J, Flowers HM (1986) Microbial treatments for nutritional upgrading of wheat straw Biotechnol Bioeng 28:381-386

Overend RP, Chornet E (1987) Fractionation of lignocellulosics by steam aqueous pretreatments Phil Trans Roy Soc London A321:523-536

Pauss A, Naveau H, Nyms E-J (1987) Biogas production In: Biomass Hall DO, Overend RP (eds) Wiley pp 273-291

Philips GO (1989) Rediscovering cellulose. Chem in Britain 25:1006-1009

Ragg PL, Fields PR (1987) Development of a process for the hydrolysis of lignocellulosic waste Phil Trans Roy Soc Lond A321:537-547

Reese ET, Sui RGH, Levinson HS (1950) The biolopgical degradation of soluble cellulose derivatives and its relationship to the mechanism of cellulose hydrolysis J Bact 59:485

Reid ID, Kirkpatrick N, Magoon J, Paice MG, Ho C, Jurasek L (1989) Lignin degradation during biological bleaching of kraft pulp with *Coriolus versicolor* proceedings of the 4th International Conference on Biotechnology in the Pulp and Paper Industry, Raleigh USA May 16-19th, pp 46-47

Reilly PJ (1981) Xylanases: structure and function In: Basic Life Sciences, Trends in the Biology of Fermentation Hollaender A (ed) vol 18 Plenum pp 111-127

Reveley A (1985) A review of cellulose derivatives and their industrial applications Wood and Cellulosics Kennedy JF, Phillips GO, Williams PA (eds) Ellis Horwood pp 211-225

Salkinoja-Salonen M, Sundman V (1980) Regulation and genetics of the biodegradation of lignin drivatives in pulp mill effluents In: Lignin Biodegradation, Microbiology, Chemistry and Potential Applications Kirk TK, Higuchi T Chang H-M (eds) Vol II CRC Press pp 179-198

Shepard WJ, Lipinsky ES, Overend RP (1987) Chemicals from biomass In: Biomass Hall DO, Overend RP (eds) Wiley pp 293-306

Tautorus TE, Chalmers WT (1984) Pilot plant production of single cell protein utilising *Chaetonium cellulolyticum*. Dev Ind Microbiol 25:621

Tubb RS (1984) Genetics of ethanol producing microorganisms Crit Revs Biotechnol 1:241-261

Wood D (1985) Useful biodegradation of lignocellulose Proc Phytochem Soc Europe 26:295-309

Wood TM, Bhat KM (1988) Methods for measuring cellulase activities In: Methods in Enzymology Vol 160A:87-112

Young RA, Achmadi S, Barkalow D (1985) Direct modification of cellulose in woody biomass and sludge In: Cellulose and its Derivatives Kennedy JF, Phillips GO, Williams PA (eds) Ellis Horwood pp 417-424

Yu EKC, Saddler JN (1985) Biomass conversion to butanediol by simultaneous saccharification and fementation Trends in Biotech 3:100-104

Van Zyl C, Prior BA, Kilian SG, Kock JLF (1989) D-xylose utilisation by *Saccharomyces cerevisiae* J Gen Microbiol 135:2791-2798

Chapter 12

Commercial Aspects of Bioconversion Technology

B. F. P. Little

Introduction

Extensive research and a small number of commercial scale applications have failed to convince industrialists that biotechnology can offer viable alternatives to traditional chemical methods. However, a resurgence of interest and significant activity, particularly in the market niche of waste treatment, is hope for the future.

This chapter looks at the current status of bioconversion technology and projects into the future. Reference is made to two areas identified as having the greatest commercial potential, namely the production of speciality chemicals and bioremediation of environmental contamination. Lignin, a major component of biomass with worldwide availability in excess of 30 million tonnes per year, is the main example for discussion.

Production of Speciality Chemicals from Biomass using Biotechnology

A recent report (Walker 1990) has highlighted the dilemma of biotechnologists who have expended much energy in developing new processes only to find few commercial uses established in the market place. If this is examined more closely it is found that biotechnology has been evaluated by many industries as a process tool to achieve particular end results. It has had a major impact in several areas including medicine (diagnostics, vaccine and pharmaceuticals production), genetics/molecular biology (microbial strain improvement and plant/animal breeding) and the environment (waste water treatment and toxic waste neutralisation).

Other industries which have invested significant expenditure on biotechnology include the chemical industry (e.g. manufacture of speciality fine chemicals and agrochemicals), the dairy industry (e.g. waste treatment and food processing) and the brewing industry (e.g. waste treatment, fermentation technology and yeast strain improvement). It is only in the mature industry of bulk chemicals that biotechnology has had a negligible effect, largely due to the more economically favourable production from oil which continues to be readily available and inexpensive.

Clearly the cost of introducing biotechnology as a working tool in many industries has been perceived as being in excess of their profitability. Mature industries are essentially driven by the cost:benefit ratio, i.e. net profits must be increased by the adoption of biotechnology-based processes. Even in industries which demand excellence in product performance and profitability, e.g. healthcare, many cost constraints exist or can develop as patent protection ends and competitive products are introduced. The hurdles to the successful introduction of biotechnology are numerous but can be split conveniently into four groups (Table 12.1)

Table 12.1. Obstacles to the successful introduction of biotechnology into industry

Regulations	-cost of product testing and securing patent protection
	-length of time to gain clinical approval
Marketing	-high rate of failure of new product launches
	-timing of entry into the market
	-quick response to competition with similar products
Technology	-development costs exceed budget
	-development work unsuccessful
	-competitors' patents are infringed
Manufacture	-product quality fails to meet market expectations
	-manufacturing costs exceed budget
	-process yield fails to meet expectations

Many examples of the above obstacles have been reported in the trade press but a further important aspect to note is the importance of raw material costs and the inter-relationship of supply/demand patterns for the various sources of such raw materials as petroleum and biomass.

It is emerging that two industrial applications have been able to take advantage of the rapid development of biotechnology. These are environmental control and production of speciality chemicals which are essentially in the mid-ground of modern industry. Product performance and the need to maximise process efficiency are balanced for speciality chemical manufacture. However, the growth in demand for solutions to the world's environmental problems has been a major incentive to the introduction of new technology with, at present, not too many pressures on cost performance factors. The use of biotechnology in these applications will be considered in greater detail with particular reference to biomass use.

Oil has remained the premier raw material for chemicals of all types including many speciality chemicals. Certain biomass sources have become established raw materials for the production of some speciality chemicals but only a very few involve biotechnology, usually a fermentation process. Figure 12.1 illustrates the complex petrochemical and biomass routes to organic chemicals.

Considerable discussion and a great deal of work has concentrated on the need to develop alternative feedstocks to the established petrochemical pyramid. Political manipulations of the base petroleum price and, in turn, related natural gas and coal prices provide the occasional spur to investigate alternative feedstocks. Much research,

PETROCHEMICAL ROUTES   BIOMASS ROUTES

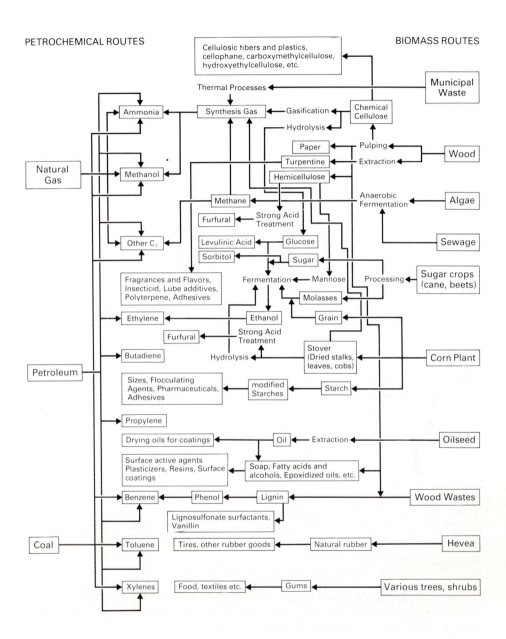

Fig. 12.1. Petrochemical and biomass routes to organic chemicals.

often in very good faith, has been supported by governments at excellent research
establishments such as the Institute for Applied Biology, University of York, to
establish viable technology. However, vested interests in the form of established multi-
nationals which can have sales turnovers in excess of the Gross National Product
(GNP) of many countries has limited the competition debate and the commercial
introduction of new processes. If a company has invested $200 million in a plant to
use a particular feedstock and the plant life is calculated to be 20 years, it is extremely
unlikely that new technology will be adopted if it means substantial capital
expenditure. However, forward planning is possible and a good example is the purchase
and development by Shell of substantial forestry interests in South America.
Consequently, we have the present scenario:

i   alternative feedstocks available - yes
ii   utilisation technology - yes
iii   end users of (i) and (ii) - no
iv   green customers - yes

   In order to make predictions on the adoption of biotechnology in the future it is
important to know when and how this situation will change and when the many
dedicated workers in the field will obtain a return for their efforts. Also it would be
useful to know if and when the petrochemical companies' monopoly can be broken.
Many of the alternative feedstocks are abundant in lesser developed countries and the
implications for these should also be considered. Possibilities for the future will be
discussed more fully later.
   The established petrochemical pyramid is very well established, supplemented with
natural gas as a source of methanol and conversion of coal to toluene as relatively
minor feedstocks. On the biomass side of the equation are a range of feedstocks and the
commercial utilisation, availability and countries of origin are very diverse. Looking at
the various biomass sources, there are many driving forces and influencing factors
(Table 12.2).

Table 12.2. Biomass sources
Waste derived from sophisticated processes/countries
Municipal waste/sewage
Manufacture of wood pulp
Wastes derived from agricultural/farming/forestry (non-pulping activities)
Sugar crops
Corn
Oilseed
Hevea
Trees/Shrubs
Products from marine algae

These are important categories because they are indicative of both long and short term
availability, closeness to end-user markets and support services. However, on the basis
of availability and closeness to potential sophisticated, industrial end-users, lignin is
the premier biomass and perhaps the most interesting chemical. Other biomasses, in
the form of municipal waste and sewage, will be briefly discussed later in the context
of environmental control.

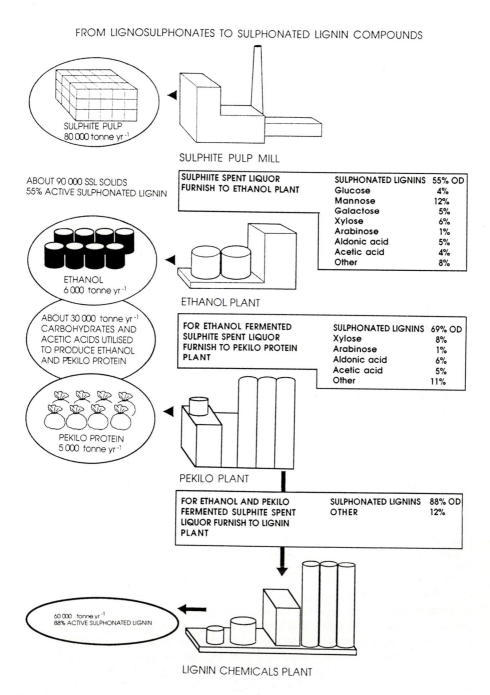

Fig. 12.2. Clean sulphonated lignin technology using the Metsä-Serla exclusive purification process for sulphite spent liquor (SSL).

Commercial Opportunities for Biotransformation of Lignocellulose

We have seen earlier that lignocellulose is the major renewable resource in the world and that in the pulp and paper industry about 30-50 million tonnes per annum of lignin and a similar amount of hemicellulose are available as by-products. Hemicelluloses are hetero-polysaccharides and Figure 12.2 describes a commercial process in which the waste liquor from the production of pulp by the sulphite process is progressively purified by two fermentation processes to yield high performance dispersants and significant quantities of ethanol and protein. A review including the potential for pentose fermentations was published recently (Dart and Betts 1990). However, with regard to hemicellulose from the kraft process, there are certain difficulties which presently restrict biotransformation opportunities. Consequently, we will concentrate our attention to the biotransformation of lignin.

Lignin Biotransformation

Derivation

Lignocellulose is generally considered to be the most abundant organic chemical amounting in total to some 50% of the world's biomass (Lynch 1987). This 300 000 million tonnes of biomass consists primarily of cellulose, lignin, hemicelluloses and some minor constituents (Table 12.3). Further details of the biosynthesis and structures of these components are provided by Betts *et al.* in Chapter 7 this volume.

Table 12.3. Lignocellulose components

	Lignin	Cellulose	Hemicellulose
Hardwoods	18-25%	40-55%	24-40%
Softwoods	25-35%	45-50%	25-35%
Grasses/Straws	10-30%	25-40%	25-50%

It has been estimated by various workers that the annual rate of production of lignocellulose is in the range of 2×10^{10} to 5×10^{10} tonnes (Kirk and Fenn 1982). Lignocellulose biomass is derived from both hardwood and softwood trees and from a broad range of grasses. In total, from the yearly growth of the world's forests, i.e. 7×10^9 to 9×10^9 cubic metres of biomass, some 1.4×10^8 tonnes of cellulose and about 5×10^6 tonnes of lignin are formed. This lignocellulose biomass represents some 50% of the world's total.

A major use of lignocellulose is in the pulp and paper industries and totals some 1.2×10^8 - 2.0×10^8 tonnes per year, mainly in the form of softwood and hardwood trees. Only cellulose is required for paper manufacture so that up to 50% of this biomass is often simply burnt as a fuel at the pulp mill or is buried in landfill sites. Many workers have attempted to develop bioconversion processes to release cellulose from lignocellulose by total degradation of the lignin (Kirk *et al.* 1986) but no commercial scale processes have to date been commissioned. Lignin is obviously a massive renewable resource which is presently considered as a hindrence or waste and is under-utilised.

The production of high grade cellulose demands the removal of the maximum amount of lignin and other compounds (hemicelluloses, sugars and other minor extractives) achievable in an economic way. At present, the kraft or sulphate process is the premier process and a world scale pulping plant will produce about 1 000 tonnes per day of cellulose.

Lignin and the other by-products are collected in an aqueous alkaline stream called black liquor which is burnt to provide energy and to recover the inorganic chemicals which can be recycled. The lignin can be extracted from the black liquor by acidification and subsequent ultrafiltration is a useful technique to both purify and select particular molecular weight fractions.

Perhaps at this stage, it is worthwhile to clarify the distinction between lignin and lignosulphonates. In the tree, lignin is there to provide strength so that it is strategically placed in the cellular structure of the tree. As soon as the tree enters the pulping process, the lignin starts to undergo change. The employment of heat, alkaline conditions and the availability of oxygen ensure that the lignin undergoes polymerisation and condensation reactions, resulting in substantial increases in the average molecular weight. In the sulphite process, the conditions provide for the addition of sulphite groups to the lignin molecule and, if sodium bisulphite is used, then sodium lignosulphonate results. However, magnesium bisulphite is generally used when the lignosulphonate liquor is to be burnt.

If the lignosulphonate is to be extracted and marketed, the liquor is first treated to remove the sugars and, as Figure 12.2 illustrates, undergoes a substantial amount of processing. Lignosulphonates are water soluble products which find many uses as binders and dispersants. Lignin is water insoluble and has found few commercial uses *per se* (Little 1989). In the only commercial operation to extract and market lignin, a significant quantity is converted to high quality dispersant grade sodium lignosulphonate. Westvaco Inc. of the U.S.A. process about 50 000 tonnes per year.

A number of new pulp processes have achieved commercial status (Table 12.4) but generally the lignin is of lower molecular weight than that obtained from the kraft process; an indication that the lignin is relatively unchanged in these new processes. There are about eight sources of so called technical lignins, i.e. lignins which are commercially available and these range from soft/hardwood kraft lignins, hydrolysis lignin, bagasse lignin, to the lignins derived from the new solvent pulping processes.

Table 12.4. New commercial pulp processes

Name	Company	Process
Organosolv	Organocell Gmbh, Munich, Germany	solvent/acid
Acetosolv	Repap Technologies Pennsylvania, USA	solvent/acid peroxyformic acid

Structure

Identification of the structure of lignin has occupied many scientists around the world for over 50 years. Slowly, more reliable data has become available as new analytical tools have been developed. It is now accepted that lignin is a three dimensional polymer made up of phenylpropane subunits. The range of ring substitutions and intermonomeric bond types allows for considerable variations in structural detail (see Betts *et al.* Chapter 7 this volume).

With so many species of tree and the enormous tonnages of material available, a general classification method was required in order to provide guidelines for selection of the appropriate lignin for specific applications. With much analytical work reported, this system has now been published having the following basis:

OH group, syringyl:guaiacyl (S:G ratio), p-hydroxy benzyl group.

Applications

Much work was achieved without a full understanding of the structure of lignin and, as a result, much effort has been wasted. No doubt some work will need to be repeated using lignins now considered structurally more suitable and which are commercially available. So what of the biotransformation possibilities for lignin? The two key commercial application areas are degradation to monomer or dimer products and modification of the basic polymer structure to enhance its properties. Let us consider each of these in greater detail.

Lignin degradation and modification

Degradation of lignin by chemical methods has not been commercially exploited (other than oxidation of sodium lignosulphonate to vanillin) because of very poor yields resulting from competing condensation reactions. The products of degradation are dependant upon the basic lignin structure. For example, eucalyptus lignin - a commercially available hardwood lignin - has the properties shown in Table 12.5 and a structure which has a high percentage of syringyl groups. Chemical oxidation typically yields the products shown in Table 12.6.

Table 12.5. Properties of eucalyptus lignin

Molecular weight distribution		Typical analysis	
> 4000	15.5%	Klaison lignin	89.7%
4000-2000	16.2%	Ash	1.7%
2000-1200	17.9%	Methoxy	21.3%
1200-800	27.6%	Reactive sites	0.5%
< 800	21.1%		

Table 12.6. Products from the chemical oxidation of eucalyptus lignin

Guaiacol	0.28%
Vanillin	1.05%
Acetovanillone	3.07%
Syringaldehyde	5.77%
Acetosyringaldehyde	2.10%
2,6-Dimethoxyphenol	Detectable
Total	12.27

More recently, electrochemical oxidation has been investigated and high yields of a variety of phenolic compounds are claimed to be produced. However, there is still much work to complete before a commercial scale is reached.

The biodegradation of lignocellulose has been extensively studied with the aim of releasing the cellulose fibres for paper making. There is a ready market for cellulose in the paper making industry and the major (kraft) pulp process releases extensive quantities of lignin. A number of research groups have started to investigate the specific biodegradation of lignin in lignocellulose (Crawford 1981).

While it is clear that the massive availability of lignin is a driving force, improved biotransformation technology and a greater understanding of lignin structure should this time around ensure that commercial applications develop. Particularly, the work of Hutterman (1989) on the enzymatic modification of lignin for technical use is noted. The use of lignin containing natural polyphenol groups as a feedstock for adhesives in wood composites has attracted much attention but few commercial applications have developed. The low cost of lignin compared with traditional petrochemical based resins of the phenol-formaldehyde type was perceived as being particularly attractive. However, during the kraft pulp process lignin undergoes significant changes, notably condensation. Lignin from some of the new solvent pulping processes may have a molecular weight which is too small and, like kraft lignin, is water insoluble. Treatment with enzymes using the conditions developed by Hutterman (1989) results in a lignin which has a reasonably high molecular weight and with high reactivity provided by reactive functional groups. Perhaps more importantly, it produces a homogeneous adhesive system.

To summarise, biotransformation reactions can achieve the several changes in the lignin molecule, including solubilisation, demethylation, changes in phenolic and aliphatic hydroxyl contents, and changes in molecular weight distribution. All of these changes are expected to lead to industrial uses, particularly when coupled to other techniques, e.g. ultrafiltration to narrow molecular weight bands.

Transformation of Biomass: Environmental Control

Clearly environmental concern can also be a major driving force in the utilisation of novel technologies to develop derivative end uses. Early industrial activity was characterised by a total lack of concern for the environment, a situation which is only slowly being rectified. Even today, Western Europe produces in excess of 2.6×10^{7} tonnes of hazardous waste each year, with the chemical and metal working industries being key polluters. However, over 500 000 sites are contributors to this waste problem and, if non-hazardous wastes are added, the problem is so enormous as to be beyond the resources of many countries to respond to public demands for a clean environment. The present drive to introduce waste minimisation as an alternative to end-of-pipe solutions is the only long term strategy which will significantly reduce waste arisings. Never the less, there still remains the problem of removing or treating and stabilising waste which has been dumped without due care for the environment.

Microbiological Treatment of Waste

Waste Minimisation and Landfill Treatment

Both waste minimisation and waste at landfill sites offer opportunities for microbiological treatment. Collection of methane at landfill sites in the UK is now common and provides a cheap source of energy for local companies. Many organisations have introduced microbiological treatment of wastes as part of their effluent clean-up programmes and are also selling their technology to other companies. The treatment of wastes is considered to be a strong driving force for the commercial development of biotransformation technology.

The destructive capability of microorganisms has been recognised for some time. Under the appropriate conditions, bacteria and fungi can decompose virtually any organic material, from wood and coal to pesticides and PCBs. In any given soil sample, it is likely that microorganisms can be identified that will have the necessary genetic profile to decompose specific compounds. There are also a variety of ways to multiply the microorganisms present in natural environments and to enhance their activity.

Genetic Ecology

Following rather simple experiments of ploughing waste land and spraying with nutrients to stimulate bacterial growth, technology has evolved into what is now called genetic ecology. Detailed studies of how environmental processes can be controlled at the genetic level in microorganisms have enabled methods to be developed which result in the destruction of toxic wastes in both land and water. Conversely, the extraction of materials from the land and their subsequent use can be assisted by biological treatment prior to extraction. It has been estimated (Goldstein and Olsen 1988) that by the use of bacteria to destroy toxic waste, site clean up can be reduced by a factor of ten.

Natural processes that break down complex organic molecules into harmless subunits usually involve many separate reactions, each catalysed by a specific enzyme. Currently under study is the enhancement of the natural duplication and transfer of genes that control the degradation of specific toxic materials. Unlike the laboratory-based genetic engineering work, using microorganisms, found in nature, should minimise regulatory problems. Finding suitable microorganisms requires a combination of field and laboratory work resulting in a model being developed which will predict the effect on site of introducing environmental change. The objective of the work is, through varying changes in temperature, oxygen enrichment and the addition of different nutrients, to increase the activity of those microorganisms and to activate more genes. Finally toxin breakdown against time is studied. Figure 12.3 describes three approaches in the application of bioconversion techniques to waste treatment.

Waste Water Treatment

There are a growing number of industrial applications of microbial transformations, ranging from the removal of fat, which accumulates in fat traps in food-processing factories, to the elimination of mercury contamination in lakes. However, the largest use of applied microbiology in the world is aerobic waste water treatment. Unlike fermentation processes in the brewing and pharmaceutical industries, these aerobic treatment processes operate as open ecosystems with the result that the whole microbiology of the process is in a state of flux. Consequently, the systems are prone to failure due to the loss of vital components of the biomass. Pre-selected microorganisms could therefore be used to establish or re-establish, replace or supplement key biomass components and thereby overcome the treatment problem. The application of this technological concept is termed bioaugmentation.

The basic principle of aerobic waste water treatment involves the stabilisation of organic pollutants by a heterogeneous population of microorganisms in the presence

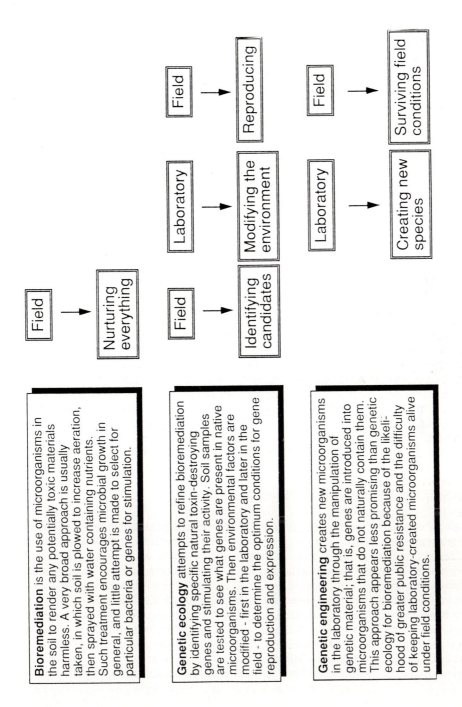

Bioremediation is the use of microorganisms in the soil to render any potentially toxic materials harmless. A very broad approach is usually taken, in which soil is plowed to increase aeration, then sprayed with water containing nutrients. Such treatment encourages microbial growth in general, and little attempt is made to select for particular bacteria or genes for stimulation.

Genetic ecology attempts to refine bioremediation by identifying specific natural toxin-destroying genes and stimulating their activity. Soil samples are tested to see what genes are present in native microorganisms. Then environmental factors are modified - first in the laboratory and later in the field - to determine the optimum conditions for gene reproduction and expression.

Genetic engineering creates new microorganisms in the laboratory through the manipulation of genetic material; that is, genes are introduced into microorganisms that do not naturally contain them. This approach appears less promising than genetic ecology for bioremediation because of the likelihood of greater public resistance and the difficulty of keeping laboratory-created microorganisms alive under field conditions.

Fig. 12.3. Fine distinctions in biological cleanup.

of free oxygen and essential nutrients. The resultant reaction primarily produces new biomass, carbon dioxide and water. Two methods have evolved for achieving this, namely suspended growth systems and fixed-film reactors. A company active in the provision of microorganisms for this application is Interbio Ltd.

In the operation of a typical biological waste water treatment plant in the chemical industry there are many indirect pressures on the effectiveness of the heterotrophic bacteria and these are described in Table 12.7.

Table 12.7. Indirect selection pressures acting on heterotrophic bacteria

Plant Design	- Suspended growth
	- Flow regime
	- Fixed film
	- Type of media
	- Design loading rate
Mode of Operation	- pH
	- Dissolved oxygen
	- Temperature
	- Nutrient addition
	- Sludge age/loading rate
Nature of the Influent	- pH
	- Nutrients
	- Types of organic pollutants
	- Flow pattern

Microbiological Treatment Methodology

The successful application of microbiology is dependent upon four major factors. First, microorganisms must be isolated/selected that are capable of degrading common environmental pollutants (Fig. 12.4). Second, these microorganisms are subjected to selection pressures which result in strains with the ability to preferentially biodegrade the target pollutant instead of an easily fermentable substrate (Johnsrud and Eriksson 1985). Third, the freeze-dried strains are blended to produce the three basic components of a product (biopolymer production, preferential biodegradation and broad spectrum biodegradation capabilities) (Fig. 12.5). Finally, the selected microorganisms are introduced into an environment conducive to their establishment.

In Situ Microbiological Remediation

With an increasing worldwide concern for the environment many of the problems derived from past industrial activity are considered as requiring attention and it is no longer acceptable to allow a wide variety of wastes to lie untreated for future generations. A greater understanding of the toxicity and carcinogenicity of products which were perhaps not considered too dangerous in the past is a further driving force. Typical of the many examples is the treatment of petroleum residues.

In many countries, particularly the UK and other coal producing areas, town gas was produced by the destructive distillation of coal in vertical retorts. Other processes involved heating coal with steam or thermally cracking petroleum. All of these processes left thick residues containing potentially toxic materials which were simply buried. However, as more has been learned about environmental and public health

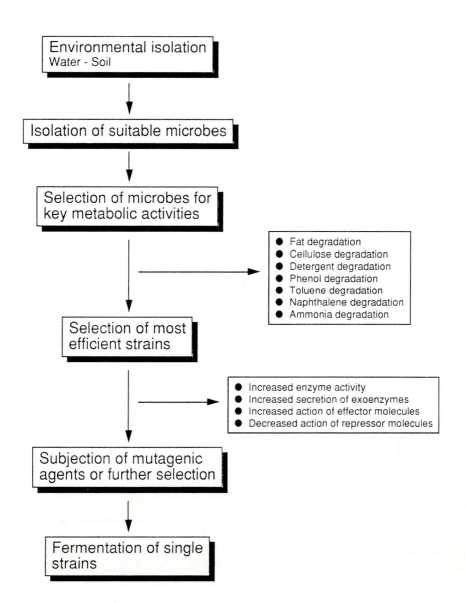

Fig. 12.4. Product development.

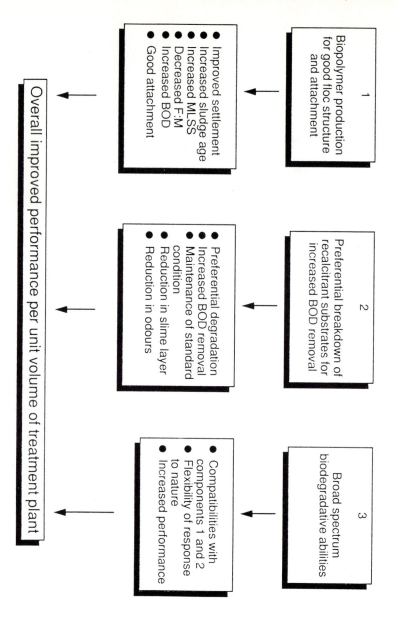

Fig. 12.5. Product components.

hazards, there has been increasing demand for technology to render these sites safe. Conventional techniques which usually involve digging up the wastes, followed by incineration or treatment with chemicals has become increasingly expensive. Typical of the contaminants found on these sites are polycyclic aromatic hydrocarbons (PAHs). Bacterial action can render these toxins and carcinogens harmless. Early studies with naphthalene demonstrated the mechanism by which two operons - one with six genes, the other with seven - control microbial production of the enzymes that drive the 13 reactions required to transform a molecule of naphthalene into pyruvate, a common harmless substance found in plant and animal bodies. Today, there are a number of companies capable of assessing sites, recommending suitable bacterial treatment and restoring the land to domestic use, all without removing any material from the site.

The Way Ahead

The world is faced with many problems, of which the need to minimise waste and to maximise utilisation of available biomasses as alternatives to the traditional petrochemical routes to chemicals are major challenges to scientists of many disciplines. After much faltering, progress is being made and a number of industrial scale applications have been established. However it is unlikely that new technology, as it becomes established in the heavily industrialised countries, will be transferred to the less developed countries; the technology gap is likely to widen rather than diminish.

Increasing knowledge of the fundamental structure of many biomasses is resulting in renewed interest in the use of bioconversion technology to produce speciality chemicals. Past disappointments, particularly in the use of biotechnology to produce high value pharmaceuticals, must be overcome. Sustainable commercial applications of biotransformation of biomass will develop due to the availability of improved bioreactor technology and the recognition of more specific and efficient bacteria. The biodegradation of lignin and, alternatively, the biomodification of the polymer structure should lead to the utilisation of substantial quantities of this important resource.

The successful use of biotechnology in meeting new environmental standards will increasingly show the way ahead. Typical of the more novel approaches now reaching commercialisation is the use of highly specific bacteria to enable activated sludge plants to meet new and more demanding ammonia discharge standards. Ammonia, even at low levels, is toxic to fish and invertebrates, and causes oxygen depletion resulting in increased costs of potable water treatment. The rate limiting step is normally the oxidation of ammonia to nitrite and is particularly sensitive to the parameters in the growth environment, e.g. temperature. Consequently, it is often possible to find two distinct degradation profiles. Often, in order to allow the nitrifying organisms time to become established and to ensure complete nitrification, plant capacity has to be extended but this is a very expensive option. Interbio, one of the leading companies in this field, have developed a range of bacteria which can augment the established system and maximise plant performance.

This innovative approach by biotechnologists to solving real industrial problems has only been achieved through a thorough understanding of the customers' needs which must surely must be the way ahead.

References

Crawford DL (1981) Microbial conversions of lignin to useful chemicals using a lignin-degrading Streptomycete. Biochtechnol Bioeng Symp 11 pp 275-291

Dart RK, Betts WB (1990) Lignocellulose and its potential, Laboratory of the Government Chemist, DTI, UK pp 1-40

Goldstein R, Olsen E (1988) Applying genetic ecology to environmental management, Environ Sci Technol 22: 370-372

Hutterman A (1989) Enzymatic degradation of lignin for technical use, Am Chem Soc 00976156/89/0397. Symposium series 397, 361-370

Johnsrud SC, Eriksson K-E (1985) Cross-breeding of selected and mutated homokaryotic strains of *Phanerochaete chrysosporium* K-3. New cellulase-deficient strains with increased ability to degrade lignin. Appl Microbiol Biotechnol 21:320-327

Kirk TK, Tien M, Johnsrud SC, Eriksson K-E (1986) Lignin-degrading activity of *Phanerochaete chrysosporium* Burds: comparison of cellulase-negative and other strains. Enzyme Microb Technol 8: 75-80

Kirk TK, Fenn P (1982) Formation and action of the ligninolytic system in basidiomycetes. In: Decomposer basidiomycetes Swift MJ, Frankland JC, Hedger JN (eds) Br Mycol Soc Symp 4, Cambridge,Cambridge University Press pp 67-90

Little BFP (1989) Lignin: a nuisance or an opportunity. In: Cellulose sources and exploitation: industrial utilisation, biotechnology and physico-chemical properties. Kennedy JF, Phillips GO, Williams PA (eds) Ellis Horwood London pp 473-482

Lynch JM (1987) Utilisation of lignocellulosic wastes, J Appl Bact symp supplement pp 71s-83s

Walker A (1990) Biotechnology benefits will be limited to major investors European Chemical News 19:22

Subject Index

Printing: Mercedesdruck, Berlin
Binding: Buchbinderei Lüderitz & Bauer, Berlin